MAN
IN THE
MIDDLE

DISCERNING RIGHT AND WRONG
IN A CULTURE THAT'S LOST ITS WAY

Eph. 4:15

S. Hower

S.D. HOWER

I love a good story. Steve Hower masterfully spins a brilliant tale of a retired journalist's close encounters of the best kind with the real and active presence of the creator, redeemer and sanctifier of human race and its environment. This is extraordinarily timely in a world mired in two (well at least two) self-evident realities: too few people have a clear concept of truth, and so many of us have clouded moral compasses. The protagonist, Jim, addresses the big, controversial, culturally and spiritually challenging existential issues of our time. He tackles this as a man who has and is struggling to understand his own identity and beliefs. In the end, Jim discovers his relationship with Jesus provides the balance between truth and love he needs. I love this book, and it's worth a read and repeated reread.

John D. Eckrich, M.D.
Grace Place Wellness Ministries
Author of *Vocation & Wellness,*
Fear, Anxiety & Wellness, Resilient Aging & Wellness

As usual, when Steve Hower writes, he makes me think. His latest work draws us into the surprising and reluctant adventure of Jim King, a retired reporter. Through Jim, Steve leads us to wrestle with the important questions and tensions of our day. *Man in the Middle* is insightful, honest, and challenging.

Greg Finke
Executive Director, Dwelling 1:14
Author of *Joining Jesus on His Mission, Joining Jesus Show Me How*

Steve Hower will capture your attention with the significant truths with which one must struggle. He has a remarkable way of taking the complex and making it simple. As a pastor who has lived out his faith in very practical ways, Steve offers much wisdom. He has significantly changed my life and will change yours too! This is a great read and a great gift for someone struggling to practically engage others in matters of faith.

Todd Moritz
Director, Strategy & Donor Enhancement, Pastoral Leadership Institute
Former Executive Director, St. John (Pathfinder) Church

Stephen Hower does a masterful job of not only crafting a story but also striking a beautiful balance of bringing God's love and truth into some confusing and potentially divisive topics. As the world becomes more polarized, rather than running to the fringes, Stephen's work will encourage people to come together to continue to have the hard, but crucial, conversations we still need to have.

Zach Zehnder
Author and Founder of *Red Letter Challenge*
Pastor, The Cross Family, Mount Dora, FL

This book speaks to any American who feels confused about the controversial issues of the day and is searching for truth in the midst of chaos. Addressing both sides of our current issues, Stephen Hower promotes serious thinking in a relevant, interesting, homespun manner. Whether you agree or disagree, you will be prompted to think and to find a moment of resolute peace. Every American should read this book and give a copy to their grown children.

Rev. Dr. Gary Schaper, D.Min., CCLC
Shirley Schaper, MAR, MSW, Family Therapist

Insightful and inviting! In a world defined by "anti-tribes" that coalesce around who or what one is against, Hower invites a conversation with fresh clarity. He writes with subtle honesty, offering both reassurance and challenge. You will enjoy it. We recommend *Man in the Middle* to anyone who hasn't known what to say—or how or when to speak—regarding today's most challenging issues.

Gail and Jock Ficken
Co-leaders, Pastoral Leadership Institute

"Don't hold back! Remember that the faithful need the reassurance and the skeptics need the challenge." "There is power in truth." "Our job is promotion, not sales." "I was a man on a mission from God..."

These quotes from *Man in the Middle* remind us that for as long as we have known him, Stephen Hower has been a "man in the middle" himself. He's been reading, learning, thinking, talking, and writing in ways that bring people unfamiliar with the truth into the presence of the truth...and then helping them to learn how to seek it, embrace it, love it, and share it. As our pastor, Stephen constantly preached us into the presence of Jesus, who is the Truth. As an author, he is every bit as bold and courageous. Like his main character, Jim King—who is divinely called, encouraged, and equipped to bring truth to people in ways that they can actually see and hear—Stephen also has a history of not holding back, of stirring up the status quo, and of choosing "God's simple answer over man's complicated explanations." This book is the informed, creative, and easy-to-read outcome of Stephen's life and ministry. The main character is a "modern-day Don Quixote, willing and capable of tilting at the windmills of the politically correct culture"— a man whose past experience and career path have positioned him "for such a time as this." We thoroughly enjoyed reading *Man in the Middle* and can't wait to use it (and the discussion guide that comes along with it) as the basis for our neighborhood Bible study and discussion group. We are convinced God will use the book to bring us and our neighbors closer together.

Dr. Lori Utech, M.D., Family Physician
Rev. Dr. William Utech, M.Div., S.T.M., D.Min.
Mission Executive, Minnesota South District, The Lutheran Church Missouri Synod

TENTHPOWERPUBLISHING
www.tenthpowerpublishing.com

Design by Inkwell Creative

Softcover ISBN 978-1-938840-39-5
E-book ISBN 978-1-938840-40-1

10 9 8 7 6 5 4 3 2 1

Dedicated to the Next Generation of Truth Seekers

Especially:
Brooke, Luke, John and Cami

I want to express my appreciation to those who came along side this project to offer suggestions, proofreading, and various comments, including: My wife Carol who gave each chapter its first scrub. Our two sons: Joshua and Jacob, both theologically trained business professionals. And two good friends with editing expertise: Susan Bentzinger and Jennifer Baehr.

TABLE OF CONTENTS

PROLOGUE

Jim and Sarah King are typical 21ˢᵗ Century American adults, recently retired. They raised their children to know the difference between right and wrong and believe there are good, better, and best choices to be made in most situations. Jim is a Man in the Middle, not especially religious, but one who believes in right and wrong.

Sarah had a successful career as a real estate agent. Jim is a recently retired reporter for the *St. Louis Herald*. Their life is turned upside down by the appearance of an angel sent to recruit the retired journalist as God's representative to an increasingly secular world. Jim's former editor simultaneously recruited him to write a weekly blog to bolster *The Herald's* syndicated online presence.

Jim, who considers himself biblically illiterate, is reluctant to accept God's call, but is convinced by Sarah and his longtime Christian friend to accept the challenge. He agrees to write the column if he is free to address the hot-button social issues of the day: race, diversity, same-sex marriage, gender, unalienable rights, capitalism vs. socialism and other controversial topics.

Jim is guided along the way by people, encounters, and observations he believes are prompted by God. The assignment forces Jim to reexamine his faith and his understanding of God's truth. The reader will benefit from Jim's struggle as well as Jim's TRUTH BE TOLD columns that are included in the pages of this book.

It is hoped the time you spend reading *Man in the Middle* will cause a thoughtful examination of what is good, better, and best for you, those you love, and for our nation.

STEPHEN D. HOWER

"I miss the way you used to talk to me when you were a kid."

—*God*

CHAPTER I

Night Vision

I saw what I saw. I heard what I heard. It happened. But what was it? I couldn't be sure. A dream? A ghost? An angel sent from God? It was vivid, that much was certain.

I can't pretend it didn't happen. It's a part of me now. A moment carved into my memory, like the two-inch scar on my right hand acquired when batting away a pitchfork tossed in my direction by my brother on our grandparent's farm. Everyone has moments like that. Experiences we recall with absolute clarity. We still visualize those encounters with amazing detail decades later: the objects in a room, the presence of others, their proximity to us, their expressions, light, shadows, smells, sounds, and mostly our thoughts.

They are the defining moments of life. The day you quit your job because you had enough, the moment your fiancée dropped to his knee, holding your newborn, the sights, sounds and panic of a crash, when confusion turned into clarity, an answered prayer, the weight of a matter lifted off your shoulders. I've had those moments. We all have. This was different. Those are normal. This was not normal. This was paranormal.

I awoke in the middle of the night to see a man in glowing white garments standing next to my bed. It was a clear, star-filled night. The rays of a full moon were streaming through the transoms casting shadows on the walls. It was surreal. He stood silently like an oversized Oscar near the red carpet at the Academy Awards. There was a sense of calm in the room. I was not startled, which seems odd in retrospect. I glanced around the room, assessing its surroundings. A faint green light glowed from the smoke detector above the door. The soothing click, click, click of the clock was still keeping time. The man in white remained motionless. His gaze fixed on the opposite wall. I felt no compulsion to defend myself or challenge his intrusion. There was a peacefulness about him. His appearance was shocking but seemed strangely normal, almost familiar.

Was this for real? I rubbed my eyes, expecting him to vanish like every other dream I've ever had. But it was not a dream. He raised his hand in a gesture of peace. He didn't speak in an audible voice, but I "heard" him just the same. His purpose was expressed in a resonate and steady tone, not a whisper despite his proximity and lateness of the hour. His thoughts came to me clear and precise. His message was as unexpected as his appearance.

"Fear not. I have been sent by the Father. He has witnessed the confusion of His people. Good is called evil and evil is declared acceptable. He has chosen you to be His spokesman to this generation. The people He loves have lost their way. They've mistaken His grace for indifference and His compassion for compromise. Truth without love falls on deaf ears, and love without truth is impotent.

As in the day of the Judges, the Father has chosen to raise up a prophet from their midst. You are that voice. A voice of one calling in the wilderness, 'Make ready a way for the Lord.' The Holy One has sent me to prepare you and to open your heart to His prompting. You must acknowledge your limitations and lay down your assumptions. His spirit will lead you on a pilgrimage of truth.

People will challenge and resist your message. Do not be

angered, nor surprised. Those who have ears to hear will hear. The beliefs of this age are well-intended but misguided. People's opinions may seem equally valid and reasonable, but they are not. Error disguised as truth is a hollow tree, appearing strong but susceptible to the next storm. The Father's ways are not the ways of the world. As high as the heavens are above the earth so are the Father's ways higher than man's ways and His thoughts higher than the thoughts of earth. Open your heart to learn all the Father will reveal.

Declaring truth is easy. Leading the misguided to the knowledge of the truth is not. Human reason limits what the mind can accept. You must be willing to accept the unacceptable and recognize as reasonable things that seem unreasonable. The foolishness of God is wiser than the wisdom of humanity and the weakness of God is stronger than the power of error.

Lack of clarity is not the source of error. Lack of faith to accept the truth is the cause of all confusion. Error's path is wide and many follow it. The Father's ways are righteous and his truth is sure. From Him and through Him are all things. The Father alone is able to bring light out of darkness. You have been chosen to reveal His light to this generation.

For truth's sake, and for the sake of His glory, the Lord will pour out His spirit of wisdom on you. Weigh all truth in the light of God's Word for His Word is true. Many false spirits roam the earth to deceive the people. They disguise themselves as teachers of truth, but their deeds are evil. Test the spirits. Be vigilant. God's Word cannot be broken. His truth is like a sharpened sword, able to separate light from darkness and truth from error. The truth of God's Word alone has the power to set men free."

And then he was gone.

The man in white left as mysteriously as he appeared. I blinked and blinked again. What just happened? Was it a vision? Was it an angel? I had more questions than answers.

- Dare I tell anyone, even my wife?
- Of all the people in the world, why me?
- What was a "pilgrimage of truth?"
- What now? What next?
- How was I supposed to make the Father's truth known?
- Would anyone believe me? Would anyone care?
- I had questions. Why had I kept silent?
- Was the man in white an angel or something else, possibly Jesus?
- Would it happen again?

I was wide awake but dared not move. My mind was a blur. Every moment, every word was flashing like shooting stars in my head. I don't believe in visions! I'm not sure I believe in angels, at least not the kind that visit the irreligious. Before this instance I had laughingly considered such claims the side-effects of oxygen deprivation, drug abuse or a shear lunacy. *Maybe I was losing it.* I analyzed the implications. If anyone within my sphere of influence claimed an angelic visitation, I would question their sanity. I was sure of one thing; I would be keeping my "vision" a secret.

I replayed the incident over and over in my head. That's what I called it. The incident. Unlike so many other dreams that evaporated in the morning light, this one remained vividly clear. "Fear not. The Father has seen the confusion of His people. Good is called evil and evil is declared acceptable. He has chosen you as a spokesman to this generation. Without vision, the people perish. As in the day of the Judges, the Father has chosen to raise up a prophet from their midst. You are that voice. The voice of one calling in the wilderness, 'Make ready a way for the Lord.' The Holy One has sent me to prepare you for all you must experience and to open your heart to His prompting."

What the man in white said was true. My level of frustration over what the politically correct culture considered acceptable had become unbearable. I considered myself Christian, but my links to the organized church were strained at best. I had about as much use for the institutional church as I did those who challenged everything they stood for. Most Christians seemed to fall into one of two camps: They are either rigid, judgmental, and arrogant, or maintained no standards at all. In a failed attempt at inclusion, many evangelicals have adopted a "live and let live" theology that didn't square with me either. I was a spiritual orphan.

I still believed in right and wrong. If there was right, by definition, there had to be wrong. As a father of two, I knew love sometimes requires saying "no" to your children. Even so, my children never doubted my love. They still believed I had their best interest at heart, even when I challenged their choices and exercised my parental authority. Could it be the same between the Heavenly Father and His children?

Jesus taught the disciples to pray, "Our Father... the One who lives in heaven." The comparison was not perfect. I was not "in heaven." My parental wisdom was earthbound and limited. I did my best but was never sure if my best was wise enough. The Father in Heaven, on the other hand, is without human limitation. Somewhere in the Bible it says,

> "Oh, the depth of the riches of the wisdom and knowledge of God! How unsearchable his judgments, and His paths beyond tracing out! Who has known the mind of the Lord? Or who has been His counselor?" [1]

I could not agree more. No wonder it stuck with me over the years. God's ways often seem more confusing than sensible. Someone needs to explain it to the likes of me, to the likes of everyone for that matter.

If it was possible for God to use my inadequacies for His purpose, I was willing to let Him. The man in white predicted many, perhaps even most, would reject the truth even if it were made clear. I had not considered that, but I knew he was right. The truth needs to be declared, even when it is opposed. Truth needs an advocate. I attempted to do that my entire life as a newspaper man. Truth has a mysterious power that cannot be easily dismissed.

Our politically correct culture is well-intentioned but seriously flawed. No wonder God wants to initiate a course-correction. The prospect was a bit overwhelming. In His famous sermon on the mount Jesus predicted:

> "Blessed are you when people insult you, persecute you and falsely say all kinds of evil against you because of me. Rejoice and be glad, because great is your reward in heaven, for in the same way they persecuted the prophets who were before you." [2]

That passage hung next to my computer screen for the last decade. It explained a lot but never gave me much comfort.

*"After all these years, I see that I was mistaken about
Eve in the beginning; it is better to live outside the
Garden with her than inside it without her."*
—Mark Twain, Diaries of Adam & Eve

CHAPTER 2

The Morning After

5:37 AM Those numbers glowed red on the alarm clock next to my bed. I promised Sarah I would not get up before 6:00 AM, but it was a promise I struggled to keep.

I recently retired after 40 years of chasing stories for *The Herald*, but old habits die hard. Five hours of sleep seemed sufficient. I was accustomed to staying up late and/or getting up early to draft, edit, or research a story, doing whatever it took to meet a deadline. That ship had sailed but I had yet to figure out how to reset my internal clock. I still woke up at 5:00 AM, alarm or no alarm. Forcing the issue only made matters worse. I was like a kid on Christmas morning screaming from my bed, "Can I get up yet?!" But at 65, my screams were of the silent variety.

Today was different. After the surreal night vision, or whatever it was, there was no way I could lie quietly for another 20 minutes. Sarah was wired differently. She had been a successful real estate agent for 20 years. Her work schedule was a moving target, revolving around her clients' availability, mostly on weekends and evenings. Mornings have always been her down-time. So I slipped quietly out of bed, grabbed my jeans and sweat-shirt and closed the bedroom door behind me. Bogey was already waiting expectantly by the front door for his morning walk. Apparently, the dog and I were both creatures of habit.

After Bogey's morning constitutional, I started the coffee and went looking for a Bible. I have always been an avid reader, but not an avid Bible reader. I consume history books, mostly biographies and autobiographies. It isn't history so much that interests me as the stories of people who lived through historic moments. I made my living writing stories about people in challenging circumstances, so I have a professional interest in how a person's story is told. Human behavior fascinates me. In my experience the proverb held true, "The same water that softens the potato hardens the egg." In other words, "If you want to know what a person is made of, watch how they respond to adversity."

Lately I'd been spending the first hour or two of every morning reading my book de jour, but today was different. As intrigued as I was to discover how an African American Jazz-man with the strange name of Nat King Cole, became the favorite singer of white, middle-class housewives like my mom, would have to wait. Today I needed to learn more about angels.

The only angel story I could remember was the one they retell at church every Christmas-eve. As a child I had been assigned the role of a shepherd in the Christmas-Eve program, bathrobe and all. I still vaguely remembered my part,

> "There were shepherds living out in the fields nearby, keeping watch over their flocks at night. An angel of the Lord appeared to them, and the glory of the Lord shone around them, and they were terrified." [3]

If only I could find our Bible. I gave up looking and resorted to what I knew best, an electronic notebook. A quick google search gave me all the help I needed. Boom! There it was. Jesus' birth is described in Luke chapter two, just like I remembered. But the part I was most interested in reading was the angel's appearance to his mother Mary nine months before his birth. That was in chapter one. Luke describes how God sent the angel Gabriel to Nazareth to recruit Mary, an unsuspecting virgin to become the mother of the promised Savior.

"In the sixth month of Elizabeth's pregnancy, God sent the angel Gabriel to Nazareth, a town in Galilee, to a virgin pledged to be married to a man named Joseph, a descendant of David. The virgin's name was Mary. The angel went to her and said, 'Greetings, you who are highly favored! The Lord is with you.'

Mary was greatly troubled at his words and wondered what kind of greeting this might be. But the angel said to her, 'Do not be afraid, Mary; you have found favor with God. You will conceive and give birth to a son, and you are to call Him Jesus. He will be great and will be called the Son of the Most High. The Lord God will give Him the throne of his father David, and He will reign over Jacob's descendants forever; His kingdom will never end.'

'How will this be,' Mary asked the angel, 'since I am a virgin?'

The angel answered, 'The Holy Spirit will come on you, and the power of the Most High will overshadow you. So the Holy One to be born will be called the Son of God. Even Elizabeth your relative is going to have a child in her old age, and she who was said to be unable to conceive is in her sixth month. For no word from God will ever fail.'

'I am the Lord's servant,' Mary answered. 'May your word to me be fulfilled.' Then the angel left her." [4]

There were some striking similarities between Mary's experience and my night encounter.

- Mary was surprised and a little frightened by the sudden appearance of an angel. (I can relate.)

- The angel announced to Mary, as he did to me, that she had found favor in the sight of God. Neither she nor I anticipated the visit or felt worthy. (God's choice of Mary made perfect sense, but His choice of me remains a total mystery. Surely, He knew I would have trouble locating our family Bible.)

- Mary had not asked to be chosen. It came as a complete surprise. (Ditto!)

- God sent an angel to recruit Mary for a mission that would change her life. (That thought gave me pause. I was pretty happy with the status quo of my existence.)

- He promised to send the Holy Spirit to Mary. (I was certain it would take a Holy-Spirit-partnership to accomplish my mission too. In fact, I reasoned my appointment would require an even greater miracle considering my total lack of resume for the task at hand.)

- When the angel left, Mary undoubtedly had more questions than answers. It happened so unexpectedly. Why her? Why now? How would her fiancée Joseph take the news of her "divine pregnancy?" Should she, could she, tell her parents? Who else knew? And if Jesus' birth was to take place in Bethlehem, why did God choose Mary who lived a hundred miles northwest of that obscure village. At the time it must have seemed significant.

- I could relate to Mary's lingering confusion. Why me? Why now? Was the world about to end? Was this God's last push for truth? Did the man in white honestly expect me to assume the role of a modern day prophet? I don't do robes and sandals. That wasn't going to happen.

As a journalist, I was intrigued by Luke's telling of the story, the angel's words to Mary, the circumstance of her pregnancy, the unexpected taxation requiring Mary and Joseph's journey to Bethlehem at just the right time, the angels, shepherds and the manger. Obviously, God was capable of working out the details and delivering on His promises.

There was also Mary's response to consider... "I am the Lord's servant. May your word to me be fulfilled." I don't recall saying anything like that. I don't even recall thinking anything like that. Where did Mary find the presence of mind to engage the angel in conversation? I was in a state of shock the entire time. Mary took it all in stride. Maybe my angel, if that's what the man in white was, had his wires crossed. That might explain things. I reasoned, if business hires fail about 50% of the time, perhaps angelic acquisition of needed talent might also miss the mark now and then.

I was not in the habit of praying other than childhood prayers, at meals, and then more out of habit than intention, sometimes not much more than a nod of the head. But then it began. Before I even realized what was happening, I found myself "talking to God". I'm not sure if it would qualify as a legitimate prayer per se, but my mind was racing over the implications of my encounter. Is that the same as praying? I wasn't sure.

"Why did you choose me? I thought You were omniscient. How could you possibly think I'm qualified to represent You to the public? The world needs some serious redirection. Have you seen what's going on? Of course you have. You're God. I'm not the only one frustrated by political correctness run amuck. But disagreeing with people and calling them out are two different things. As a student of history, I know The Declaration of Independence says, 'We hold these truths to be self-evident.' What happened to that? Is nothing self-evident anymore? Has tolerance of every aberration and opinion robbed us of self-evident truth? Everyone's entitled to their own opinion on most things but that doesn't mean all opinions are equally valid. A wise person once said, 'When the student is ready, the teacher will appear.' In my experience, forcing an issue before a person is ready to listen rarely changes their opinion. If You are the teacher, teach me. If You want a spokesman, teach me what to say. If You don't show up this will not end well.

What is truth? I have an opinion on most subjects and I've taken sides in past columns, but this seems different. When does one person's freedom become another person's imposition? I can make a case for almost any viewpoint but not all points of view are created equal. If there is right, there must be wrong. I believe that and I think most people do too. Some opinions are dangerous. Those who believe that 'might makes right,' or 'majority rules' are a threat to a free society. Our founding fathers established a Republic, not an absolute democracy for a reason. They declared, we are all 'endowed by our Creator with certain unalienable Rights, to which the Laws of Nature and of Nature's God entitle them.' Is that still a thing? Is belief in God enough? Muslims, Jews, and Christians all believe in god, but not the same God and certainly not the same 'Bible.'

The world has lost its way, no doubt. But who am I to intervene? I recall the story of Jonah I learned as a child. He ran the other way didn't he? It seemed the sensible thing to do at the time. But You didn't let him abandon ship, did You?

Like most, I find it hard to say nothing when people I care about are headed down a path of self-destruction, but I'm not courageous by nature. If my child was running wild, I would say something. Love compels caring people to care. But calling out complete strangers? Can one person turn the world around? I know, I know, Christians are called to 'love their neighbor as they love themselves.'[5] Love as a theoretical concept is easy. But love in real life is hard. How can I love someone, even a stranger, and not step up? But if I step up and step in, I might alienate the wayward. I'm so confused. Does looking the other way make me complicit? I didn't ask for this assignment, Lord. I'm a, 'mind my own business and let the chips fall where they will,' kind of guy. What goes around comes around. Karma is real. Good will ultimately be proven right and wrong will ultimately fail. Won't it?"

The longer I sat in my study, eyes closed, mind racing, lips mumbling, I became more relaxed as if God was sitting in the chair to my right.

"Do You expect people to honor the Ten Commandments, Lord? What about all the other laws in The Bible? Some of them seem pretty far-fetched. How can a person know which of your rules are valid and which are not? Isn't it disingenuous to honor some and not others? I don't feel qualified to make that distinction. You won't find any seminary diplomas hanging on my wall. And even if there were, religious leaders, no matter how well educated, never seem to agree on much anyway.

I have questions, Lord. You confuse me. Questions about heaven and hell for starters. Who gets in and who doesn't, and on what basis? What about race and racism, Lord? What were you thinking when you created racial diversity? Why are some prayers answered and not others? I have questions about poverty, evil, and on what basis we decide one faith is right and another is wrong. Just being sincere can't be enough. It's possible that some are sincerely wrong. And of course, there is the matter of suffering. Good people suffer and bad people flourish. How can You be okay with that? I have questions.

What should I do with all my questions? Climb a mountain and wait for You? How did that work out for Moses? Not so good. The world hasn't gotten any better since he brought the stone tablets down from Sinai."

My one-way conversation with the Lord was interrupted by the opening of the bedroom door. I could hear Sarah's slippers shuffling down the hallway. Bogey noticed too and ran to meet her. She stopped to acknowledge him, then proceeded to the kitchen and the coffee she could smell brewing. Only then would she seek me out for a morning kiss and greeting. Priorities.

The room always brightened a bit when Sarah entered. Resting her hand on my shoulder, she leaned in for our morning embrace. "You *almost* made it to 6:00 AM," she said with a smile.

"I'll get there" I replied, "but it may take some time."

She noticed the iPad resting on my lap in the place of my usual book. "Catching up on the over-night news?"

"No. Catching up on my Bible reading."

"Did you say, Bible reading? Aren't you full of surprises?"

I had anticipated this moment. "I know what you're thinking. But I have my reasons. There must be a thing or two even I can learn from the Good Book," I said without revealing my purpose.

"You won't get an argument from me."

"About what? My sudden interest in the sacred? Or still having a thing or two to learn?"

Ignoring my attempt at humor, Sarah continued chiding, "I'm just guessing here, but it looks like you couldn't actually find our Bible?"

"You could say that again and be right both times," I smiled. But the online version might actually be the better choice. Did you know you can type any word or phrase into the search-engine and locate every instance when that word or phrase is used in the entire Bible? Technology is a wonderful thing!"

"No doubt, but I'm more curious to know what peaked your sudden interest in the Bible. What's going on? Since when did you start your day with a dose of God? Are you thinking about a second career in the priesthood? 'Cuz if you are, I'm pretty sure they don't allow wives in the rectory, sweetheart."

Ah. The moment of truth. "I'll tell you but first you must promise not to laugh."

Sarah sensed the serious tone in my answer. She nestled further into her favorite chair, cupping the mug in both hands while savoring the aroma she peered back at me over the rim. In a calm and affirming voice she replied, "I won't laugh."

Slowly, with a degree of hesitation, I began to relate the events of my middle-of-the-night visitation. Sarah had not heard or seen a thing. From her perspective, last night was like the one before and the one before that. Had the visitor put her in some kind of suspended animation? Is that possible? She's normally a light sleeper. How could she not have awakened, but I could tell she was being totally honest. She pressed for details as I expected she would.

Without doubting my version of the event, she probed further for a logical explanation of my experience. Had I been troubled about anything in particular before going to bed? Had I watched any programs recently that included angels, visions, or strange dreams? Had I read anything that might have planted spiritual notions in my subconscious? Had I taken any sleeping aids or other meds? And how did I know for sure it was an angel and not a hallucination or dream?

It was a candid exchange. No, I had not taken any medications. No, I was not upset about anything. No, I could not recall any unusual show or stories I had watched or read recently about paranormal activity. I was halfway finished reading a biography about Nat King Cole, not exactly spiritually explicit material. As hard as I tried, I could find no logical explanation for my experience. I answered Sarah's questions to the best of my ability and came up empty. She was always the logical one and a good check of my thought process. It was one of the things I loved about her. To be honest, she was more open-minded than me, especially when it came to belief in God and the possibility of miracles.

"Just suppose the guy in white was in fact an angel," Sarah suggested. "Suppose for a moment God has chosen you to be His spokesman."

"But why would He do that?" I argued. "I'm not squared away on matters of faith. I'm not even especially religious."

"Exactly. It sorta makes sense. You're a writer. You aren't a religious-nut-case. You've spent your career reporting on current events and human interest stories. You aren't naïve. You've been around long enough to know things aren't always as they seem. So-called religious experts believe they have all the answers. You, on the other hand, have no preconceived notion of what's right or wrong. You study a story from every angle. You are unconventional. Think about it. Who better to investigate God's take on life and the consequence of political correctness run amuck than an investigative reporter? No one would ever accuse you of being a Bible-thumper! Haha. You couldn't even find our Bible this morning! If I were God I would totally choose a guy like you. It makes perfect sense."

I looked at her and she smiled, but she was completely serious.

I shook my head. "I'm not so sure."

Sarah was definitely open to the possibility that God still cared about people even if people no longer cared about Him. "Maybe He's decided enough is enough." Sarah seemed more convinced of God's calling than me and she hadn't even caught a glimpse of the intruder.

I was still on the fence. "'A man's strength is his weakness.' You've heard me say it a thousand times. I'm not a Bible-thumper and that may be to my advantage. But it has a huge down-side too. I'm what the faithful call a 'Chreaster,' a guy who shows up for worship only twice a year at Christmas and Easter to check out the poinsettia and lily displays. You have to admit, when it comes to the contents of the Bible, I'm more than a tad deficient."

"That's never stopped you before. What did you know about incarceration, charter schools, the effect of multiple-deployments on military families, secondhand smoke, or equal pay for women and minorities? But you won awards for reporting on all those things. *The Herald* is begging you to write a monthly column for their online website. They even promised nationwide syndication. Why not take God up on His offer and butcher a few sacred cows? What have you got to lose? You're retired. They can't fire you, and if they drop the column you can go back to criticizing everyone else's editorials and playing golf. It's a great opportunity to do what you love and strike a blow for common sense.

"Why not? 'Cuz I could ruin my reputation as a fair-minded journalist? Have you thought about that? People will think ole James has finally lost it completely."

"Nonsense! Columnists are supposed to be controversial. No one's asking you to go all John the Baptist. Just challenge the politically correct crowd with a different perspective. There's no danger of anyone mistaking you for a fundamentalist preacher. You can't tolerate pious rhetoric any more than blatant immorality. You will be an equal-opportunity offender." She smiled. "You are a man in the middle. There are probably more people like you than not. You've always challenged the status quo. That's what good writers do. This could be just the angle, or angel you've been waiting for. Pun intended sweetheart... pun intended. God knows there are no lack of issues worthy of divine re-direction."

"If I do this I'm gonna need help... and sweetheart, I don't mean to offend you... but your eight years in catholic school doesn't meet the standard."

Sarah smiled her wry grin. I loved moments like this. The energy between us was palpable. We could banter back and forth on almost any topic without danger of offense.

"You'll get no argument from me. I'm no Bible scholar. I was sent to catholic school to keep me on the straight and narrow. A Bible scholar is not what the world needs. We have plenty of those. God could have His pick. The majority of Christians we know are of the 'closed-minded' variety. I doubt even an angel suddenly appearing at their bedside could get them to think a new thought."

"Exactly my point. Who's going to listen anyway? People pretty much have their minds made up." My cynicism was showing.

"Everyone's sure of themselves until confronted by the truth. You've said it a thousand times. 'Truth has a way of breaking through the best defense.' This mission is perfect for you. It's going to require someone who's not afraid to ask tough questions and is willing to follow wherever the truth takes them. You've always done that. If Bible knowledge is what you lack, you know plenty of people who can quote chapter and verse, and there is always google search," she said with a smirk. "I suggest you start with George."

"George? I'm pretty sure he considers me a lost cause. He's been trying to get us to attend his church for years. I don't think he's ever met a person who didn't need converting," I laughed. We both knew it was true. It was what we loved and hated about him at the same time. Say what you will about George, but when it came to faith in God he was all in.

"All the more reason he'll be glad to help. Isn't he an elder, or something like that at that big church near the stadium? Why don't you take him to lunch and get his take on your idea of writing a column on current social issues?"

Her suggestion amused me, "Yeah, I can hear it now. 'Hi George. James King here. How are you doing? I had an angel intruder the other night over at my place. You know, the middle-of-the-night variety, dressed in a white robe who asked me to pursue a mission from God. What do you know about angels and God's recruiting policies?' Ha! He'll think I've finally lost it!"

Sarah laughed at the prospect. "I agree, baby. I wouldn't tell George about your night vision. At least not yet. Just ask what he knows about angels, dreams, and visions. Tell him you're researching a story."

"'My night vision?' Is that what we are calling it now?"

"You know what I meant," Sarah moved to the loveseat next to me. "Maybe he can suggest some Scriptures to read, or a book or two on the subject. He's a good guy. I'm sure he'll be happy to point you in the right direction. It won't hurt to ask."

"No harm in asking," I agreed.

I've been playing golf in the same foursome with George for years. He's never been too pushy with his faith, but never shied away from an opinion either. Clearly I needed advice from someone on a first name basis with the Lord. If last night was the beginning of an ongoing encounter with the unknown, I was a student in need of a mentor. If it was just a case of jalapeno-hallucination, I'd chalk it up to a gastric distraction and move on. The man in white said I needed to lay aside what seemed "reasonable" and open my mind to things that seem "unreasonable." I'd give "unreasonable" a try and see what happened.

I glanced down at my iPad still opened to Luke, chapter one. Mary said, "I am the Lord's servant. May Your word to me be fulfilled."

Sarah touched my arm in a show of support. "I believe in you baby. I've never seen you back down from a challenge. Wow! Life is crazy huh? Yesterday you were newly retired, without a care in the world. Today, you've been recruited to turn the world on its ear."

What a difference a day makes.

*"I don't need a friend who changes when I change and who
nods when I nod; my shadow does that much better."*

—*Plutarch*

CHAPTER 3

Due Diligence

S aturday is my favorite day of the week. Weather permitting, it
begins early on a nearby golf course with three of my closest friends.
Golf has always been therapy for me. The five-mile walk provides
ample opportunity to gain perspective. I prefer walking to riding so I have
quiet time alone as well as group time on the tee box and greens. If life is
treating me well, I take pleasure in thoughts of gratitude and if not, the
walk provides perspective. My foursome includes like-minded guys. We are
competitive but not to the point of tossing clubs or swearing at a missed
shot. The banter is friendly and the personal digs are given and received
with a smile.

I've always considered golf the perfect combination of both physical
and mental challenge. The golf swing requires good hand/eye coordination,
synchronized upper and lower body movement, and mental focus. An
inch off at the point of contact spoils everything. Hitting it pure brings
an immediate sense of accomplishment. By the time most of the world is
stumbling from bed towards their first cup of coffee, I've finished the first

nine holes and lowered my blood pressure by ten points. There is nothing like the smell of freshly mown grass, the morning dew glistening on the fairway and the sun rising over distant trees. Perfection.

But before a word is said, a ball struck, or score card opened, the ritual of the practice range must be observed. With little more than a nod, golfers pull on gloves, uncover clubs, and scatter practice balls across the grass. They attempt to loosen their stiff backs and aching shoulders in search of a repeatable swing they can take to the course. Only the clank of struck balls, self-rebuke, and moans of frustration break the silence. Such was my Saturday ritual.

I quickly learned our usual foursome would be reduced to a twosome. Gary was on vacation, and Jim was playing in a charity event across town. Just as well, I wanted to talk with George about my encounter with the man in white without the distraction and well-intended advice from the other two. George and I walked the course and carried our clubs so there would be plenty of opportunity to talk as we made our way.

George broke the protocol of silence on the first tee box.

"How's retirement treating you? Are you making progress on Sarah's honey-do list?" It was his usual attempt to poke at me while I lined up my first swing.

"It's all good. There is always something that needs attention but nothing major. Not a lot of loose ends there. We've been thinking of downsizing the operation. The kids are out of the house. It seems silly to maintain a four-bedroom home for the two of us. But that's a big decision. No need to rush. How about you?"

George waited on my tee shot before answering, shielding his eyes against the sun to track the flight of my ball.

"Down the middle. Again! Don't you ever get tired of hitting it straight? Your game is so boring!" He stuck his tee in the ground and drove his ball down the right side of the fairway just short of the bunker guarding the approach to the green.

"Nice shot, George."

"Just trying to keep up with the King."

Good ole George. His antics amused me. He loved making fun of my name and overt praise was one of his favorite attempts at distraction.

We shouldered our bags and stepped off the box. "Elizabeth and I crossed the down-sizing bridge a couple of years ago. No regrets, I might add. We got rid of our mortgage, and we have all the space we need. We still have a guest room and the lower level provides a place for grandkids to crash when they visit. It was time to cash out. We even made some money. A seminar at church provided the push we needed to make the change. We have no regrets. You and Sarah should consider it."

There it was. We had not reached the first green before George mentioned his church. I had to smile. It was pure George. He rarely missed an opportunity to inject the subject of faith into our conversation.

"Speaking of church," I seized the moment. "I've been wanting to pick your brain about a few things."

"That door is always open, James."

The conversation continued as we walked. We loved the game but weren't fanatics. A conversation about something other than golf was always welcomed.

"I'm free-lancing a series of articles on what's right and wrong in popular culture. I think most folks still believe in the concept of right and wrong, but fear of being called out by the PC police causes many to tolerate all kinds of aberration. Didn't Pontius Pilate ask Jesus, 'What is truth?' I feel like that sometimes. How can people be certain of anything if they have nothing to base their opinions on? The truth of the Bible appears up for debate, even among theologians. In the past God sent angels and caused prophets to dream dreams and see visions. Do you think things like that still happen?" (I was secretly proud of my subtlety.)

"Visions and dreams? Sure. I think that happens more often than people are willing to admit. There is a passage in the Bible that says, 'Many have entertained angels unaware.'[6] In other words, angels are all around us but most often take on the appearance of normal people, so we rarely notice. God can do whatever God wants to do. If He wants to send an angel or grant a vision or a dream, He can certainly do so. It happened all the time in the Bible. But I'm of the opinion we are suffering a spiritual drought, a famine of The Word so to speak. Everyday theophanies, are another matter. When it comes to theophanies, I guess you could call me a skeptic."

"Theophanies?"

"Right. It's a Greek word that means 'God-appearance.' There are examples throughout the Bible when God showed up at an opportune time. Moses and the burning bush, the pillar of cloud and pillar of fire that led Israel through the wilderness, the time the Lord confronted Paul as he rode to arrest Christians in Damascus... times like that."

"Interesting. Why do you suppose theophanies are so rare? And what's a famine of the Word? I've never heard that term before."

After hitting his second shot ten feet from the flag, George continued, "There's a reference to a famine of the Word in the Old Testament of the Bible. It's in the Book of Amos." George had obviously given the subject some thought. He recited the verse from memory. *"The days are coming,"* declares the Lord, *"when I will send a famine on the Land. Not a famine for bread or a thirst for water, but a famine of hearing the Word of the Lord... people will stagger from sea to sea but they will not find it."*[7]

I marked my ball on the green and began lining up my putt. I was impressed by George's Bible acumen but had to ask, "Why would God do that?"

George pulled the flag and laid it down near the edge of the green. "The days of Amos were especially evil. People had become greedy, showing little concern for the poor. The Bible says they called good bad, and bad good. They lost their moral compass. There was no such thing as right or wrong. Everything was a matter of personal opinion. The Bible says everyone did what was right in their own eyes. They had lost their way."

"Thank goodness those days are long gone!" My cynical nature was on full display.

George sounded exactly like the man in white. "The people have lost their way. They've mistaken grace for indifference and compassion for compromise. In an effort to be inclusive, they have set aside the truth."

You'd have to be asleep at the wheel to miss the connection between the days of Amos and today's "anything-goes" mentality. Although George and I were like-minded on many things, there was a major difference between us. For George it was always about honoring God's standards. From God's mouth to his ears, no questions asked. I was more pragmatic, more interested in the cause and effect of human behavior. Bad choices lead to bad outcomes. Good decisions lead to good outcomes. Maybe the two were the same. Maybe God established His standards of right and wrong for humanity's benefit, not just a means of testing faithfulness. It makes perfect sense when you think about it. Could it be as simple as the Creator knows what's best for His creation?

George shook his head. "God eventually grew tired of watching the people He loved suffer from the consequence of their own bad choices. Amos was God's last attempt at course correction. People are stubborn. Frustrated prophets called them stiff-necked. Few if any listened to Amos. They thought they knew better. A few years later Assyria invaded the country, killed their leaders, enslaved the people, and sowed their fields with salt. Those ten tribes were never heard from again."

Over the next forty-five minutes George lost focus, and it showed in his game. He three-putted the next two holes. I smiled to myself. He wanted to swear but lacked the experience. I felt bad about distracting him, a definite violation of golf etiquette. We played golf to de-stress, not aggravate each other.

"I owe you an apology, George. I didn't mean to ruin your game. I should have known better. We can change the subject if you like."

"No worries, James. Golf is just a game. Some days you have it and some days you don't. No one died here today." He smiled. "But I am worried for our families and our nation. The patience of God has limits."

"I see your point. I'm far from a model Christian myself. I can't quote chapter and verse, but I don't believe an 'anything goes mentality' can be sustained for long. Things are getting out of hand. The one thing the politically correct culture can't seem to tolerate is someone who dares to believe in right and wrong. I'm a man in the middle. I refuse to join the ranks of self-righteous Christians who condemn anyone who doesn't agree with them. They drive more people away from God than crooked politicians. But I can't bring myself to accept immorality in the name of tolerance. If there is right, there has to be wrong."

I mumbled to myself after pulling the next tee shot into the trees left of the fairway. George hardly noticed. "You said you were doing research on dreams, and visions? What's the point? Are you finally working on that book I've been urging you to write? Now that you're retired, you have the time."

"I've been asked to write a column for a syndicated website. They are giving me editorial freedom to write whatever I want—as long as it's controversial enough to get people to read it. I'm thinking of addressing some of the big issues of the day, religious and otherwise. I'd like to embody the wisdom of a Billy Graham with the orneriness of Andy Rooney. What do you think?"

"Sounds good. If it were me, I'm pretty sure I would overwhelm your readers with Bible quotes and offend them immediately. Ha! Like you said, you're a man in the middle. You often share my perspective but from a different point of view. You have the credibility and you definitely know more about writing a column than you do about golf."

George's insult was shared with a smile, "Thanks," I replied, "but that's not much of an endorsement."

The conversation turned to politics (as it often did) and the lunacy of expecting elected politicians to restore any semblance of right and wrong. The Supreme Court appears unwilling to acknowledge the existence of God despite the views of the Founding Fathers who used terms like, "... *the Laws of Nature and Nature's God.*" The Continental Congress didn't hesitate to say truth, "is self-evident," and that people are "endowed by their Creator with certain unalienable rights."

We finished our round and grabbed a cup of coffee, sitting down to tally our scores. It was one of those days the outcome didn't seem to matter as much as time spent in conversation with a good friend. Mark Twain once called golf, "A good walk spoiled." But then what did he know? He also said, "It is better to remain quiet and let people think you a fool than to open your mouth and remove all doubt." Today had been a good day despite the spoiled part of the walk.

"One last thought before you go, George. We both believe in right and wrong, but how can we be sure our opinion is the correct one? Not even Biblical scholars agree on the interpretation of Scripture. These days you can find a church willing to teach whatever you already believe."

"It's not so hard, James. A person knows right and wrong when they hear it. Don't let the experts confuse you with their theories and complicated theological explanations. Knowing right from wrong doesn't require a doctorate in theology. Study the issue. Study the Bible. Choose God's simple answer over man's complicated explanations. Don't get tangled up in the rhetoric of the truth-twisters. The good book says, *'God is not a God of confusion.'*[8] What was true for the Greeks was true for the Romans, was true for the Jew and Gentiles alike. It's still true. There were no exceptions. Fashions change, the weather changes constantly, but absolute truth never changes."

"Is that all? Anything else?"

"Keep praying and expect God to guide you. Maybe this famine of the Word is about to break. Perhaps God has chosen you to bring the rain," George said with a wink and a smile. "Let me know if I can help in any way. I'd love the honor of proof-reading your columns if you think it might help."

"I might take you up on that. Thanks, George. I got the coffee. It's the least I can do after ruining your game."

"Actually, it may have been the best game I've had for a while." George smiled as he headed towards the locker room.

I was beginning to sense a pattern. "Expect God to guide you," George said. My visitor said the same thing in so many words. But how would God guide me? That remained a mystery. I felt a sense of affirmation and encouragement from Sarah and now George. They were both eager for some response to the growing chaos of our time. I was becoming more open to the possibility of allowing God to use me in some small way. A week ago I would have laughed at the thought.

After changing shoes and stashing my gear in my locker, I headed to the parking lot. The clubhouse was buzzing with conversation and laughter. Quite different from four hours earlier when we began our round. The parking lot was full. It was hard to find an open space at mid-day. I walked past several rows of cars to my usual parking spot in the shade of a large oak. I punched the fob and was reaching for the car door when I noticed something scribbled across my trunk lid.

Scrawled in the pollen covering my trunk was a strange reference to *"Jeremiah 29:11–13."* I snapped a picture with my phone and slid behind the wheel. It hadn't been there when I parked in the nearly empty lot at sunrise. I suspected George was responsible. His car was sitting in its usual spot. He was in the habit of showering and changing clothes before leaving. I guessed he had stepped out to retrieve some clothes or put his clubs in his trunk before heading to the shower. I presumed the reference came to him after our earlier conversation and it was his way of having the last word.

As the AC kicked in and my car began to cool, I grabbed my phone to text him.

> Thanks for the message. I will
> check it out when I get home.

He must have been sitting by his locker with his phone in hand. I got an immediate response.

> What message?

> The one you wrote on
> the trunk of my car.

> I don't know what you are talking
> about. What did it say?

I texted him the photo.

> I know the passage, but I didn't write it.

> God must be trying to get your attention.
> Do you think? I'll check it out.
>
> Let me know how I can help. I
> think God has plans for you.

"God has plans for you?" Where did that come from? I had avoided all mention of the encounter with the man in white. George's comment implied God was reaching out to me. Maybe He was. I would definitely check the reference when I got home.

I noticed Sarah's car was gone as the garage door swung up. She was probably running her usual Saturday errands. I started a fresh pot of coffee and headed to the shower. I would typically replay my game shot-by-shot in my head. That's what golfers do. But today was different. I was too busy recalling my conversation with George. Was I losing my mind? Is this what happens when guys retire? Or was I beginning to believe I'd actually "entertained an angel unaware"?

George's mention of the prophet Amos and his prediction about a famine of the Word stuck with me. He said, "Maybe God wants you to bring the rain." George knew I was not religious. Why would he assume that? I got dressed and looked for the tablet, but couldn't find it. I was not surprised. Sarah was in the habit of taking it with her in case a client called about a listing, or she needed to check out a property online. Old habits die hard.

No worries, Sarah had placed our Bible next to the chair in the den where I normally sit. I looked again at the picture I had taken of my trunk lid. "Jeremiah 29:11–13." A quick glance of the index took me to page 1114. I turned a few more pages and found chapter 29.

> "I know the plans I have for you,' declares the LORD, 'plans to prosper you and not to harm you, plans to give you hope and a future. Then you will call on Me and come and pray to Me, and I will listen to you. You will seek Me and find Me when you seek Me with all your heart.'" [9]

No wonder George said, "I think God has plans for you." That guy knew his Bible.

Next to the passage in our Bible, was another reference written by hand in the margin. It was certainly not something I wrote and it wasn't Sarah's distinctive cursive either. "Mark 9:24."

Another visit to the index had me turning to page 1503. Mark 9:24. "Immediately the boy's father exclaimed, 'I do believe; help me overcome my unbelief!'"

I took a moment and read the rest of the story. A father brought his son to the disciples to have him healed of epilepsy. The boy was troubled with seizures that sent him into convulsions that had nearly caused his death more than once. The disciples were unable to help, so the boy's father appealed to Jesus. "If you can do anything," the father asked, "take pity on us and help us." Jesus replied, "If I can? All things are possible for him who believes."

I compared the story to the Jeremiah reference, and wondered about the connection between the two. Jeremiah was predicting God's plans to prosper his people if they sought him with their whole heart. The father of the epileptic son was begging Jesus to heal his son and help him rise above his lack of faith. Perhaps God's plans to prosper a person required faith on the part of the one seeking His blessing?

Who wrote the passage on my car? Who added the reference to my Bible? Both passages applied directly to my situation. Was God messing with me? Had my visitor struck again? According to Jeremiah, I needed to seek God with my whole heart. And, according to Jesus, I needed to lay aside my doubt.

My professional instincts kicked in. I needed to start recording this stuff before I forgot most of it. I went to my office and found an empty journal, grabbed a pen, and began writing.

ENTRY #1:

- Luke chapter 1: The angel Gabriel appears to Mary.

- Mary responds: "I am the Lord's servant. May your word be fulfilled in me."

- Theophany: Greek for "God appearance."

- Moses and the burning bush, the pillar of cloud and pillar of fire, Paul on his way to Damascus.

- Amos – a famine of the Word.

- God was tired of their unfaithfulness and turned their songs to dirges and make their life bitter.

- Keep it simple. Right and wrong does not require a doctorate in theology. God is not a God of confusion.

- Pray and expect God to guide you.

- Maybe God is expecting you to bring the rain?

- Jeremiah 29:11–13 God has plans for you… you will find Him when you seek him with all your heart.

- The notebook was gone… I had to use the actual Bible. Strange reference in the margin – asked Sarah about it.

- Mark 9:24 "Lord I believe. Help me with my doubts."

"Seeking the Lord with all my heart," was going to take a concerted effort. I wondered if people would notice, besides Sarah of course.

Tomorrow was Sunday. For the first time in months I actually thought about attending a local worship service. They call it God's House for a reason. But my doubts were making a strong case for the status quo.

I couldn't remember the last time I felt "close to God" in any church. Like most of my friends, I attended services for funerals, weddings and my annual pilgrimages at Christmas and Easter. I reasoned it wasn't entirely my fault. I was rarely if ever moved by the experience. My participation, if I'm honest, might say more about me, than God, or even the pastor. Expectations dictate outcomes, everyone knows that. Maybe that was true about worship too, mine were never very high. "Lord I believe. Help me with my doubt." [10]

I wondered if I should begin some kind of Bible reading plan? I was sensing an urge to become more methodical in my search for God's direction. The man in white and George had both urged me to "weigh my observations in the light of God's Word." If I was going to stay open to God's direction, I would need to spend more time reading what He had to say.

Was I becoming some kind of Jesus' freak? The possibility unsettled me. If I was going to be useful, I would have to keep it real and not get preachy and "holier-than-thou." No one listens to a religious fanatic. I never gave those types the time of day. No one did.

Maybe Sarah was right. My lack of Biblical expertise might be more useful than not.

I was after all, an expert when it came to skepticism.

"I have been driven many times upon my knees by the overwhelming conviction that I had nowhere else to go. My own wisdom and that of those about me seemed insufficient for that day."

—Abraham Lincoln

CHAPTER 4

Church

I f the Lord came to my house, perhaps it was time to return the favor.

A quick check of the website listed worship times on Saturday evening at 5:00pm and Sunday morning at 9:00 & 11:00 AM. The last service time was my preference. That option provided plenty of time to enjoy breakfast and glance at the paper per my usual Sunday routine. And besides, I didn't want to seem too eager.

Sunday is my day to take things easy. I still roll out early and take Bogey for a walk, but the rest of the morning was always left intentionally unstructured. Since retiring I look forward to perusing the stories published by my colleagues at *The Herald*. You never know what might capture their interest. With few exceptions Sunday editions are "soft-news days" in the business. Most of their columns are written in advance to give everyone a break from deadlines. The articles focus on human interest stories that are rarely time sensitive for obvious reasons. The sports page may be the exception. They are obligated to keep their fans up to date on the scores and outcomes of weekend competitions, but even they flesh-out their section with an interview of a popular athlete, or a do-good project of a known player.

A headline on the Religion page caught my eye, "The Most Segregated Hour in America." Headlines are written to capture the curiosity of the reader and this one did its job. It was drawn from a famous speech given by Martin Luther King Jr. in 1963, at Western Michigan University in Kalamazoo. A faculty member asked, "Don't you feel that integration can only be started and realized in the Christian churches, not in schools or by other means?"

No one knows if the question was prompted by an honest search for a solution, or an attempt to deflect any sense of responsibility by university faculties like the one at WMU, Kalamazoo. The professor was suggesting that Christian churches and pastors, not educational institutions, are better positioned to address the issue of racial prejudice. The decisive answer of Dr. King was not what anyone expected. He could barely contain his frustration over the racial divide in America's churches.

"We must face the fact that in America, the church is still the most segregated major institution in America. At 11:00 on Sunday morning, when we stand and sing that Christ has no East or West, we stand at the most segregated hour in this nation. This is tragic. Nobody of honesty can overlook this."

His candor must have surprised those who expected King to praise the church for their efforts to bring racial change to America. Racial tensions that year were at an all-time high. Only a few weeks earlier, King had made his watershed "I Have A Dream" speech on the steps of the Lincoln memorial. President Kennedy, a strong advocate for racial equality, had recently been assassinated in Dallas. Five years later, Dr. King would himself be gunned down in Memphis, while advocating for the cause. Clearly, the 1960's were the defining decade of the civil rights movement. But according to *The Herald's* story, now more than 50 years later, not much had changed.

Sunday morning is still considered the most segregated hour in America.

The article was syndicated, written by a nationally known journalist. I didn't know her personally but was familiar with her work. I liked her "detached approach" to the subject. I couldn't tell by reading her assessment if she was a Christian or not. She let the story tell itself without interjecting her opinion about the findings. I respected that kind of writing. It was the same approach I worked hard to maintain throughout my career.

No one, it seems, wants to tackle the question of race relations in America, but like it or not, no one escapes its impact. I felt drawn to the issue like a child to a puddle. It was the proverbial elephant in the room. It touched every aspect of society. How could we continue to ignore it? The origin of racial diversity and God's creative purpose in designing this human condition were high on my list of questions to ask the man in white.

Throughout my career covering breaking news or social trends, I was rarely assigned a story without a racial component. It was impossible to ignore. No matter what the subject: employment, education, housing, crime, business, or politics, racial diversity played a part.

As a journalist I had reached the conclusion race is not a white and black issue. It's a humanity issue. No race is more or less guilty than the next. As Dr. King said, and statistics verify, all races demonstrate separatist attitudes. African American churches still attract mostly African American Christians. And churches with Anglo-Saxon roots attract white people of European descent. Segregation by personal choice is not limited to Sunday mornings. Division along racial and ethnic lines is also noticeable on university campuses, in our neighborhoods, restaurants, commercial centers, as well as in the music, clothing, and entertainment industries. Well-meaning politicians can pass all the laws they want forbidding racial division, but they can't keep people from making personal choices. And those choices routinely occur along racial, ethnic, and socio-economic lines.

My mind was racing with thoughts stirred by the story as Sarah and I drove to our first other-than-holiday worship service in a long, long time. I expected my experience to validate *The Herald*'s findings. After all, we too were W.A.S.P. Christians (White, Anglo, Saxon, Protestants) headed to an historically W.A.S.P. church by choice.

Church-going Americans have been portrayed as more accepting of diversity than society in general. I'm not sure it was ever true, but it remains a popular perception. Most of the Christians I know believe God makes no distinction between people on the basis of race, gender or age. But the observation of Dr. King and articles like the one I just read, confirm that the social behavior of people who participate in organized religion or not, behave pretty much the same. Preachers of every race talk-the-talk of integration and equality but the racial make-up of their congregations and the weekday choices of their members demonstrate a different reality. Everyone knows that.

Sarah and I immediately noticed things about church have changed since I was a kid, and I was glad to see it. Back in the day, Dad wore a suit and tie on Sunday, but you wouldn't catch him in that "monkey suit," (as he called it) any other day of the week. Back then everything about church was squared-away and ritualistic. Women almost always wore dresses. The pastor wore a black button-down robe covered by a frilly white gown with a colorful stole draped over his shoulders. It could be 100 degrees in the non-air-conditioned sanctuary. He'd be sweating like a ditch digger, but that was what he did. Sermons were preached from a high pulpit so he could be heard before the age of digital mics. But mostly it gave the impression that the laity were being "talked down to," or "preached at," a term eventually applied to anyone who came off as self-righteous. If that wasn't intimidating enough, the inflection most preachers assumed when speaking took on a deep authoritarian tone reserved only for that purpose. Growing up, it all seemed odd and a bit scary. I reasoned it was the adult thing to do and I would grow up to see the wisdom of it. But I never did.

As a kid my family attended a church called St. Peter. The church Sarah and I were planning to attend is called, "Reliance." I like the sound of Reliance. It suggests more than a continuation of the ancient past, repeating the same liturgy, the same songs, sung to the same organ, surrounded by the same architecture and the same zoned-out parishioners. The name Reliance implies a present-day application of timeless truth. That concept appealed to me.

Fresh from reading *The Herald* article earlier that morning, my attention was drawn to the nonverbal clues of the church environment. Guys in suits and women in dresses were the exception, not the rule. And none of those men wore ties. Jeans appeared to be the norm, but shorts were not uncommon. We were offered a cup of coffee and invited to carry it into the worship center if we wanted. It made me smile as I thought back to St. Peter and how anyone carrying coffee into the sanctuary would have been turned back in the days of my youth. The culture of Reliance was definitely outside my childhood experience, and I knew things back at St. Peter hadn't changed much. Well that's not exactly true. The once full pews were now pretty much empty. They were probably a year or five away from closing their doors for good.

It was a sad commentary on the focus of many historic churches. People were still seeking divine direction but had moved on to churches delivering the ancient truth in culturally relevant ways. Those changes were for the better in my opinion. Maybe things were better racially too. I was curious to see if the teaching had also shifted to mirror the popular beliefs of the culture. Could the ancient truth be dressed in new clothes without losing its substance. That remained to be seen.

The stage at Reliance (the term "chancel" didn't seem to apply) was professionally lighted and contained a drum kit, guitar stands, keyboards and microphones in preparation for the band that would soon welcome hundreds of people streaming in from six or seven entrances across the back and sides of the room. It looked more like a civic center than a place of worship. Padded chairs with arm rests had replaced the oak pews of my youth. Huge projection screens hung along the wall behind the band with flat-screen-monitors scattered here and there as well. Camera-operators stood on platforms and a roving tech team dressed in black stood ready to capture close-ups of the singers, the pastor and the congregation. It was definitely not your momma's church.

As Sarah and I found our seats, I noticed a 20-something African

American was sitting behind the drums and a Hispanic woman was one of the four lead singers. The bass guitar was played by a Caucasian teenage girl, and a 60ish white guy with a ponytail was playing lead guitar. I couldn't help but think he had played in a 70's rock band in a former life. I wondered if the church leaders were intentionally trying to address the problem of the "Most Segregated Hour In America," by modeling greater diversity in the worship team.

The quality and energy of the music stirred the audience who raised their hands and clapped not unlike a crowd at a rock concert. The ethnic diversity of the band was more noticeable than in the audience. The worshippers appeared to be a mostly homogenous bunch, with some people of color visible here and there across the room. I gave the leaders credit for trying, but evidence of segregation by choice was still on display in the room. I was not in any position to pass judgment. My decision to attend this particular church was likewise based on an expectation of a familiar demographic and a style of worship that made me, a recently retired white dude, feel comfortable.

The pastor was Caucasian, perhaps in his late thirties, but no more than forty. He wore a wireless mic, designer jeans, and a long-sleeve shirt rolled up his forearms. His manner was relaxed and personable, not words I would use to describe the pastor of my childhood. He began his message telling a story from his past, then transitioned to a Scripture reading displayed on a flat-screen next to the stool on which he sat. He read the story line by line guiding our eyes to highlighted words and phrases with his hand. He did the same later emphasizing the key points of his message. It was very similar to presentations I have often experienced in business conferences, only better organized and visually illustrated. Reliance was definitely in touch with the electronic culture of the day.

The pastor's message was based on the story of the Good Samaritan from the gospel of Luke. I think most people probably know bits of the story, even if they're unfamiliar with the Bible. The term, "Good Samaritan," has become slang for do-gooders everywhere. In the story, a man in the crowd asks Jesus His opinion about how to obtain eternal life. Jesus discerned that the man had asked his question as a test, not because he was confused about the answer. Jesus turned the tables on the guy and asked the man for his own opinion. The challenger quickly (and perhaps arrogantly) replied that the way to attain eternal life was to,

> 'Love the Lord your God with all your heart and with all your soul and with all your strength and with all your mind' and, 'Love your neighbor as yourself.' [11]

The pastor suggested Jesus must have smiled at that point, realizing the motive of the man had been revealed. *"You have answered well,"* Jesus replied. *"Do this and you will live."* In other words Jesus was saying, *"Good luck meeting that standard!"* Undaunted, the man asked, *"Who is my neighbor?"* In answer, Jesus told the story of the Good Samaritan.

The Bible story begins by describing a Jewish traveler who was robbed and left for dead along a deserted stretch of road. Two religious men, one after the other, came upon him and fearing for their own safety and estimating the inconvenience of stopping, passed by quickly. Then a Samaritan came along, from a race of people despised by the Jews. The Samaritan also saw the injured man, treated his wounds, and took him to an inn where he paid in advance for his continued treatment. Jesus asked, *"Which person turned out to be a good neighbor to the man who was robbed and left for dead?"*[12] The answer was obvious.

The pastor quickly turned his message back to the original question that prompted the story, *"What must I do to have eternal life?"*[13] Like a good journalist, he looked deeper than the mere facts of the story. He emphasized the impossibility of achieving perfection, and the necessity of God's grace. But I was more interested in the story behind the story, the racial component. The man who rendered aid was a Samaritan. People of the Jewish race and the Samaritan race didn't play nice together. That aspect of the story had my full attention.

Who were the Samaritans? Why did the Jews despise them? I started my day reading an article about racial prejudice in the modern church. I came to church and heard a Bible story about racial prejudice during the time of Jesus. The subject had my full attention. Why was racial diversity such a big deal for people? And if God knew racial diversity would be the source of so much trouble, why did He create it or allow it to exist? I made a note to find out more about the difference between the Samaritans and Jews and why they hated each other. Racial prejudice is evidently an issue that has plagued people of every culture even before the days of Jesus, maybe forever.

The service continued as expected. I couldn't help but think about the concept of "church," and its unique place in our culture. Where else do people gather in large numbers on a weekly basis just to hear lectures about life's values and purpose? Business professionals attend conferences and trade shows a few times a year for the sake of profit, but thousands more attend weekly services and freely contribute hard-earned money to support ministries and to assist the less fortunate. It seemed like a good place to start looking for answers to the hot topics of our day. All my journalistic instincts were kicking in. It felt right.

After worship, Sarah and I drove to a nearby deli to grab a bite and discuss our morning. Over lunch we discussed how our childhood experiences formed our opinions about race in America. We were both old enough to remember the 1960's, the black and white images (no pun intended) of protests, marches, speeches and racial violence that dominated the evening news. I'm sure we overheard many an adult conversation on the subject, but I couldn't recall any strong opinions expressed by my parents one way or the other.

I was raised in a small town in the Midwest. Sarah was raised in a Texas city of more than a million people. I don't recall any students of color attending my elementary school. Sarah's experience was more diverse but Caucasians were still the majority in her neighborhood and church. High School was more integrated for both of us but already the "birds of a feather" axiom was in play. Segregation was apparent in various forms, not just race. Farm kids hung with farm kids, affluent students with kids from the same zip codes, and the working class found their peer group too. It seems wrong now but felt perfectly normal at the time.

My first serious consideration of race came as a freshman in college. I had been recruited to play basketball for a small Christian college in Texas. Unsure of my academic ability, I turned down the scholarship in favor of intramurals, deciding to devote myself to my studies. I loved the thought of heading South for the winter. When I went to sign up for classes, I discovered the registrar had flagged my name. I was directed to the Dean of Students' office but had no idea why. I hadn't been on campus long enough to get in any trouble.

The Dean was a pleasant man. He quickly assured me there was no reason for concern. The college was small, only a couple hundred students in each class. In addition to recruiting me, they had also recruited an African American basketball player from Alabama. The college had a number of local African American students attending classes, but my roommate Jerome Jones, would be the only resident black student on campus. The Dean reasoned that since we were both athletes and I grew up north of the Mason-Dixon line, there would be less risk of racial issues if he roomed with me rather than with a southerner. Jerome and I both laughed at that logic. I knew plenty of white athletes from the north who were just as prejudiced as any southern boy, but that's how I ended up sharing a room with Jerome from Alabama.

It was an interesting year for both of us. I was shelter by my childhood, naïve to say the least. I knew absolutely nothing about the Jackson Five, had never seen a hair pick, or heard of afro-sheen. But despite our cultural differences, Jerome and I got along just fine. I'm sure he was equally curious about my love of hunting, ice hockey, and country music. It's a toss-up who was more uncomfortable: Jerome when he attended a social event on campus, or me when I tagged along with him to a party hosted by the black students who lived in town. I don't recall any arguments between us, but there were more than a few cultural differences we chided each other over. Jerome only attended college for one year. It was a simple case of home sickness. That, and an understandably difficult adjustment to the Texas' "cowboy culture." We parted as friends but lost touch over the years, both of us drawn back into our respective cultural corners.

As Sarah and I left the Deli, my attention was drawn to a commotion near our car. A tricked-out, oversized pickup truck was stranded with its hood raised. I noticed a large bumper sticker proclaiming, "Black Lives Matter" on the tail gate. A larger-than-average African American man, whom I assumed to be the owner, was engaged in an animated conversation with four Spanish-speaking men who had piled out of their landscaping truck and trailer to offer assistance.

One of the lawn crew noticed us walking past and yelled in English, "Hey James, can you give us a hand?"

His words caught me by surprise. I turned to see if he was talking to someone behind me. Seeing no one, I responded, "Are you talking to me?"

"Yep, you. Can you give us a hand here James? Henry needs a jump and our rig is too long to get close enough without blocking traffic. Can you pull your SUV over? I have jumper cables."

Ignoring his request for a moment, I had to ask, "Do I know you? Have we met?"

His response only deepened the mystery. "We met once, but you wouldn't remember it. It was late and you were tired. You work for the newspaper don't you?"

"I used to, but not for a while." Maybe that was it. Maybe he knew me from a story I had covered, or from the picture on my byline. It was not unusual for people to greet me on the street as if they knew me. It was a hazard of the profession. People remembered me from a story I had covered, and assumed I remembered them too. But I'd covered hundreds of stories and interviewed thousands of people. Remembering names was not my strong suit.

We walked over to assess the situation and shake hands. "I'm James King and this is my wife, Sarah."

"Hi Sarah." Sam, the English-speaking member of the landscape crew shook my hand with a double grip and a slight nod of his head. "I'm Sam, Sam Gooding," he replied. "Henry needs a jump. It will only take a moment."

"Okay. Sure thing." I asked Sarah to bring our car over, while I greeted the rest of the men. Sam fetched the jumper cables from his trailer.

It didn't take long. Sam knew what he was doing and quickly had Henry's truck running and on his way. I was impressed by the encounter, Hispanic landscapers stopping to help an African American they had never met, asking a middle-aged white guy to give them a hand. In a moment of honest reflection, I wondered if I would have offered to help if Sam had not stopped me. His example made an impact. I was inspired by his compassion to buy Sam's crew lunch out of respect for their kindness.

"Mighty nice of you James, but you and Sarah were just leaving. You don't need to do that."

"We'd like to do it anyway. I was impressed by your willingness to help Henry and besides it won't take long."

So back we went into the restaurant. Sam's crew placed their order and I handed my credit card to the cashier. It amuses me how little it actually costs and how unusual it seems to be considered generous in our society. The bill for his entire crew came to less than $60.

We followed Sam to his table to make sure everyone had all they needed and say our goodbyes.

"Funny how it works," Sam said with a smile. "You thought you were just going to church today, but God wanted you to be the church."

"How do you know we just came from church?"

Sam laughed. "Am I right? I have a sixth-sense about these things. Going to church can be good, but what matters most is how you apply your faith after you leave. Am I right? Christians like us have the opportunity every day to make a difference in things that matter. Think about what you just experienced James. A bunch of Mexicans helping a black man by recruiting a white guy to solve a problem. It doesn't get any better than that!" he said with a laugh.

"Is that what just happened? I'm even more impressed than I was before," I said with a smile.

"That's a story worth telling James. It's not what people expect. Our differences aren't a bad thing. They create opportunity! Opportunity to do the unexpected. Opportunity to love in action and not just words. You gotta love that." He was fired up.

Who thinks like that? Who talks like that? I suddenly wondered if any of this had been a coincidence. His perspective struck me as unusual. I asked again, "Sam, how did you say we met?"

"I didn't say, James," Sam replied with his characteristic smile. "Let's just say the Lord brought us together." And with that, he shook my hand, thanked me for lunch, and returned to his crew.

I couldn't help but wonder about the entire encounter. "Our differences aren't a bad thing. They create opportunity," he said. And, "Let's just say the Lord brought us together." Was God messing with me? Was Sam who he appeared to be or was he another angelic stalker like the man in white? I remembered George mentioning encountering angels without realizing it. Was God trying to get my attention? Was he asking me to address racial prejudice in America? Was that what today was about?

Sam Gooding? Good Sam? Good Samaritan? My instincts were working overtime. It was too much of a coincidence to be a coincidence.

They say "all kids are born color-blind," but we grow up and begin to "see" things and people differently. The reality of racial difference is ever-present, but rarely discussed outside of our own clan. When it comes to racial issues, we live in a "them and us" culture. It doesn't have to be a negative stereotype to still be a stereotype. We categorize and make assumptions about "them," and "they" categorize and make assumptions about "us." Our morning experience piqued my interest. How, when, and where had race occurred? I had no idea.

I just spent Sunday morning in a worship service where I expected to find God. It seems God was definitely trying to teach me something. It was time to put my investigative reporter hat back on and go to work. "Check your sources," was S.O.P. in the journalism business. I had leads I needed to follow. *The Herald* article about segregation mentioned Pentecost as the birth of the Christian church. One of the article's statements referred to John's vision of heaven as a multi-racial, multi-lingual reality. I needed to check that out.

The pastor's message this morning also spoke to me. I resonated to his emphasis on grace as the great equalizer. I've never been tempted to claim any personal merit or worthiness before God. My struggle is just the opposite. I find it hard to believe God could actually care about a sinner like me. But what had captured my greatest attention was the racial issue in the story of the Good Samaritan. Was Jesus the Savior of everyone, or the Jewish Messiah only? Did He come to save Samaritans as well as Jews? And if he is truly the world's Messiah, how prepared are modern day Christians to recognize our racial prejudice and accept the Samaritans (and everyone else who is racially, ethnically, or economically different from us) as equally important to Him?

If the Bible account is to be believed, humanity is universally descended from a single couple, Adam and his wife, Eve. So where did racial diversity come from? How could God be happy with the current state of Christian diversity, or more accurately, the lack thereof?

I was willing to do my part, but it was the Lord's idea to recruit me. I don't recall volunteering for the job of modern-day prophet.

I was definitely in need of divine assistance.

"It is time for parents to teach young people early on that in diversity there is beauty and there is strength."

—*Maya Angelou*

CHAPTER 5

Mordecai

"Can I help you young man?"

Sarah sometimes chides me by saying, "You've aged well for an old guy," but I have not been called "young man," by a stranger in a while. I turned to see a middle-aged African American man standing just off my left shoulder. He had a pleasant smile, was well dressed, with salt and pepper hair gracing his temples. I suspected he was about my age, give or take a couple of years.

"I just finished my last book and am looking for another," I responded.

"Anything specific, Jim? From what I've noticed, you gravitate to biographies and American history."

It didn't take a psychic to notice I was looking at books in the biography section of The Footnote, my favorite used bookstore. But how did he know my name? This was the second time in a week a stranger had called me by name.

"I'm sorry. Have we met? I'm not great with names, but I rarely forget a face."

"Mordecai Taylor," he replied as he stuck out his hand. "You write for *The Herald* don't you? No reason you should know me, but I've seen you in here a few times. We have the same taste in books. I've been a regular for a couple of years. Two weeks ago I watched you snag the Nat King Cole biography I was eyeing."

The Herald connection again. "I used to write a column for them but recently retired. I finished the Cole book. I could loan it to you if you'd like. It was not well written in my opinion, but contained some great quotes and excerpts of articles from the 1940's. It was worth the effort it took to read it. I'd gladly give it to you for that matter, but I have a hard time parting with one of my children," I said with a smile.

"I hear you. I'm the same way about books. I like to sit in a room surrounded by the thoughts and stories of gifted people. It's like having coffee in a room full of extraordinary personalities. Nat Cole was one of a kind," Mordecai added. "He blurred the lines between jazz, pop, instrumentals, vocals and race too. His appeal was universal."

I smiled in agreement. Cole said he was a musician at heart but sang because the public buys it. I sometimes listened to his recordings after reading a chapter or two from his biography. He was smooth and sang with a thoughtful poise honed by struggle. The contrast of his preacher/father's influence and his love of the music he heard as a child in the honky-tonks of Chicago comes through in his art. But what especially captured my interest was his impact on race relations in America. My mom, along with millions of blue-collar white women bought his records during the 40's and 50's, one of the most segregated times in America. That fascinates me."

"What's the greatest thing you can learn? To love and be loved in return!" Mordecai said with a smile.

He was referencing lyrics from Nature Boy, one of Cole's early mega-hits. He obviously knew a few things about Nat Cole and his music.

"That lyric goes to the heart of it. That's what caught my interest. I'm trying to gain a better understanding of the African American perspective of life in a predominately white culture. The good, bad, and ugly of race relations is complicated. I've read the biographies of Nat King Cole, Booker

T. Washington, Mohamed Ali, Ray Charles, Martin Luther King, George Washington Carver, Frederick Douglass and Malcolm X, and others I can't recall."

"That's quite a list. I bet I can predict what you discovered."

"That there is no one, united, African American opinion about race relations in the United States of America?" I said with a smile.

"Ding, ding, ding... give this man some applause. He just answered correctly!" Mordecai said with an infectious and disarming laugh. "If you read Douglas, Washington, King and Malcolm X, you know that for sure. You are closer to the truth than you realize. Their wisdom is best understood through their experience, not their words. I'm not sure they even fully understood the importance of their own contribution to the subject of race relations in America." He looked away in thought, then added, "I have learned the lesson that great men cultivate love and little men cherish a spirit of hatred. I learned that assistance given to the weak makes the one who gives it strong; and that oppression of the unfortunate makes one weak."

I recognized the quote immediately from Booker T. Washington's autobiography, *Up from Slavery*. I consider Booker T.'s book one of the most important biographies in my library. I quoted him often in my columns and tried to live by the principles he espoused. Washington's wisdom and his work at Tuskegee Institute is one of America's great treasures. People resonate to his perspective. His is the kind of truth grown from struggle that needs no validation. I responded to Mordecai with a favorite Washington quote of my own. "'I will permit no man to degrade my soul by making me hate him.'" I actually have a first edition copy of *Up from Slavery*, and another copy I have highlighted, underlined, and notated so much it's falling apart and hard to read."

There was something mysterious about Mordecai. I have no memory of seeing him in The Footnote, and yet he mentioned seeing me there often. It didn't seem possible. I only perused potential purchases along a twenty-foot section of the bookcases. Mordecai was not the kind of person who blended into a crowd. He was distinctive in his appearance and manner.

I sensed there was more to Mordecai than he was willing to share. My experiences over the last few days prompted me to prolong the encounter.

I invited him next door to continue our conversation over a cup of coffee. "I'm buying and you should definitely take advantage of that rare occurrence," I said with a wink. I was glad he agreed rather than cut and run as is the custom of most men when things get real. Mordecai was different, not just racially but in his demeanor. There was an air of authority to his comments. And yet he didn't come off as arrogant, just confident, and sure.

I began the discussion. "You seem to know my story. What's yours? Are you still gainfully employed?"

"You could say I've dabbled in education most of my life. And like you, I've always been interested in why people do what they do, no matter what their race, creed, or social standing." His answer was short on specifics. "It's funny isn't it, how guys ask about each other's professional lives, not each other's family status." Mordecai smiled knowingly.

I felt a need to share more about my quest for truth. "I told you I was retired, but actually I've been asked to freelance a series of stories on any topic of my choosing. I've been thinking about the concept of political correctness run amuck in America. Don't laugh, but the lyrics of Buffalo Springfield's song, *For What It's Worth,* keep running through my mind. The political mantra denounces the battle lines being drawn between people of different race, political opinion, attitudes towards war, peace, and social status. The song makes the obvious but overlooked claim that if all people and all positions are denounced as wrong, nothing can be declared right. Truth exists. To declare something right, something must be declared wrong.

"That's a classic. The lyrics are relevant because they are still true. I'm not especially religious but I believe in right and wrong. Every opinion can't be equally valid. I'm just getting started on my assignment and feel drawn to address the subject of race-relations in America. It's been controversial ever since God made dirt and doesn't seem to be getting better any time soon. I don't understand why it's still such an emotional issue 150 years after the Civil War. What's your opinion? How and when did racial differences enter the picture? Will people of different races, creeds, and cultures ever get along? Have they ever gotten along? If you could speak a word of advice to help broaden my perspective, what would you say?"

"I'm convinced God got it right. That's what I'd say. If I could wave a magic wand and make the whole world the same color, speak the same language and share the same culture I wouldn't do it. A diverse world is a better world in my not-so-humble opinion. Try to imagine a world without color... the purples, reds, and yellows of a sunset, the brilliance of autumn, the beauty of wheat dancing in the breeze." Mordecai leaned across the table, emphasizing his point.

"A world without color would be a boring world. In the same way racial diversity makes the world more interesting. It also creates a perfect opportunity for the best of us to give and receive God's love to one another, just like we are doing now. Do people mistreat and stereotype others on the basis of race, creed, and culture? Absolutely! They always have and always will. The world is a sinful place filled with sinful people. But the potential for evil was even greater before diversity existed, when the people of the world were all the same."

He spoke with conviction. "What makes you so certain? If the value of diversity is so obvious, why is it the source of so much conflict?"

"I have no doubt when it comes to God's truth, Jim. Your assignment is important, but don't assume people will accept the truth just because it's true. Manage your expectations. Remember, they killed the prophets and crucified Jesus. There is a Scripture that says, 'Our words are wise because they are from God, telling of God's wise plan to bring us into the glories of heaven. This plan was hidden in former times, though it was made for our benefit before the world began. But the great men of the world have not understood it; if they had, they never would have crucified the Lord of Glory.'" 14

Mordecai had my full attention. He was obviously a spiritual person. His perspective was grounded in a deep but practical understanding of God's Word. I can't explain why, but I resonated to what he said. Maybe it was the conviction in his tone, his certainty. I'm not sure. My editor always said, "Truth has an edge to it. It cuts through the B.S." He also said, "You can often tell the power of an article by the negative reaction it generates. People can't let it pass. It reaches out and grabs their attention." My father-in-law, raised on a farm in Wisconsin called it, "Plowing close to the corn." I smiled to remember it.

"You said, 'The potential for evil was unlimited when the people of the world were all the same?' What did you mean? When was that?"

"Check out the story of the Tower of Babel in the Book of Genesis," Mordecai suggested. "Before sin entered the picture race, faith and cultural unity was a powerful force for good. But along came sin and changed everything. The power of unity to accomplish good became Satan's means to accomplish evil. The devil attempted to turn God's blessing into a curse. It all came to a head at a place called Babel. To limit the destructive capacity of evil God created division. The creation of diversity limited mankind's evil intention to unite against the Lord and the Lord's plans for humanity's good."

I was impressed by Mordecai's insight. I hadn't thought about the downside of one race, one language, one culture. I had assumed that was the ideal we should be striving to establish. "I suppose there are two sides to every coin," I injected. "We are limited by what we've experienced. People with different experiences and perspectives have the potential to contribute a greater blessing. I never considered the destructive nature of unity under the control of sinful people, or the advantages of diversity."

"Jim, the world is a mess to be sure. But God has redeemed the world. He's not the cause of evil, He's the solution. God snatched victory from defeat. Whatever the devil attempts to do in an effort to destroy God's design, God uses against him to bless His creation."

Mordecai waved our waitress off when she offered a refill. I felt the opportunity for more dialogue slipping away, but something Mordecai said prompted the need to ask one more question. "You said I should manage my expectations. You predicted truth will always be met with skepticism. What's the point of truth if people are unwilling to accept it?"

"Jim, truth matters, even if the majority of people reject it. There is power in truth. The faithful need its reassurance and the skeptics need its challenge. A skeptic by definition is not easily convinced of anything. The truth has the power to turn a skeptic into a believer, more than you realize and more than they care to admit. Every generation needs to hear the truth. Our job is promotion, not sales. Hasn't that always been your challenge as a journalist?"

"I suppose so. You've given me a lot to think about. Thanks for taking the time. By the way, how can I get the Nat King Cole book to you?"

"Don't worry about it," Mordecai said with a smile. "I have access to the primary source."

Before I could question the meaning of his reply, Mordecai was shaking my hand to leave. "I'd like to talk again. How can I reach you?" I asked.

"No need for that, Jim. I'm sure we'll bump into each other often enough. In the meantime, you have your work cut out for you."

He was right of course. I had more leads than I had for most of the stories I'd covered for *The Herald*.

Sarah had dinner waiting when I got home. She was eager for me to keep this project moving and post my first articles. I told her about meeting Mordecai and our unexpected conversation. Sarah had the same sense that this project was unlike any other I had ever tackled. It had a life of its own, guided it seems, by promptings and meetings beyond my control, beyond explanation really.

I needed to capture my latest interaction on the Link Chart I had created on the wall in my office. I used the same technique throughout my career to visually display the leads I considered most important to a story. It consisted mostly of Post-it notes on topics, resources and people that were grouped according to categories with lines of string linking cross-connections, thus the name. This project included four categories. 1.) Historic Insight, 2.) Ancient Beliefs, 3.) Personal Encounters, and 4.) Popular Opinion.

Under Historic Insight I posted: Consult biographies and autobiographies, followed by notes containing the names and documents I considered relevant to the topic. The question of race relations was not a new interest of mine. My shelves and files contained articles, biographies and autobiographies that touched on race and racial prejudice from the time of the founding fathers to Nelson Mandela and Barrack Obama. The list was not limited to political figures. It included artists, sports figures, military, and industrial leaders who had made an impact on the question of race, intentionally or not.

Under Ancient Beliefs, I posted Scripture passages I needed to study based on my limited Christian background, The Herald article, and my conversations with George and Mordecai. The list already included the Book of Genesis, the story of Babel, the Good Samaritan, The Samaritan Woman, the Book of Philemon, Pentecost, as well as the description of heaven found in the Book of Revelation.

I hesitated to include personal encounters as a category. No self-respecting journalist would give much credibility to an anecdotal source, but personal encounters had led me to other important discoveries and posting them on the Link Chart would prompt my recall. The list included, my night visitor, The Herald article, George, Jerome Jones, Pastor Martin, Sam Gooding, and now Mordecai Taylor.

The category of Popular Opinion would help me focus on the purpose of my op-ed. Right or wrong, popular opinions had to be acknowledged. There was no point in addressing questions people were not asking. I also needed to consider the confusion created by opinions that were deemed "politically correct." Everyone acknowledged the problem of self-imposed segregation, but no one knew what to do about it. If I hoped to impact popular opinion, I needed to understand it.

I tackled the category of ancient sources first. It had been a while since I intentionally read the Bible. We kept one around like most people keep a dictionary or thesaurus, for reference when the occasion called for it. I reasoned it was like riding a bike once you mastered the basics, you might wobble a bit after an extended hiatus but would quickly recall the essentials.

From my past reading of the founding fathers, many of whom were slave owners, until the passage of the 13th Amendment outlawing slavery in the United States, I knew that slave holders and abolitionists had both used the Bible to justify and denounce slavery. Could any two positions be more diametrically opposite? No wonder people say you can prove anything from the Bible! I was eager to explore the arguments of both extremes.

Even before being recruited for the task at hand, I had read the so-called Biblical arguments supporting slavery and racial prejudice. They were contrary to everything I believed about the nature of God. Yes, slavery had existed in Bible times, so had stealing, lying and murder but that didn't exonerate those crimes either. The arguments used to endorse slavery required a twisting of Scripture and didn't ring true. No educated student of the Bible could endorse racial prejudice based on Scripture.

The most popular secular theory suggested racial differences were the natural result of geographic isolation of a people group. It was believed their proximity to the equator over time had caused certain ethnic groups to develop darker or lighter pigmentation and other features. This theory is absurd on face value with no scientific or biological basis of support.

South Africa was colonized by the British 200 years ago, and the Dutch before them, and yet South Africans of European descend are still born fair skinned with no greater African-racial tendencies than their ancestors. People do not become more or less Asian, African, or Caucasian by living for generations in a certain region of the world. Darkened features caused by exposure to the sun are not transferred through birth. If the Bible is to be believed that teaches we are all descendants of one man and one woman, then something drastic happened that forever changed God's original design. According to Genesis, God himself altered his design and created the races for the greater good of mankind. But how and when?

Some of the sources I checked referenced the "mark of Cain," Adam and Eve's firstborn son and the murderer of his brother Abel, as the origin of racial distinction and justification for prejudice. But that bucket doesn't hold water. The mark of Cain was the "branding" of a single person, for the sake of his protection after he killed his brother Abel, not the establishment of a distinctive race or a justification for prejudice. And besides, there is not just one racial variation in the world but many.

Other sources referenced the curse of Ham, Noah's youngest son, as an explanation for the origin of race. I checked that out too. After the flood

Noah planted a vineyard and got drunk. Ham discovered him lying naked in his tent and urged his two other brothers to check it out. Shielding their eyes, his brothers covered their father in a show of respect. In response to Ham's disrespect, Noah proclaimed that his descendants would become servants (some translations say slaves) to the descendants of his older brothers. It's absurd to believe Noah's words had anything to do with the establishment of race or the justification of prejudice. Noah's prophecy was fulfilled when Israel, under the leadership of Joshua, entered the Promised Land and conquered the Canaanites (the descendants of Ham). That historic reference has nothing to do with the establishment of race or prejudice.

I took the time to read the entire Book of Genesis. I could find no reference to race in the creation accounts. Strangely, I noticed a hand-written reference in the margin of our Bible next to the story of The Tower of Babel which Mordecai had mentioned. The notation looked recent but how it got there I have no idea. At this point, I was beginning to expect the unexpected without question. The reference directed me to a poignant story involving Moses and his siblings Aaron and Miriam. It led me to the Book of Numbers.

Moses' first wife was a Midianite of Arab descent. But after her death Moses married a woman from the land of Cush, an African tribe. Miriam and Aaron criticized their brother for marrying an African woman and, based on what appears to be racist attitudes, challenged his continued standing as Israel's leader. God descended on the camp of Israel in a thick fog to resolve the dispute. When the fog lifted, Miriam, the instigator of the gossip, was turned completely white by leprosy. It was as if God was making a point about skin color. "You prefer white? I'll show you white!" Ever-compassionate and forgiving Moses immediately interceded for his sister. But God declared she must remain a leper for seven days, an entire week to consider the consequence of her prejudice.

The only credible reference to the origin of race contained in the Bible is the one suggested by Mordecai in the coffee shop. The story of Babel that he mentioned from the Book of Genesis (which occurred long before Moses married the woman from Cush), offers an explanation the other theories do not. To be sure, it's a bizarre story. I'm not suggesting it is scientifically reasonable. It is not, but neither is the concept of God creating the first man out of the dust of the ground and his helpmate from his rib. Miracles are unreasonable by definition.

The account of Babel requires a good deal of faith in the veracity of the Bible to accept the story as factual, but based on my own recent experiences that seems to be God's way. The account explains God's reasoning for creating diversity and describes the place and time in history when He drove a supernatural wedge between the heretofore homogeneous Jewish nation. It is a clear, concise, and candid telling of the means and the motive for the creation of diversity.

Nothing in Genesis chapter eleven definitively says God created racial distinctions at Babel, only that He confused their languages so they could not understand each other. There are hints that God's interference involved more than language. Assessing the problem God said, "If as one people, speaking the same language they have begun to do this..." Language appears to be only one aspect of the lockstep God considered troublesome. It does not require a leap of faith to believe the Lord created other distinctions including race that drove people into distinctive and separate camps. For those who believe God can do anything by virtue of being God, the account of God's intervention at Babel appears entirely possible. It is a simple question of trusting or not trusting the Bible's explanation for the origin of human diversity.

From my reading in Genesis, God clearly commanded humanity to be fruitful, increase in number, inhabit the whole earth and rule over it. When sin entered the picture, man's desires and God's expectations were no longer in sync. The Babel story describes man's rebellion against God. Instead of spreading out to occupy the entire world in obedience to God's directive, they were determined to stay in one place.

"Let us build a city for ourselves" they declared, "with a tower reaching into the heavens, so that we have a place for ourselves;

otherwise we will end up scattered over the face of the earth." [15]

If they would not voluntarily occupy the whole earth in obedience to His command, God decided to make it happen another way. Observing their defiant nature God surmised,

> "'If as one people speaking the same language, they have begun to do this, then nothing they plan to do will be impossible for them. Come, let us go down and confuse their language so they will not understand each other.' So the LORD scattered them from there over all the earth, and they stopped building the city. That is why it was called Babel." [16]

Before humanity could succeed in obstructing God's intention for world-wide inhabitation, the Lord intervened, creating confusion. God's concern was greater than disbursement. He reasoned, *"If they have begun to do this, nothing they desire to do will be impossible."* [17]

For the last 100 years Sunday school teachers have taught stories of Jesus befriending, healing, and comforting all types of people no matter what their race or status in society. The accounts of Jesus' kindness to all people demonstrate God's love for every age, race, creed, and gender. The ultimate purpose of Babel was not segregation as some suggest, but an increased appreciation for diversity designed to bless the entire world.

According to the facts of the story, God created diversity as a means to an end, not an end in itself. It was the means by which God's original objective was achieved. It demonstrates how and why God brought an end to limitless evil. Journalism taught me to use the facts to interpret and better understand the parts of a story that were less clear. Everyone knows God is love. As love personified, God cannot be the source of hate and division. Consider the evil Hitler perpetuated in an attempt to establish his so-called superior Aryan race by destroying every other race he considered inferior. God's establishment of diversity at Babel demonstrated His unwillingness to allow a single race to dominate the world. He would not permit it at the time of Babel, nor under the tyranny of Hitler, and He won't permit it now either.

A Post-it note on my Link Chart brought me back to the article from the Sunday Herald. It referenced interviews with Christian scholars who were adamant in their belief that segregation was never God's intention, not then, not now. They contend those who value God's principles, are in a position to reclaim the miraculous power of unity for good. Pentecost, they said, was a reversal of Babel, a restoration of unity's power for the benefit of the entire world, regardless of racial and cultural diversity. They propose people of every race, language and culture were reunited by the power of the Holy Spirit at Pentecost, not by a denial of their differences but by the acceptance of a common faith despite their differences.

Pentecost is considered the birthday of the Christian church. It is so-named because it occurred fifty days after Jesus' ascension just as He had promised. On that day God sent His Spirit to enable the Lord's disciples to speak languages and dialects they had never learned, and for good reason. The audience who witnessed the miracle was extremely diverse.

"Parthians, Medes and Elamites; residents of Mesopotamia, Judea and Cappadocia, Pontus and Asia, Phrygia and Pamphylia, Egypt and the parts of Libya near Cyrene; visitors from Rome (both Jews and converts to Judaism); Cretans and Arabs—we hear them declaring the wonders of God in our own tongues!" Amazed and perplexed, they asked one another, "What does this mean?" [18]

A quick read of the account in the Book of Acts, chapter two, confirmed those in attendance had come to Jerusalem from across the world where they'd been disbursed since the days of Babel: Italy, Africa, Saudi Arabia, Iraq, Iran, Mesopotamia, Egypt and Turkey. It is safe to say the birth of the church on Pentecost embraced people that were ethnically and racially diverse but spiritually unified

The news article was openly critical of segregation evidenced in contemporary Christianity, calling it an aberration of God's intention. The article referenced Biblical prophecies that predict heaven will be racially, linguistically, and culturally diverse. John's vision as recorded in Revelation describes a restoration of God's original design.

> "I looked, and there before me was a great multitude that no one could count, from every nation, tribe, people and language, standing before the throne and before the Lamb." [19]

The book of the Bible that interested me even more than Revelation was the letter the apostle Paul wrote to a man named Philemon. As a lifelong student of history, I knew that before the civil war, the pro-slavery faction and the abolitionists both appealed to the Book of Philemon to justify their positions. As it turns out, Philemon was the "owner" of a runaway slave by the name of Onesimus. I discovered the entire book contains only twenty-five verses and is located near the end of the New Testament. Onesimus became known to Paul because of the kindness he demonstrated during the apostle's Roman imprisonment.

When Paul learned that Onesimus was a runaway slave, he sent him back to his Christian owner carrying a personal letter to Philemon. Pro-slave advocates made much of Paul's decision to return Onesimus to Philemon as his rightful owner, who was considered to be a Christian in good standing by the apostle. Paul's decision to send a slave back to his owner, they said, validated the ownership of slaves.

But the pro-slave faction conveniently ignored the content and purpose of Paul's letter. Paul begins by saying he could "order" Philemon to do "the right thing." (The right thing being, to free Onesimus.) But instead Paul preferred that Philemon would release Onesimus out of love through the voluntary exercise of his Christian faith. Paul calls the former slave Onesimus, a beloved brother and urges Philemon to "welcome him as you would welcome me."

Paul goes as far as saying that if Onesimus wronged Philemon in any way or owes any debt, that it should be forgiven or charged to Paul personally. Paul concludes by expressing a confident expectation that Philemon will do even more than Paul asks of him. It is lunacy to believe the Bible supports slavery and the segregation of race based on anything in Paul's letter to Philemon.

Abraham Lincoln once said, "God must love the common man. He made so many of them." Based on Lincoln's logic, the thought crossed my mind, "God must find beauty and delight in racial diversity, he made so many people who neither look, act, nor speak the same." God is obviously a fan of racial diversity.

Based on ancient and modern history, the example of others, the study of Scripture, and my own experience, God has made the truth about race and its purpose clear. All that remained was to summarize my findings in a concise and intriguing Op-ed for *The Herald*.

I was fascinated by God's plan to use a recently retired reporter using a syndicated blog on the world-wide-web to declare His ancient truth. The more things change, the more people and issues remain the same. God evidently intended to broadcast His unchanging truth in ever-changing ways to an ever-changing culture.

When the people of God were unwilling to occupy the whole earth as God had commanded, God forced their hand. He would not be denied. If people today are unwilling to read the Bible or attend the church of their choice, God is determined to bring His truth to them using unconventional methods. God's love for the lost and misinformed will not be denied.

I was warming to the idea that God could use my professional experience to make a difference in things that matter. I remembered Mordecai's advice to manage my expectations. "Remember," he said, "they killed the prophets and crucified Jesus." But Mordecai also urged me not to be discouraged. "The faithful need truth's reassurance, and the skeptics need truth's challenge," he'd said. "Our job is promotion, not sales."

It will be fascinating to see how this plays out.

"For an idea that does not first seem insane, there is no hope."

—*Albert Einstein*

CHAPTER 6

Testing the Water

I remember a column I wrote on the subject of dementia, the source of memory and the essential nature of sound sleep. Crucial biological and neurological reprogramming occurs during meaningful sleep. Conversely, lack of sleep exposes people to a wide variety of health risks.

Meaningful sleep occurs in stages, but the most important are (SWS) slow wave sleep, and (REM) rapid eye movement sleep. SWS shuts down our motor impulses, slows our breathing, decelerates our pulse, and lowers our blood pressure. This enables our body to remove stress toxins that we accumulate during our waking hours, preserves and prioritizes memories and helps us lock down newly learned information. It explains why we often wake up with an answer to a problem that's been frustrating us for days. It might be as simple as a solution to a crossword puzzle or we suddenly remember the name of an old classmate we could not recall the previous day. REM sleep allows our mind to reset causing us to dream and think new thoughts.

This explains why you wake up one morning with a song stuck in your head that you haven't heard in years. It was the only logical explanation to my recollection of a Biblical quote from the Old Testament hero, Joshua. "Choose today whom you will serve, but as for me and my house we will serve the Lord." [20]

Nothing else made sense. Why else would that random passage have entered my mind? I'd seen the quote countless times on plaques in the homes of my Christian friends. Maybe it was a subconscious recollection of a bumper sticker from the parking lot at Reliance Church. Who knows? But why now? Maybe my reset-mind was urging me to act. If I was going to accept the offer to write a column, I needed to get off the fence and make a decision.

I've known Brad for years. We had worked as colleagues chasing stories for the paper before I declined their offer as Editor in Chief and he accepted. It was a good decision for both of us. He was an editor's editor. He could sharpen a lead, rearrange a story and clean up sloppy writing with a few swipes of his pen. Watching him work was like watching a master carpenter join crown molding, everything looked tighter when he was done. Rarely did anyone complain. That job held no appeal for me. I wanted to be on the front line, not correcting the work of other writers.

He was happy to receive my phone call and eager to discuss the column's potential. We decided to meet at Mulligans later that same afternoon, a locally-owned diner just around the corner from his office. Offsite made sense. It would keep me from explaining a dozen time to former colleagues, "How's retirement going?" and reduce the office gossip.

I wondered how Brad would warm to my thoughts about the direction of the column. I saw no reason to discuss my recent encounters with the paranormal. Brad would think I'd lost my mind. How I chose the subject of my articles was not as important to him as the content, especially when it came to editorials. He would either like them or not.

I do some of my best thinking on the driving range at the club. I typically pick a spot at the far end of the practice area and beat balls down-range while working out my issues uninterrupted. Not unlike slow-wave-sleep, it tends to clear away the clutter and helped me focus. I discussed my plans for the day with Sarah and hit the road. She seemed happy to hear I was finally taking action. In typical Sarah-fashion, she didn't press me for details.

We rarely talked much about my work unless I initiate the conversation. It wasn't that she didn't care, she knew I needed time to work things through alone. Forcing an issue before its time never produced a good outcome. Her hands-off approach worked to our mutual advantage. I began the habit of reading most of my stories to her out loud before submitting them to Brad. There is something about reading a column out loud that uncovers its strengths and weaknesses. Sarah has been a good sounding board over the years. She might or might not suggest a change but never felt obligated to inject an opinion one way or the other. Like a stand-up comedian, I needed to work out new material before a friendly audience. Sarah was my safe place before facing the criticism of the public. Unlike Sarah, they always had an opinion one way or the other. The more they disagreed, the stronger they expressed their displeasure.

I grabbed my clubs and lashed them to a cart before heading to the range. I was surprised to see a tall well-dressed golfer hitting balls from my favorite spot. He looked vaguely familiar. Without looking up, he greeted me by name but made no attempt to close the space between us. He kept his eyes on his work, hitting laser-like shots towards the flags that marked off the distance from tee to target.

"How's it going Jim?" I immediately recognized the voice.

"Mordecai, great to see you. I never expected to run into you on the practice range. I've been a member for ten years and don't recall ever seeing you here."

"Every day is full of surprises, wouldn't you agree?"

I'm not sure what he meant but it appeared Mordecai was up to his old habits of avoiding the question.

"By the looks of your swing, you've been playing a while," I responded.

"What brings you out today Jim? Do you have a match or are you just here to work out the kinks?" Something about his manner led me to believe he already knew my purpose.

"No. I just needed time to think through a few things and hitting a bucket of balls on the range seems to clear my mind."

"What have you decided? Are you going to write the column?"

Mordecai caught me by surprise. "How do you know about the column?"

"When we talked at the bookstore, you mentioned being asked to write a series of editorials. You pressed me for my opinion on political correctness, and more specifically racial diversity. Have you decided to step back into the fray?"

"Mordecai, your memory is a sharp as your swing. As a matter of fact, I'm meeting with my editor this afternoon. But yeah, I'm leaning in that direction. It remains to be seen what he'll think of the concept."

"Don't hold back, Jim," Mordecai injected. "Remember what I said, 'The faithful need the reassurance and the skeptics need the challenge.'"

"You also said I should manage my expectations. That I should not assume people will accept the truth just because it's true. I recall you saying, 'Our job is promotion, not sales.'".

My response caused Mordecai to chuckle out loud. "I can see there is nothing wrong with your memory Jim. No wonder you've been chosen. The Lord doesn't make mistakes. Did you know Moses refused his calling five times before God convinced him to challenge Pharaoh? He reminded old Moses, 'Who gave man his mouth? Who makes him deaf or mute? Who gives him sight or makes them blind? Is it not I, the LORD? Now go; I will help you speak and will teach you what you are to say.' [21]

"There you go again quoting Scripture like you wrote it. Mordecai. Who are you, really?" I asked.

"Who I am is not important. My name was given in honor of Queen Esther's uncle. Esther was married to Xerxes, king of Persia. He had the power to save the Jewish people from certain annihilation, but first Esther must risk her life to request the king's action."

"It was Esther's uncle Mordecai who urged her to accept the risk on behalf of God's people. 'If you remain silent at this time, deliverance for God's people will arise from another place... Who knows, perhaps you have achieved your position for such a time as this.' [22] Remember what I said,

Jim, 'Don't hold back.' If ever there was a time when people needed to hear truth, it's now."

"Are you...?" My words came slowly. "Are you...?" I couldn't bring myself to say it out loud. It sounded too strange, even silly. "Are you an angel?"

"I'm here to help Jim. I'm the Lord's messenger. You've been given an important task and will need all the confidence you can muster. Stay watchful. Pay attention to the things you hear and see. The Lord will provide the needed direction at the proper time. You are to speak the truth, truth that can set people free. Weigh your opinions in light of God's Word. It is not only trustworthy; it is helpful. In these last days false prophets will fill the earth with lies, hoping to deceive even God's children. Even the faithful will be tempted to accept as fact the opinions they want to hear. You're called to be a spokesman for God in the midst of the chaos. Popularity is not proof of validity. Remember, the road is wide that leads to destruction and many follow it, but the way is narrow that leads to life that is life indeed. Stay on the narrow road. The unpopular road... the road less traveled."

And with that, Mordecai slung his bag over his shoulder and prepared to leave the range.

"Wait. I have more questions. How do you hit your long irons so pure?" I said with a smirk. "Seriously though, tell me, how is all this going to work? When will I see you again? How can I get in touch with you?" Mordecai just smiled but hardly slowed his pace as he walked past me.

"Keep the faith Jim. The Lord will provide all you need when you need it. What you're doing is important. You should feel honored to be chosen. Don't worry, you'll never be alone. It may feel like it sometimes, but the Lord is as close as your shadow. We'll see each other from time to time."

And with that, he was gone.

Mordecai's words, and his unexpected appearance left me stunned. Did that just happen? Am I actually awake and standing on the driving range? I could not be dreaming. It was the middle of the day. How bizarre. I left my clubs on the cart and walked to the locker room. I needed to make some notes. I couldn't afford to forget any of it.

It was still too early for lunch. I went back to the range to continue my practice. I thought it might help me recall the encounter. This morning I began my day with Joshua's words on my mind... "How long will you sit on the fence? Make a decision. Get on with it. Serve the Lord." Just now I had encountered Mordecai for a second time. This was no coincidence. His name was not listed on the roster of members posted in the hallway by the 19th hole. I checked. I knew from the first time we met there was something different about that guy. "Many have entertained angels unaware," George told me. I knew it was true.

I vaguely remembered the story of Esther and Mordecai from Sunday school. I recognized her name. She often cited by women rights advocates as a heroine of ancient times. I made a note to reread her story when I got back to the house. Mordecai said she was caught in a conundrum. Like Moses, she was asked by God to risk her life for the sake of His people. It was Mordecai who urged her to act." My Mordecai had quoted his namesake, "Perhaps you have achieved your status for such a time as this. But if you fail to act, God will choose someone else and you will have missed the opportunity."[23] The similarity to my situation was striking.

The poet wrote, "God moves in mysterious ways, his wonders to perform." I agreed whole-heartedly. It sounds biblical. My situation was beginning to feel like old times, one interview leading to another and another, until a story came together. *Maybe there* was *a reason God chose me for this task.*

I returned my clubs to the bag room, grabbed my notebook and headed for the grill. I took a seat in the back corner, away from the bar so I could be alone with my thoughts and notes. It was my old routine. Everyone knew when they saw me sitting alone at a table covered with paper, they should keep walking. It was a perk of membership. Whether I was meeting someone for a story, or jotting down my thoughts, that kind of privacy was impossible to find in a public restaurant. I decided not to tell Sarah just yet about the Mordecai encounter. It would only lead to a lively conversation and I needed to settle my thoughts and focus on my meeting with Brad.

I got to Mulligans a bit early so I could score a booth near the back of the room. We were old friends so no one who knew us would give our meeting a second thought. It wasn't long before Brad showed up. Deadlines were second nature in our business. We spent our careers living and dying by the clock. He was right on time for a change and smiled to see me already there and waiting.

"How the hell are you, Jim? I suppose you've lowered your handicap by a shot or two by now."

"Funny thing about that, Brad," I replied. "It seems the more I play, the more there is to learn. Ignorance is bliss buddy. I'm trying to simplify the game. I have way too many swing thoughts running through my mind these days. My bible-thumping friend George likes to quote the Scripture, 'The one who knows what to do but does it not, for him it is sin.' [24] I chuckled. "By that standard I've been sinning a lot."

"How about you, Brad? How are things at *The Herald*? How's the paper adjusting to the changing trends in how and where people get their daily dose of news?"

"That's why we're here, Jim. The ownership knows we need to change with the times. It's already begun. We now have more online business than we have subscription to the newspaper. It isn't either bad or good, but it sure is different. We make as much money from the hits on our website as we do from the junk mail inserts and paid subscriptions for the paper. The more people click on our stories, the more our advertisers are willing to pay. That's why I was glad to get your call. We need your byline attracting people to the website. Our online presence isn't limited to local subscriptions or even local advertisers. If the content is good enough we can attract advertisers from across the nation, even the world."

"I knew things were headed that way. It's fascinating, even amusing, to see how legit news outlets are using social media 'click-bait' to capture the attention of people who would never buy their paper or watch their news channels."

"And once we get them to make that first click, there is always the chance that another story, interview, or advertiser on the site will capture their attention. That's why we need you, Jim. Your experience in choosing stories and hooking readers is a gift. You can write your column from anywhere. We don't need you to cover hard-news. We have stringers for that. We need you to tackle the issues of our day. I don't care how controversial you get as long as you tap into the curiosity of the public."

That comment made me smile. "You say that now, but wait till the heat rolls in. You might change your tune."

"We both know controversy sells. I trust your judgement. You're bold without being offensive. You have to crack a few eggs to make an omelet." Brad smiled. "Just don't burn the bacon. What do you say? Are you in?"

"Don't you want to hear my concept? I've had time to think about the things that interest me. I don't have a particular axe to grind but there are some sacred cows that need milking and a few that would be better off butchered. I'm neither right nor left on the political spectrum. It's always been my job to report the news, not make it. You can trust me to give both sides of an issue equal time, but I do believe there is right and wrong. Everyone teaches their kids to accept certain values and reject others. But on what basis? I want to tread on the politically correct culture of our time. Everyone seems so afraid of offending the public that they no longer take a position on anything. That's not me."

"What kind of sacred cows are you thinking about milking, Jim? Tell me more."

"You said you want me to tackle some of the issues of our day. There are no bigger issues than racial prejudice, gender bending, subjective truth in place of absolute truth, socialism verses capitalism, immigration, patriotism, globalism, gun control, environmental issues, creation vs. evolution, pro-life vs. abortion... it might get messy. I promise to tackle each issue with compassion and fairness, but I can guarantee some people won't like it. These are 'third-rail issues.' Are you okay with that? Because if you aren't, there really is no point in wasting your time or mine."

"I think I'm okay with that. Let's run it up the flagpole and see how it flutters. It's extremely polarized out there, Jim. No matter what your opinion on any subject, you can expect strong opposition and even a few personal attacks... or twenty." Brad smiled again.

We both knew he was right. It would be impossible to write an editorial about anything these days and not raise the ire of people with a different point of view. The days of Paul Harvey, Abigail Van Buren and Erma Bombeck are long past. That ship has sailed. I'm not sure even Oprah could do her thing and be as popular today as she once was. She'd have to work overtime defending and constantly explaining herself on social media after every show. Common sense, it seems, has been martyred on the altar of tolerance. Even those who agree with a common sense position are afraid to admit it. People default to silence, avoiding controversies of every kind. "Live and let live," doesn't work anymore. "Keep your opinions to yourself or risk verbal, physical or public attack, is more in fashion."

"Fair warning, Brad, I ran into a friend who reminded me, 'Don't assume people will accept the truth just because it's true.' I believe there is right and there is wrong. I believe there is truth and there is error. Truth has an edge to it but like it or not, people need to hear it. Those who accept truth need the affirmation and those who don't, need the challenge. If you're okay with that, then so am I."

"This should be interesting. Like I said, let's give it a shot and watch the response. What's the worst that could happen? A riot might break out. You could be personally attacked on the street or at your home. Are you ready for that? We might be sued for slander, but what else is new? That's why God made lawyers."

"Let's talk nuts and bolts. I'm thinking your column should hang around one to three thousand words in length. Some topics may require more, some less. Online publication allows us to be flexible so long as you hold the interest of the reader. Remember, we are looking for an op-ed kind of column. The real juice in these kinds of posts is not always in the body of the article, but the quality and the quantity of the responses they generate. The articles themselves are intended to get people talking, with the hope the column will 'go viral' as they say. That means you will have to hit-and-run your issues. If the column gets too long no one is going to read it. You are going to have to break your material down into bite-size pieces.

I'm thinking of four columns to an issue, a month's worth of material if we publish weekly. That will give it shelf-life, long enough for people to comment, but not long enough to get stale. How soon can you get started?"

"I've been researching the subject of racial prejudice. Not the usual us vs. them approach. I've developed some material that has the potential to stir the pot in a positive way. But even before that, I believe we need to publish an article or two on the subject of truth in a politically correct world. Unless we establish the basis for deciding right and wrong, what's true and what's false, the column will lack perspective. People deserve to know where I'm coming from."

"Agreed. Sounds like a good place to start. The layout guys can arrange the material, but have you thought of a name for your column?"

"I was thinking 60 Minutes, Dateline, or 20/20, but I googled those and discovered they've been taken." Even Brad had to laugh at that thought. "What about, 'Truth Be Told'? I think it has a ring to it."

"That should fire 'em up for sure. Brace yourself for the feedback. It will come by the bushel basket."

"I was hoping for truckloads myself. Didn't you say, 'The juice in these kinds of columns are in the quality and quantity of the response they generate?' I'll do my best to keep it positive and thoughtful. That's all I can promise."

"That's good enough for me. No need for you to come into the office unless you want to discuss it further. Shoot me your first four columns and we can meet again to check the layout and discuss future topics. Let's get this party started!"

"Truth Be Told, I'm ready to get busy," I said with a chuckle.

Confidentially, I had no idea if this was a good or bad decision. We were all about to find out.

St. Louis Herald

An Auspicious Beginning

By: **James King**

Who is James King? Why bother reading his column?

In the interest of full disclosure, those who access TRUTH BE TOLD have a right to know the answers. The time-honored advice, "Consider the source!" serves a noble purpose.

TRUTH BE TOLD is published in an effort to provide a common-sense perspective on a host of issues being redefined by a politically correct culture gone too far. Afraid of being socially insulted and publicly attacked, the common sense opinion of many has been silenced to the detriment of all. TRUTH BE TOLD makes no claim to omniscience, but is determined to provide a reality check on issues being redefined by our PC culture.

James King is not a new face in the publication business, but he may be new to you. Here's the inside scoop on what makes him tick.

He's been a married man since bellbottoms were a fashion statement, mullets were cool, and Boones Farm was the college beverage of choice.

He holds a degree and several awards in journalism. The university that certified him as qualified to practice his trade shall remain nameless to protect the guilty. Jim got his start writing a column for his high school paper. For the last 30 years he's been a reporter for the *St. Louis Herald*.

His wife, Sarah, is a realtor, recently retired. Together they've flipped a dozen houses over the last 20 years.

They have two married sons and five grandchildren. Some say he looks too young to be the patriarch of so many. He explains those boys were the result of Sarah's first marriage, which is technically true, since he is Sarah's first and only husband.

He prefers to read nonfiction (mostly biographies), write (obviously), hunt deer and elk in the mountains, golf, and rehab houses.

He's traveled the world including Africa, South America, Europe, Russia, the Middle East, Israel and Egypt.

He's comfortable with comfort food. His guilty pleasure is a Coney Island Dog covered with sweet onions and cheddar cheese. "Life is too short to eat a cheap hot dog," is his bumper sticker of choice.

Jim believes in God but it's a tenuous relationship. He admires people of every faith so long as they are peace-loving believers. Jim is of the Christian variety, but hasn't been a dues-paying member of any one congregation or denomination since childhood.

He believes in angels, life after death, creation by God in some form, the power of prayer, and the Bible. He's decidedly undecided on the question of inspiration and inerrancy—just one of the subjects he intends to investigate in a future column. He believes karma is the natural consequence of personal choice; "What goes around, comes around, with allowance for exceptions." He also relies heavily on God's grace, mercy, and unconditional love.

He has faith in the healing power of music, the beauty of trees, flowers, birds, rivers, mountains, and all aspects of unspoiled nature.

Jim acknowledges that no person has had a greater influence on the world than Jesus of Nazareth. He accepts the New Testament assertion that Jesus is the Son of God and Savior of the world, which is a discussion worth having.

Jim believes some have experienced near-death-encounters He is willing to acknowledge a few close calls himself, but never saw the light or the tunnel, never saw Jesus, and has not encounter any dead relatives from the "other side."

He believes in good and evil and the devil. If God exists, it's reasonable to assume his nemesis is also real.

Jim invites you to join the discussion. As you've no doubt noticed, he won't be holding back. You won't be bored... angry perhaps, enlightened God-willing, and hopefully challenged to think new thoughts. At the end of every TRUTH BE TOLD column you will have an opportunity to react, agree, disagree, or tell Jim to take a long walk off a short pier. TRUTH BE TOLD looks forward to reading your opinion on the subjects under discussion.

The first order of business is a treatise of truth itself. Is it possible to discern truth from error? If so, on what basis? How should human behavior be determined acceptable or unacceptable? What role does conscience play? Why does anyone suffer guilt and shame if right and wrong are a matter of personal choice? How can parents raise children to make good, better, and best choices if right and wrong is determined solely in the eye of the beholder?

There's a lot to talk about:

- Will there be life after death or just death?
- Where and how did racial distinction enter the picture? And to what end?
- Are there limits to gender distinction, or are gender possibilities infinitum?
- When does life begin? Should end-of-life decisions be a personal choice?
- Are all marriages created equal, including heterosexual, same-sex and multiple partner unions?
- Globalism or nationalism? Do nations have a right to secure their borders? Should immigration be based on merit? Who determines what qualifies as merit?
- Why are there cats and dogs in the world but not cogs and dats? Does evolution make any sense?
- If God is good, why does He allow evil in the world?
- Capitalism or socialism?
- Who decides when my rights impose on your rights?
- Who gets to decide what is good, better, and best environmental policy?

If fence-sitting is not your thing. If you prefer a lively discussion rather than avoidance of controversial issues, then TRUTH BE TOLD is for you. Come down from the bleachers and onto the field. We are about to touch the third-rail on these and many other divisive issues.

What could possibly go wrong? ▪

St. Louis Herald

TRUTH BE TOLD   Edition 1, Column 2

Self-Evident Truth

By: **James King**

I s self-evident truth still a thing? Do people still believe that certain rights, values, and truths are so obvious no one could possibly disagree? Is there such a thing as self-evident, undeniable truth?

The sun comes up in the East and sets in the West. Snow is cold. Fire is hot. Some birds, but not all birds, migrate according to the seasons. Water runs downhill. The earth is round. The hottest parts of the earth are those along the equator because they are closer to the sun. The Polar Regions are colder because they are farther from the sun. The earth turns on its axis counter-clockwise as viewed from the North Pole. These and a thousand other scientific facts are indisputable. You could logically say they are self-evident.

America's founders declared independence from England on the basis of truth they claimed was self-evident. In other words, the reason for their action was so apparent they needed no defense. The veracity of certain truth, they believed was beyond question.

The Declaration of Independence identifies five universal freedoms all people should enjoy but which England had denied the Colonies. The Founding Fathers believed denial of their basic human rights left the colonies no choice but to declare independence and establish a new nation. They based their declaration on "the laws of nature and nature's god" that "all men are created equal and are endowed by their creator with certain unalienable (undeniable) rights, that among these are life, liberty and the pursuit of happiness." England's denial of these rights in America they believed, justified their decision to sever all ties to the British Crown. They declared their position, "self-evident."

To defend their stance, the signers listed more than 2 dozen examples of how England had suppressed their God-given freedoms. Far from naïve, they knew their declaration of independence would bring swift reprisal by the British. They placed their fate in the hands of God, making their appeal to "the Supreme Judge of the world... with a firm reliance on the protection of Divine Providence," and pledged to each other "their lives, fortunes and sacred honor".

Are there non-scientific truths that can be rightfully declared self-evident? In an age of moral relativism, self-evident truth may not be so self-evident. "You have your truth and I have mine. What is true for you may not be true for me." Can what is true still be declared on the basis of "nature and nature's God?" Is America still "one nation under God", or is belief in God no longer an American value? Can those who deny the existence of God nevertheless agree on the existence of self-evident truth apart from God; things like life, liberty and the pursuit of happiness? Was self-evident truth a valid justification for America's Declaration of Independence? Is there room in our culture for common sense positions, or is common sense no longer commonly shared?

This author believes in objective, self-evident truth. This column will demonstrate the difference between the good, the bad and the indifferent on a variety of issues facing America and the world. TRUTH BE TOLD believes self-evident truth does exist, and because it exists, opinions on a wide range of issues can often be declared right, wrong, misguided, or a matter of personal preference. Even Hollywood with its live-and-let-live mentality sides against those who cheat on a spouse. They understandably decry school shootings, oppose animal abuse and terrorist attacks. They campaign against sex trafficking and oppose slavery in all its ugly forms. The most liberal American rightfully contends that every person deserves a chance to be loved, happy and free.

TRUTH BE TOLD also believes most people (but not all people) recognize immorality when they see it. Call it conscience if you will, but something inside a person instinctively discerns truth from error and differentiates right from wrong. Like teenagers challenging parents over rules that they believe are irrelevant and old-fashioned, people instinctively desire someone in authority to defend right and oppose wrong. Self-evident truth is not dependent on approval. It exists even when it is opposed by popular opinion. The founders declared "all men are created equal" even though the majority of them owned slaves and refused equality to women. The hypocrisy of their actions did not make the self-evident nature of their declaration any less true. Truth is true because it is right not because it is the accepted standard.

America's independence was built on the foundation of self-evident truth. Some contend the Continental Army's defeat of the British was the true basis of America's independence. The Founding Fathers would disagree. The Declaration inspired the courage and sacrifice of the patriots.

Without it, there would have been no revolution and no victory.

TRUTH BE TOLD believes self-evident truth is an undeniable reality. The Founders of America risked their lives, fortunes, and sacred honor to defend its existence.

Someone said, "The truth will set you free." We would do well to ask ourselves, "How long can true freedom exist in the absence of truth?" ▪

St. Louis Herald

Is God Dead?

By: **James King**

That question appeared in bold red letters printed on the stark black cover of the April 8, 1966, edition of TIME Magazine. It was Good Friday, the day Christians around the world mark the Roman crucifixion of Jesus outside the walls of Jerusalem.

Anyone who bought the issue thinking TIME was paying homage to the Christian holy day was sadly mistaken. The cover and the article had little to do with Christianity, Jesus, or Good Friday. TIME was merely reporting on America's growing disbelief in all things divine.

Did God die on the first Good Friday 2,000 years ago as payment for human sin? Jesus may have died on the cross that day, but according to TIME's assessment, God did not.

On the contrary, Jesus' death led to greater and more widespread belief in God that spread like wildfire from Jerusalem to Rome and beyond. According to TIME, the death of God in the minds of people occurred in the 19th century.

From 1883–1885, the German scholar Friedrich Nietzsche published a series of articles that included the now famous statement, *"God is dead. God remains dead. And we have killed him. How shall we comfort ourselves, the murderers of all murderers? What was the holiest and mightiest of all that the world has yet owned has bled to death under our knives; who will wipe this blood off us? What water is there for us to clean ourselves? What festivals of atonement, what sacred games shall we have to invent? Is not the greatness of this deed to great for us? Must we ourselves not become gods simply to appear worthy of it?"*

Nietzsche argued that God existed because people believed he existed.

He died when people quit believing. He may have a point. Consider the case of the famous American poet Henry Wadsworth Longfellow.

It was Christmas 1863. Two years earlier, the love of his life and wife of 18 years died when her dress caught fire while melting wax with a candle to seal letters. Henry rushed unsuccessfully to her rescue suffering burns to his face and hands so severe he could not attend her funeral. Adding to his confusion over the providence of God, Longfellow's oldest son was badly wounded in a Civil War battle and being held prisoner in a Confederate P.O.W. camp. Christmas provided no peace for the poet who vented his consternation with pen and paper.

I heard the bells of Christmas Day/ Their old, familiar carols play,

And wild and sweet the words repeat/ Of peace on earth, good-will to men.

And in despair I bowed my head/ "There is no peace on earth," I said. For hate is strong, and mocks the song/ Of peace on earth, good-will to men!"

Then pealed the bells more loud and deep/ "God is not dead, nor doth He sleep. The wrong shall fail, the right prevail/ With peace on earth, good-will to men.

Who hasn't felt abandoned by God? Slavery and human trafficking continue. Children are aborted, abused, and neglected. The homeless sleep in the streets. Thousands around the world starve while those of fortunate birth have food to waste. Hate crimes, discrimination, drug abuse, gun violence, terrorism, war and threats of war are a daily occurrence. Our prayers seem ignored at best, at worst unheard. How can a just God tolerate such injustice? He fails to meet our needs so we declare Him nonexistent. We reject the ancient Scripture as mere words.

Or do we?

A highly respected 2019 PEW Study (A Research Center established in honor of Joseph Pew founder of Sun Oil Co.) discovered that in spite of the difficulty of their lives, the overwhelming majority of Americans, including a majority of the religiously unaffiliated (including those who describe themselves as atheists, agnostics, or nothing in particular), nevertheless say they believe in God or a Higher-Power.

- 56% of Americans profess faith in the God of the Bible, while another 33% say they believe in an undefined Higher Power or Spiritual Force. Only 10% deny any form of divinity.
- 90% of American Christians and Jewish believers have faith in God's existence. 80% of Christians believe in God as the Bible defines Him, while only 33% of Jewish believers accept the veracity of the Scriptures. An astonishing 72% of those

unaffiliated with any faith say they believe in some form of Supreme Being.

- 66% of American's over 50 believe in the God of the Bible, just 49% of those in their 30s and 40s believe the same. Only 43% of those under 30 accept the Bible as a true and reliable description of God and His will. Nevertheless 80% of those between the ages of 18–19 still believe some form of spiritual being controls the universe.

- The more educated a person is, the less likely they are to believe. 94% of those without a college education vs. 84% of those with college believe in the God of the Bible.

- Belief is also reflected in political affiliations. 70% of Republicans hold faith in the God of the Bible while only 45% of Democrats accept the Bible's depiction of the true God. The exception are Black & Hispanic Democrats who have faith in the God of the Bible 61% vs. just 32% of white Democrats.

TRUTH BE TOLD stands with the majority of Americans who profess faith in God and are willing to consider as valid the claims made by the Bible. Somewhere it states, "The fool has said in his heart, "There is no God." And "The fear of the Lord is the beginning of wisdom and a good understanding have all those who seek His truth." If we intend to discuss moral and ethical issues under debate in our culture, we need a starting place. Why not use the ancient Biblical standard that has guided civilized people since humans first put words on paper?

With some variation, the three major religions of the world, Judaism, Islam, and Christianity, have all consulted the Old Testament prophets of the Bible for truth. It's a good place to start. The guidance provided by these prophets falls into one of three categories: 1.) Laws that governed their religious ceremonies, 2.) Laws that guided their civil regulations, and 3.) those Laws that established a standard for moral and ethical behavior. Without requiring obedience in ritual and civil laws we can benefit from an understanding of God's moral standards for all people of every race, creed and culture.

According to the Genesis record, on a mountain called Sinai, God handed Moses the sum total of all moral laws etched on two tablets of stone. Commonly referred to as *The Ten Commandments*. They continue to be recognized by most as the gold standard of right and wrong. Let's start with those.

The first three commandments require humanity to honor God and respect His authority as the creator and overseer of the world. The remaining seven (depending on how you count them) provide guidance for peaceful coexistence between people: love and honor your family of origin, don't hurt or kill each other, don't steal, be faithful to your spouse, don't lie, don't gossip, don't covet other people's stuff. They don't seem like much, but they are enough.

Knowing right from wrong isn't the same as doing right and avoiding wrong. Most Godly people recognize the impossibility of living a perfect life… and perfection, (sometimes referred to as "righteousness" in the Bible), is what God demands.

For this reason, Christians believe God provided the Messiah Jesus (Messiah is translated as Christ in Greek.), to suffer the penalty of humanity's failure. Regardless of your faith or lack thereof in Jesus, we can all agree the ancients believed mercy and grace were required if sinners intend to maintain a close relationship with a perfect God and each other. Confession of sins and subsequent forgiveness from God is not a new or uniquely Christian concept. Declaring your faults and forgiving one another has been a vital part of healthy relationships with each other and with God from the beginning.

King David, who wrote the Psalms a thousand years before Jesus was born, put it this way,

"If You, my Lord should keep a record of all sins,

Who could ever stand before you justified?

But there is forgiveness with You,
So that You may be honored.
So I wait and I count on the Lord.
My soul waits, and in His promises I put my trust…
Let all the faithful put their trust in the Lord
For with the Lord there is forgiveness of sin,
And with the Lord there is abundant redemption.
He will redeem the faithful from all their iniquities." (Psalm 130)

A good friend once told me, "Aim for the moon, you may only land on your roof, but you will out-perform most." TRUTH BE TOLD believes striving to do what is right and avoiding what is wrong is like shooting for the moon. Doing only right and avoiding all wrong is humanly impossible, but that doesn't mean it's not worth the effort and unimportant.

The faithful believe in a gracious God Who forgives their failures. Living in the knowledge of God's grace keeps them from giving up in utter frustration. The motive for the faithful's good deeds therefore flows from gratitude for God's forgiveness, not from a futile attempt to impress Him by avoiding all wrong and doing only right. Unburdened from guilt and shame, the faithful are free to boldly embrace family, and strangers, friends, and enemies, in an attempt to make the world a better place without hesitation caused by fear of potential failure.

Human failure is inevitable. God's grace and mercy is sufficient to cover the shortfall. The faithful can unashamedly and boldly acknowledge their mistakes to God while simultaneously seeking forgiveness and acceptance from those they've harmed.

Extending forgiveness to others is necessary for the well-being of the perpetrator as well as their victim. Asking for and granting forgiveness doesn't always make the wrong right. It won't always heal the hurt or undo the outcome, but it is necessary to affirm what is right and denounce what is wrong. God's standards are perfect even though people are not.

Past mistakes that can't be undone must be left to God for special handling. He can bring good out of evil and use the worst circumstance to bless those who move forward in faith.

God is not dead until you declare Him dead to you. Even then, He will not give up on those who have given up on Him.

He stands by the window watching and waiting for the child He loves to come home. ∎

St. Louis Herald

R-E-S-P-E-C-T

By: **James King**

Aretha Franklin taught America how to spell "respect," during the summer of 1967. She didn't write the original lyrics and wasn't the first to record Otis Redding's massive hit, but she "owned it" like no one else. It was Aretha who added the now famous chorus letter-by-letter, "R-E-S-P-E-C-T: Find out what it means to me. Take care, TCB (i.e. take care of business), …when you get home."

The song soared to number one on the charts and stayed there for an impressive 12 weeks. It resonated as a siren call for personal and social dignity. Drawing from her experience as a young black woman raised in a segregated, disrespectful, misogynistic culture, she more than any other artist, gave the lyrics their

power. It was more demand that plea. Without respect, there would be hell to pay.

The song went public during an unsettled time in America. The nation was at war with itself. The war in Vietnam was escalating while protests against it raged on university campuses and in the streets back home. Long-simmering racial tensions boiled over in the neighborhoods of major cities. Just as the song topped the charts, the Twelfth Street Riots erupted in Detroit, leaving 43 dead, 342 injured, more than 1,000 protestors arrested, and 1,500 buildings burned to the ground. Newark, N.J., followed, adding 26 protestors to the death total. R-E-S-P-E-C-T was in high demand. People were willing to die for it.

And die they did. President Kennedy was assassinated in November of 1963, firebrand activist Malcolm X was shot to death in February of 1965, nonviolent civil rights leader Martin Luther King Jr., died by gunshot in March of 1968, and presidential candidate Robert Kennedy three months later. It could be argued that all, with the exception of Malcom X, were advocates of R-E-S-P-E-C-T for all. He chose a more confrontational approach to the nation's racial inequality.

Aretha's father and M.L.K. Jr. were good friends, pastors, and co-leaders in the Civil Rights movement of the 1960's. King often stayed at the Franklin home when visiting Detroit. As a teenager, Aretha experienced injustice first-hand, joining her father on marches with Dr. King. A year after **RESPECT** topped the charts Dr. King was gunned down in Memphis. Aretha sang at his funeral in Atlanta. No wonder she sang with such passion.

If Aretha's song was the movement's anthem, M.L.K. Jr.'s, *"I Have A Dream"* speech was its Declaration of Independence. Delivered from the steps of the Lincoln Memorial, built to honor the assassinated Great-Emancipator of the 1800's, it was an inspired message worthy of the setting. Unfortunately, there is something about a demand for R-E-S-P-E-C-T that incites violence in some, and martyrdom in others.

Dr. King never advocated R-E-S-P-E-C-T through violence, just the opposite. He urged the oppressed to rise above their oppressors, meeting physical attacks with what he called, nonviolent soul-force.

"In the process of gaining our rightful place, we must not be guilty of wrongful deeds. Let us not seek to satisfy our thirst for freedom by drinking from the cup of bitterness and hatred."

Despite the violence of the era, he had a dream that justice and R-E-S-P-E-C-T would come. A day when, *"the sons of former slaves and the sons of former slave owners will be able to sit down at the table of brotherhood."*

There will always be a difference of opinion among people. Show me a family, a marriage, a team, a church, a business, a subdivision, a community, a nation or an alliance of any kind that exists in lockstep-unity and complete harmony, and I will show you people who lack the courage of their convictions. Diversity and disagreement can be a good thing if expressed with mutual respect.

Someone said, "If two people look, act, and think exactly the same, one of them is unnecessary." But differences in race, culture, gender, age, and belief should not compel attacks against those whose views are different from our own. Rick Warren, author of The Purpose Driven Life has said,

"Our culture has accepted two huge lies. The first is that if you disagree with someone's lifestyle, you must fear or hate them. The second is that to love someone means you agree with everything they believe

or do. Both are nonsense. You don't have to compromise convictions to be compassionate."

Only small-minded people hate people and perspectives they don't agree with. It is the very definition of prejudice – to "pre-judge something or someone" without taking the time to understand.

I saw a sign that read, *"Those who remove restraints from conformity place themselves in peril of further and more alarming accommodations."* TRUTH BE TOLD does not agree with that viewpoint. It is the old slippery slope argument: Gradually the unthinkable becomes tolerable, then acceptable, then legal and then praised. Religious leaders have quoted the Bible to support their belief that the slippery slope theory is justified. *"When the foundations are destroyed, what will the righteous do?"* (Psalm 11:3)

TRUTH BE TOLD (TBT) contends the foundations of the righteous are in no great danger if they are true. The righteous should trust that foundations built on truth are able to withstand the assault of falsehood.

Somewhere it says, "The letter of the law kills but the spirit gives life." Jesus didn't abandon compassion for fear of the slippery slope.

- He gleaned wheat on the Sabbath.
- Healed on the Sabbath.
- Welcomed prostitutes to approach Him, granting them compassion and acceptance.
- Talked to gentiles.
- Touched lepers.
- Conversed freely with people of questionable character.
- Ate in the homes of known sinners.
- Welcomed a tax collector and a thief to join his disciples.

TRUTH BE TOLD does not accept the slippery slope theory. TBT believes truth needs no protection, just opportunity. Wrong-thinking is light-adverse. Like the morning dew, it evaporates quickly when exposed to the light of day. Attentive listening and sincere inquiry are preferred over argumentative and demeaning reaction to error. TBT believes intimidation accomplishes little and changes nothing. Those convinced against their will remain unconvinced.

TBT won't avoid controversial issues for fear of upset. We expect to be challenged and welcome a discussion of what is right, wrong, best, or optional. We expect to uncover a blind spot or two of our own. People must learn to respectfully listen to each other if we intend to achieve Dr. King's dream, *"...when future generations will not be judged by the color of their skin but by the content of their character."* Mutual R-E-S-P-E-C-T will be required to turn Dr. King's dream into reality.

Two years before Aretha's historic call for R-E-S-P-E-C-T, another famous singer and personal friend of hers by the name of Sam Cooke wrote a song she also covered in 1967. The song's refrain declares

that change, though it's been a long time in coming, is on the way.

It's time. It's past time. ∎

"You don't seek power or popularity. You simply ask, is the thing right in itself? If it is, then I must do it, no matter the cost."

—*J.K. Rowling*

CHAPTER 7

Early Returns

N o one was sure how TRUTH BE TOLD would be received. Until now, it was pure speculation. My work was well known in St. Louis. A few of the investigative series I had written for The Herald had been syndicated, mostly in the Midwest and a few times in larger markets. But while a syndicated series is personally gratifying, it doesn't necessarily translate to national recognition.

Editors and journalists across the country knew my byline, but I was no Mike Royko, or Art Buchwald. It was enough that my column was recognized and awarded locally. A series I wrote on gang recruitment, and another on an organ transplant scandal had been nominated for a Pulitzer, but that's as far as it went. If this venture had legs, it would be due to content, not reputation. I was okay with that.

An artist friend once lamented his work came into demand only at the end of his career. Just when he was ready to slow down, he achieved the notoriety he had pursued for decades. It was hard for him to turn down the commissions his new-found recognition brought after years of working in the shadows. I resonated to his consternation. Good things happen when you least expect it.

The life of a reporter is unpredictable. You never know when or where the next big story will fall into your lap. Sarah's work as a realtor was just as demanding and uncertain. We were both looking forward to the boredom of predictability, time with grandchildren and being untethered from phones and laptops. I was definitely looking forward to better tee times and more opportunity to chase the little white ball.

Sarah's enthusiasm for the TBT project caught me by surprise. Rather than discourage me from pursuing syndication, she was gung-ho. She called it, "A rare opportunity to influence thousands without the burden of meetings and throwaway assignments of no importance." Besides, she reasoned, I could write the column from anywhere. She proposed a new tag line for my business card, "Have laptop will travel." She considered me, "the right man, at the right place, at the right time." So did my editor, Brad. But I was not so sure. They had grown accustomed to my style. They understood me and resonated to my methodology. I couldn't help but wonder if I might be an acquired taste.

I entertained no illusions of grandeur or harbored lofty expectations for the column. I had some skills but considered myself more a utility player than a franchise star. My expectations rested on the visitation of the man in white and half a dozen unexplainable encounters since then. I accepted the assignment on the premise this undertaking was God's doing, and if he wanted it to succeed, not even I could mess it up. It remained to be seen if TRUTH BE TOLD was capable of attracting a national following.

Local advertisers were willing to back the launch based on my street cred, and the sales team had done a good job scoring some national sponsors willing to take a flyer on the concept. But we all knew writing an op-ed was new to me. I was about to discover the world of analytics that publishers use to measure the commercial viability of blogs and websites. The first four columns were published and the early returns were better than anyone expected.

Brad asked me to meet with the analytics team so we could gain the benefit of their findings. They threw around terms like "Web Traffic, Search Rankings, Time on Page (TOP stats), Social Media Shares, Inbound Linkage (IL's), Click-Through Rate (CTR's), and Calls To Action (CTA's)." I was impressed and also a bit troubled by the amount of information they could discern from tracking online activity.

They were able to discern what percentage of clicks were the result of a key-word search or if the targets (Yes, they actually used that term.) had arrived on our page via referral from a related story or partner site. They knew immediately if a target clicked through the entire article or only glanced at the content and moved on. They could precisely report how many people shared the column, posted it to their social media page, or "liked" the article. Most importantly, from a commercial point of view, they could tell how many visitors clicked on an advertiser's promotional link.

Everything looked good. Our numbers were solid, especially for a new column by a relatively unknown journalist. The trick, they suggested, was to keep the column controversial without being offensive. The content had to be current and edgy to attract the attention of new targets drawn by curiosity to the editorial. We were fishing for "keepers" in a pool awash with tasty bait. We could buy positioning on popular search engines, but that could get expensive.

The marketing team wanted TRUTH BE TOLD to have "PICK-potential." Pithy – Informative – Creative – and Koncise. (No one seemed to care that "concise" was spelled with a K.) It made me think of an interview I once did with Berry Gordy the famous Motown producer. He said he could tell if a song had hit-potential by listening to the first three measures of the music. If it didn't grab him by then, its future was in doubt. I felt the same way about writing. The first two or three sentences had to grab the interest of the reader. If I hadn't connected by then, it is doubtful they would bother reading the rest of what I had to say.

What impressed Brad was the number of visitors attracted by one TBT article who then jumped to a second, third or even the fourth. Those numbers were off the charts. Over half, who clicked on one of the columns also clicked on another. A good number of targets also clicked on the byline or google-searched my name for more information.

It was interesting to see the order of interest in the first four columns. The *R-E-S-P-E-C-T* article got the most hits, followed closely by *Self-Evident Truth*, then *Is God Dead?* and last, but not least, *An Auspicious Beginning*. The column's title tested well. People seemed to like the concept of TRUTH BE TOLD. They were evidently looking for a thoughtful, apolitical discussion on issues of importance without the toxic rhetoric.

The site mangers could immediately discern the political, religious, gender, age, and a half-dozen other things about the targets who visited our site. They knew if a visitor had linked our article to their social media, forwarded it, copied it, or downloaded it for some future purpose. I was blown away by the amount of data and began to understand the potential for Google and other companies to capture and categorize individuals by patterns of behavior... a boon to marketing operations. It made me wonder about my own internet profile.

As the author, I was more interested in the comments and banter posted on the column's thread than the reader's profile. This was all new to me. A traditional article in a newspaper might generate one or two letters to the editor, but the ease of commenting on the web attracted literally thousands of short, often funny, sometimes mean-spirited responses. It was impossible to read them all, but their comments provided important insight into the minds of those drawn to the subject matter and the column's approach.

Understandably, the blog prompted different reactions based on the political, religious, and cultural values of the host site. Right-wing sites that carried TBT generated the most passionate tirades, sometimes advocating for their opinion with Biblical proof-texts in an adamant defense of their perspective. More progressive and liberal readers were less prone to vehement tirades. They seemed to appreciate the thought-provoking nature of the articles and were more open to alternative points of view. The exception was anyone they perceived to be a "Bible-thumper." They had a low tolerance threshold for Bible quoting. It was like blood in the water for sharks. Once provoked, reason and logic went out the window. It was eat or be eaten. It made me wonder how future articles would be received, sure to challenge their views on race, gender, marriage, poverty, wealth, abortion, and euthanasia. A wise man once told me, "Everyone respects you until you offend them. After that, nothing you write gets a fair hearing." I intended to be an equal-opportunity offender.

The most controversial of the columns so far was, *Is God Dead?*. The most universally accepted column was *R-E-S-P-E-C-T*. Almost everyone agreed there should be greater acceptance of people who disagree with a position without being attacked for expressing a personal opinion. That pleased me the most, but while they agreed with the concept in theory, they simultaneously and vehemently attacked opinions that ruffled their feathers. Some of the perspectives were shocking. The anonymity of the thread allowed people to express viewpoints that would probably never be shared in an open conversation between friends, or even enemies.

The column that got the most response, no matter the host-site, was *Self-Evident Truth*. That column struck a nerve. Most responders had opinions about what was best, right, and wrong for the good of everyone, but there was no consensus and few offered any justification for their point of view. It is a societal conundrum. Many have "a sense of what is right or wrong," but feel no need to defend their perspective. Some argued the old saw, "Everyone should be free to do whatever they want as long as the exercise of a person's freedom does not impose on another's." That can be a troublesome stance when the issue involves gun rights, abortion, pornography, prostitution, age of consent, and other moral positions that many consider detrimental to the social order.

The team programmed the column to burn posts on the thread that included obscene language or attempted to market products, but otherwise we maintained a hands-off approach. We expected the column to generate a wide variety of opinions and interaction, even passionate and argumentative exchanges between readers. We had no problem with that. The more passionate, the better. Energetic debate was one of our desired outcomes.

Analyzing the metrics held more curiosity for Brad and the sales team than for me. Right or wrong, I believed that if I did my job, the analytics would take care of themselves. I was not indifferent to feedback. As a rule, every writer wants to know what his readers think. I wanted to know if my perspective was understood or misconstrued, but it was the subject matter, not the popularity of my viewpoint that energized me. We live in an era when too few give serious consideration to the important issues of our day. People are more reactive than proactive. It's easier to let others of their "tribe" (religious, political, or racial) dictate a position that they readily adopt without much thought of their own.

It sounds like a bad imitation of the Blues Brothers' mantra, but it's how I felt. I was a man on a mission from God sent to challenge extreme political correctness. I was of the opinion that the mainstream media, talk show hosts, Hollywood elites, and the majority of politicians did not understand or represent the common man. Those who challenge the politically correct perspective are consistently labeled "racist, ignorant, or archaic." But my gut told me the majority of people still believed in right, wrong, good, better and best. I believe the majority of Americans still hold to historic values on moral issues while remaining compassionate and tolerant of those who make alternative moral choices. It is frustrating to see those who disagree with the status quo called judgmental, mean-spirited, hate mongers, bigots or worse. Those who resort to using terms like, "racist, xenophobic, misogynistic, homophobic or other phobic monikers" concede the high-ground in a veiled effort to silence a thoughtful discussion of issues. Sadly, their attack strategy is often effective. The "silenced-majority" needed a modern-day Don Quixote willing and capable of tilting at the windmills of the politically correct culture. Maybe, just maybe, my past experience and career path had positioned me, "for such a time as this."

The responses to the opening four blogs were overwhelmingly positive and well received.

R-E-S-P-E-C-T provided an affirmation of the perspective I hoped TBT would become known for.

@**turnupthevolume**: "Truth! If you can't tolerate the opinions of people who see life differently, by definition, you are intolerant."

@wornoutshoes: "God gave people two ears and one mouth for a reason. Stop talking and start listening."

@sirwinksalot: "You don't have to compromise your convictions to be compassionate. Whatever happened to polite discussion?"

@Mythstaken: "Only bullies and insecure people demand everyone accept their point of view. Truth needs no defense, just opportunity. It wields a power you can deny but never defeat."

@Alienplanet: "Unity not uniformity!"

@Easypeasy: "These three abide: faith, hope and love. And the greatest of these is love. God's standards have not changed, but neither has His love."

@tonedeaf: "Bring it TRUTH BE TOLD. It's about time someone had the courage to challenge the PC police. If we only read, listen, and watch those who say what we want to hear, nothing changes. And change is life's only path to progress."

@Endgame: "Aretha, M.L.K., and Jesus spoke the truth in love and we are better for it. Their legacy deserves R-E-S-P-E-C-T."

If TBT was going to challenge the politically correct crowd, I knew it would face its share of criticism. I was fine with that. I have never minded controversy. It's apathy I can't stand. *Is God Dead?* did not disappoint.

@Aquarius: "I gave up on god years ago and have no regrets. If it helps you to believe in a higher power, fine, but leave me out of it."

@MrObvious: People need to believe there is a force greater than themselves when they face struggles beyond their capacity. If believing in a higher power is helpful, you'll get no complaint from me. I prefer the assistance of flesh-and-blood pilgrims on the path called life."

@Hitandrun: "Some of the best people I know are believers. Some are not."

@whataretheodds: "God *IS DEAD*. Just look around. Church buildings are crumbling like the pyramids that contain the dried bones of the pharaohs who died believing they were headed for bigger and better things in the great beyond. Their bones are right where they laid them."

Interesting enough, more people argued in favor of God's existence than those who denied the possibility. It should not surprise anyone. Statistics confirm a large majority of Americans, many who doubt the veracity of the Bible, still believe in God.

@USApatriot: "In God we trust is more than a national motto. It's the reason America remains the strongest nation on earth. When America denies the existence of God, it will disappear like all the godless empires before it."

@blindfaith: "Trusting in the God of the Bible is unlike any other faith. Every other religion teaches what you must do to please god. The Bible teaches what God has done in time and history to make you pleasing. It is established on factual evidence, archeology, and historic predictions that have been examined and found accurate. Give God a chance."

@tunein: "I'm a new subscriber to TRUTH BE TOLD. If this is the kind of thinking we can expect in the future, you can count on me to spread the word! Everyone knows there is right and wrong. It's about time someone had the hutzpah to challenge the deniers!"

@truthninja: "Good luck advocating for truth in a culture that believes every opinion is as valid as another. I'm eager to see how TRUTH BE TOLD tackles the tough issues. Subjective opinions are a namby-pamby way of avoiding the issues. Bring it and let the chips fall where they fall!"

Brad was ecstatic over the analytics but more importantly, he liked my approach, especially the discussion of Self-Evident Truth. He called it, "A genius move to appeal to America's founding document." It was the kind of column he envisioned, resisting the temptation to fence-sit while inviting a difference of opinion. He wasn't interested in promoting a peacemaker. A peace-breaker was more his style, as long as it was done in an interesting and respectful manner. He invited me to join him for a beer at Mulligan's after the meeting.

He wasted no time getting to the point.

"You have to be happy with what you just heard. The early columns did a great job of establishing TRUTH BE TOLD. How are you feeling about it?"

"TRUTH BE TOLD," I smiled in reference to the byline, "I'm feeling unsure. We haven't really tested the waters yet. I've only discussed my expectations and intentions for the column. It's one thing for people to play nice and respect differences *in theory*. Wait until the column tackles some real issues and people start seeing their sacred cows being corralled for slaughter. That's when we'll find out if TBT has legs and the appetite of our sponsors for controversy in a cancel culture.

"Your next four columns are due in a week. Is that going to be a problem?

"Not for me," I chuckled. "They're ready now, but I want to run my perspective past my consultant."

"Consultant? You haven't said anything about using a consultant."

"No worries Brad, he's not a consultant in the usual sense. I don't have a financial agreement with him. He's just a friend with a wealth of experience and insight, a good sounding board. He's more muse than consultant, a straight shooter who's been 100% supportive of the column from the get-go."

"Do you think you'll need help choosing subject matter moving forward?"

"Not yet, but if that ever changes I'll give you a call. I need to sit with my thoughts for a bit before exposing them to the public. Like fine wine, they need time to breathe before achieving their full potential. I'll definitely meet the deadline. I plan to dedicate four columns to each issue, keeping the essays from getting too deep, while making sure each subject receives the focus and attention it deserves. It plan to connect my readers to the column by ending each article with a cliff-hanger to keep them eager for the next installment. Not unlike a good series on Netflix."

Brad was optimistic, but we both knew the real test was just around the corner, when the column took a stand on a controversial issue of our day. My goal was neither to be liked nor despised, only to be respected. The goal of TRUTH BE TOLD was to create an exchange of ideas that would challenge the right and the left, believers and non-believers, the common and the elite to question themselves as much as they question those with whom they disagree. I wasn't sure it was even possible, but the response to the first four columns provided a glimmer of hope.

Sarah was eagerly waiting for my return from the meeting. She showed more interest than me in reading the responses to each column. It amused her to read the threads aloud to me each evening until I reached my limit. Some were insightful, some apparently written under the influence of a mind-altering substance, and a few were outright hilarious. I purposefully limited my exposure to feedback to keep an objective perspective for future articles without anticipating reader's reactions. I needed to protect my spirit from becoming defensive and paranoid. After forty years in the industry, I had seen too many journalists implode from insecurity. I wasn't about to start down that path at this point. The effectiveness of an op-ed is often directly proportionate to the amount of negative mail it generates. As I said, it was apathy, not controversy, that I feared most.

Sarah was waiting at the door when I arrived home.

"How did it go?

"Everyone seemed pleased. The numbers were good. Lots of social media shares, and the number of hits on links to the advertisers was solid. It's always good when the money people are happy! The tenor of the threads was what we hoped for. The articles stimulated a lot of discussion, most of it positive, a respectful exchange of opinions. Everyone is eager to see how it continues. In all fairness, the columns so far have been pretty innocuous.

"Could they tell anything about the popularity of one subject compared to another?

"That was interesting. They all had their share of hits, with the column on R-E-S-P-E-C-T being the strongest. The good news was that after reading one of the articles a high percentage clicked on another in the archive, and quite a few registered to receive future posts. By the end of the month, the columns had all received about the same amount of hits. They have it down to a science... literally. They could tell how long someone stays on a page or if they are a 'click and go.' It was news to me. We surpassed the norm in almost every category by a sizeable margin. That was affirming.

"I'm not surprised. You have a way of drawing people into your stories. I wonder if the man upstairs is watching."

"Yeah. You and I are the only ones who know about that part of the effort. I would like to touch base with Mordecai or one of his 'colleagues' but don't know how to go about it. My next columns are due in a week and I would like some divine guidance before I dive into the deep end."

"Well you know where he hangs out. Why not go to The Footnote and see if he's there waiting for you. He has an uncanny way of knowing where you will be and when."

"Let's not forget, he also showed up on the practice range at the club." I replied with a smile. "All things being equal, I'd prefer to go there and see if he's working on his game."

The articles on racial diversity are in the que, but I could benefit from his insight. If I'm called to be a divine spokesman, it seems God would have a vested interest in the content of the next posts. Maybe He doesn't care one way or the other about the perspective of the column and just recruited me to start the discussion? I'm clueless at this point."

"I don't believe that for a minute. Too many things have happened to assume God has no skin in the game."

"I'll try the bookstore. I just finished that Amelia Earhart biography so I'm in need of some reading material."

"Good idea. While you are at it, maybe you could ask Mordecai whatever happened to Amelia. Enquiring minds want to know!" Sarah said with a chuckle.

"I just might do that. The truth about Amelia would be a real scoop."

"The Mystery Has Been Solved. Amelia Earhart spent the last forty years of her life enjoying peace and quiet, avoiding annoying reporters on an island in the South Pacific. Pictures to follow!"

"The older I grow, the more I am convinced that there is no education which one can get from books and costly apparatus that is equal to that which can be gotten from contact with great men and women."
—*Booker T. Washington*

CHAPTER 8

Lessons Learned

I took Sarah's advice and the next morning found myself at The Footnote in hopes of catching up with Mordecai. I convinced myself he would be there, but he wasn't. I wandered into the children's nook and walked through the romance novels, science fiction, health and fitness, business, and mysteries sections on the chance he might be there on a different mission. It was no use.

Dismissing the staff's offer of help, I bounced next door hoping to find him sipping a cup of coffee in the corner booth where we sat a month ago. Nothing. I was confused. I remember distinctly asking how I might contact him in the future, and he had said, "No need. I'm sure we will bump into each other often enough." It didn't feel like "often enough," to me. I was convinced he'd circle back once the column went public. I needed feedback, approval or not.

Discouraged, I returned to The Footnote to find some new reading material. The store was well organized by genre and author. The staff could run a computer check of their inventory by title or author but otherwise there was no way of telling in advance what you might find. Forrest Gump might say, "A used book store is like a box of chocolates. You never know what you are going to find." So long as the book was nonfiction and well written I was open to almost any possibility.

I enjoy stories of adventure, innovation, exploration, and living off the grid. Biographies and autobiographies of musicians, industrial leaders, and politicians also held an attraction, especially those of my contemporaries. I was always eager to learn the story behind the story. I prefer studying history through the lives of those who lived it. It didn't matter to me if the main character was well known like Amelia Earhart, or Mark Twain, or an unknown historically insignificant person like those described in The Glass Castle, or Angela's Ashes. Nonfiction books reinforce my sense that everyone's life is significant, and if their story is properly told, it can provide a helpful life lesson.

As I perused my usual twenty-foot section of the store, a member of the staff interrupted me.

"Looking for anything in particular Mr. King? We can check the computer and save you some time."

Her name tag caught my attention. Esther was 60ish as best I could tell, with slightly graying hair, not unlike Mordecai. Her glasses hung from a lanyard, apparently more accessory than necessity. She moved with confidence and spoke in a matter-of-fact voice, tilting her head slightly while looking me in the eye.

"Have we met?" Wow... I find myself saying that more and more lately.

"Everyone knows you write for *The Herald*. Well, not everyone I suppose. But the people who buy books probably do. How are you enjoying your new assignment? TRUTH BE TOLD appears to be off to a good start."

"Do you read TRUTH BE TOLD in the paper or online? I'm always curious."

"I noticed it in the paper at the coffee shop. *The Herald* mentioned it was also being published online, which is a good thing since I don't subscribe to their paper anymore."

"You and a gazillion other people, I suppose. What did you like about it?"

"I like that you were willing to put in print what I suspect most people believe. We have our differences and that's fine, but whatever happened to an honest, respectful discussion. R-E-S-P-E-C-T right? These days it seems everyone jumps to attack-mode from the get-go."

"I'm not sure I can keep the discussion civil. TRUTH BE TOLD is about to get a bit more real. It's one thing for a person to agree to disagree in theory. It's another thing to admit you might be wrong."

"I'm sure you will be 'gently firm.' My dad used that phrase a lot. It's okay to be firm, but it's not okay to be rude. The Bible calls it speaking the truth with love. My father liked to add, '… and when in doubt, err on the side of love.'"

"Your father was a wise man."

"Mr. Taylor was in yesterday and left some books he thought might interest you."

"Mr. Taylor? Mordecai Taylor? You know him?"

"Mr. Taylor is a regular like you, Mr. King. You are both what we call one-way customers," she said with a smile.

"What's a one-way customer?"

"Customers that take books out but never bring any back. I don't know what you do after reading them. You must have a sizable collection by now."

"I stack 'em," I said with a grin. "I don't think you would be interested in repurchasing my copies after I'm done with them. I'm very visual. I can't read a book without underlining it and making notes in the margin. It helps me retain the content, but they aren't worth much when I get done with them. Did you say Mordecai left some books for me at the counter?"

"He did. In fact, he even paid for them. Let me show you."

I followed her to the front counter.

"Esther's a name you don't hear much anymore," I said. "I had an aunt named Esther when I was a kid, but I don't recall meeting anyone with that name lately.

"My father chose it. It's a Hebrew word that means, 'star,' but I am pretty sure he chose it because it's from the Bible. He called me Queen Esther until the day he passed. It never got old for either of us."

"Queen Esther risked her life to save her people, didn't she? ...For such a time as this, and all that. Right?'" I was showing off what little Bible knowledge I had. I only remembered the passage because of my previous conversation with Mordecai.

Without answering, Esther asked, "Are you a Christian, Jim?"

Most of my friends called me Jim, but my byline and our mutual friend Mordecai always called me James. I thought he preferred my "Christian" name to remind me of my calling. I didn't care what people called me one way or the other, but their choice always made me curious. Mothers, teachers, librarians, pastors, and people past the age of 80 tended to prefer James over Jim. It seemed odd to hear the street version of my name on Esther's lips. The more I talked to her, the more curious I became.

"I am," I responded. "But I don't claim to be especially dedicated to the cause."

"God moves in mysterious ways, His wonders to perform," she said while reaching under the counter for the books Mordecai had set aside for me.

I'm wasn't sure what she meant by the reference. I suspected she was questioning God's decision to use a "Chreaster" (a person who only worships on Christmas and Easter) to advocate for truth on the issues of our day.

"Is that saying from the Bible somewhere? Maybe the Proverbs?"

"Lots of people think that. It's actually from an 18th century hymn by William Cowper. It's one of my favorites. He called the hymn, *Light Shining Out Of Darkness*. Which is what I guess you are trying to do with TRUTH BE TOLD. *'God moves in mysterious ways; His wonders to perform; He plans His footsteps in the sea, and rides upon the storm.'* In a way, that quote describes the types of books you buy. People like Springsteen, Billy Joel, and Mark Twain aren't known as pillars of faith or morality, but God used them in mysterious ways to speak truth to the culture... His mysterious ways."

"That's an interesting observation."

"Truth is where you find it and shows up when you least expect it. How many times have you read a book, seen a movie, or read an editorial and thought, 'Wow. That's so true.'"?

Esther had a manner that made me think she knew more about Mordecai and my reason for asking about him than she was willing to admit. My Spidey-senses were tingling. Like a kid venturing into unknown territory my inner voice was whispering, "Beware of strangers." First as a reporter, and now as an object of divine interest, I was reminded, "Everyone seems normal until you get to know them."

I had been frequenting The Footnote for several years and don't recall ever seeing Esther before today, yet she moved through the stacks and behind the counter like it was her second home. The more we talked, the more I suspected she was working in league with Mordecai and for the same cause. Even her name suggested a connection. As I recalled from my earlier conversation, Mordecai of the Bible was the uncle of Queen Esther who encouraged her to intervene on behalf of the Jewish nation.

"Esther, I don't recall seeing you here before today. Are you new to the store?"

"The owner's a good friend. I help her out now and then on a voluntary basis. We both love books, words, and people so I feel right at home."

I've been a reporter long enough to know when someone is avoiding the question, and Esther was definitely avoiding the question. My suspicions about her were growing. She seemed to be more than a "volunteer," helping out a friend. What are the odds?

"How long have you known Mordecai? We've only talked a few times, but he impresses me as a well-read, intelligent person. I've grown to respect his advice and observations."

"He's a keeper all right. Always polite, always smiling, and good on the eyes too," she said with a twinkle. It was good to see her reaction. It almost made her seem human... almost. Esther retrieved the books and placed them on the counter. They were tied neatly with a string like something from the 19th century. There was an envelope with my name jotted on it slipped under the binding.

"Here are the books Mr. Taylor set aside for you. He marked some places with Post-it notes and wrote your name on the envelope. I have no idea what it's all about. He didn't say much, and it was none of my business, so I didn't ask.

"Thanks for your help, Esther. How much do I owe you?"

"Nothing. As I said, Mr. Taylor already paid for them."

Mordecai had chosen three books. They seemed like an odd combination of titles. One was *Douglass – A Narrative of the Life*. It contained a collection of writings by Frederick Douglass, the well-known runaway slave, turned abolitionist. The other two were of a less historic nature, the more recently published autobiography of Bruce Springsteen called, *Born to Run*, and last but not least, *An Invisible Thread*. A friend had recommended *An Invisible Thread* to me a few years back, but at the time I wasn't interested. Evidently, it's the true story of a business woman in New York City who befriended an inner-city street kid. I did notice it carried the *New York Times* bestseller badge which was always a good sign. I also noticed the bookmarks Esther mentioned. I was curious to discover what quotations had captured Mordecai's interest.

The books were great, but I was more interested in talking to Mordecai. I needed his reaction and insight on the column. "Can I leave a check for you to give Mr. Taylor the next time he stops by? Does he come by at any certain time?"

"No money is necessary. He made that clear. He kept the receipt and said to tell you not to worry about it. He drops in from time to time but like you, there's no predicting when he might stop by again. We keep contact files for mailings and to notify customers of special orders, but Mordecai has never registered. Even if we had a profile, we couldn't share it. I'm sure you understand."

"It was worth a shot," I smiled. "Can I leave a note for you to pass on? After all, you set aside these books for me. If I wrote Mr. Taylor a thank you, maybe you could see that he got it?"

"I'm sorry. We are not in the business of passing notes between customers. Don't confuse us with the Post Office, Mr. King," she laughed. I sensed she was trying her best to stay out of the discussion between myself and Mordecai.

"What if I bought a book and left it for Mr. Taylor? Would you be willing to set it aside until the next time he comes in? After all, that's what you did for me."

"I suppose that could work, as long as a purchase is involved."

"Okay. Give me a moment. I'll be right back."

I left the books on the counter and walked to my favorite section looking for a volume of interest, something appropriate... maybe about angels, visions, or something theological. It didn't take long. My eye was drawn to a copy of *The Noticer* by Andy Andrews. Perfect. I'd read the book several years ago and still had a copy in my library. It was a story about a mysterious man named Jones who provided what he called, "A little perspective on life" by noticing things most people miss. I sat down to jot a note on my business card for Mordecai. I doubted he needed my contact information, but it provided the opportunity to make sure my email address and phone number were in his hands.

"Dear Mordecai: We need to talk. TRUTH BE TOLD is being published. I'd appreciate some feedback and your thoughts on the project. Please give me a call or text."

I opened the book to chapter six in which Jones helps a widow realize every life has meaning, regardless of your age, physical well-being, financial status, race, gender, or belief. I found just the right paragraph to underline and stuck my business card between the pages. The quotation was on point.

"In desperate times, much more than anything else, folks need perspective." This perspective leads to calm, clear thinking, new ideas, and ultimately "the bloom of an answer."

I paid for my purchase and left the book with my card for Mordecai. This must have been how the GI's felt on D-Day hitting the beach at Normandy. I was working for the Lord on a need-to-know basis and someone in authority decided I didn't need to know much. I had my marching orders but lacked an understanding of the big picture. I decided I'd complete my assignment with or without Mordecai's insight. Maybe the books he left for me would help.

I was eager to get started and open the envelope that bore my name. He told Esther I might find it useful. My curiosity was definitely piqued. I should have headed home where I could sit in the quiet of my office and give it greater consideration, but I've never been known for my patience. I headed next door for a cup of coffee and a quiet booth.

I opened the envelope first. Mordecai's message was affirming but measured. It read,

"Manage your expectations."
Galatians 1:10

Curiosity got the best of me. I used the Bible app on my phone and quickly checked the reference. Truth over popularity seemed to be the meaning.

> "Am I now trying to win the approval of human beings, or of God? Or am I trying to please people? If I were still trying to please people, I would not be a servant of Christ."

The reference provided a gentle reminder to temper my expectations for the column. It was comforting to know the Lord understood what I was up against. Just because something is true, doesn't mean it will be accepted. Mordecai was preparing me for the reaction that was sure to come.

People see what they want to see and embrace information that supports their existing perspective. It was not unlike raising our teenage boys who challenged house rules based on the behavior of their friends and the more permissive attitude of their friends' parents. They argued for concession. I never took it personally. I considered it their "job" as teenagers to challenge my authority. It was my "job" as a responsible parent to hold the line when those decisions opposed our standards. When no agreement could be reached, I held firm and gave permission for them to place the blame on their father. I suggested they respond with, "What can I say? My dad's an idiot." I didn't care what their friends thought of me, but I cared a great deal about the consequence of a decision that could be detrimental to the character and safety of our sons.

The books Mordecai left for me covered a wide spectrum of subject matter. I wasn't initially sure what Frederick Douglass, Bruce Springsteen and a marketing agent for USA Today had in common. Mordecai knew I favored biographies but there had to be more to it than that. I speculated they all had something to do with the series of articles I was about to write on race and prejudice. His bookmarks and highlights would tell the tale.

I was more familiar with Frederick Douglass than Springsteen or Laura Schroff. I had previously read the autobiographies of both Frederick Douglass and Booker T. Washington, two nationally known black leaders of the 1800's. Although there was 38 years' difference between them, both had been born into slavery. Both had risen above their circumstance to become respected leaders, famous in America and Europe. Both were invited to the White House by sitting presidents. Douglass met with Lincoln three times. The last time, just after Lincoln's second inaugural address, only a few days before his assassination. Thirty-six years later Booker T. Washington was invited by President Roosevelt to dine with his family, becoming the first black person to eat dinner in the White House. Douglass was a nationally recognized orator, pastor, publisher, and political activist. Washington founded the prestigious Tuskegee Institute in Alabama, intent on helping both black and white Southerners overcome the devastation of the Civil War.

Mordecai knew I was keenly aware of Booker T. Washington's impact on America. I remember telling him at our first meeting that I considered his autobiography *Up from Slavery* one of the most important books in my library. Frederick Douglass was lesser known to me, but no less significant.

I was eager to see which of Douglass' speeches were included in the collection and which comments Mordecai had highlighted. His most famous was given on July 4th, 1852, to an abolitionist gathering in Rochester, New York. The date's important when you consider it occurred nearly a decade before the attack against Fort Sumter, the instigating event of the Civil War. If Booker T. Washington sought to build on what was good between the races (and he did), Douglass did the opposite. His verbal attacks against racial and gender prejudice were bold and unrestrained at a time when denunciation of inequality could easily get a black man lynched. He was the Malcolm X of his generation, minus the hate speech.

I stepped next door to examine the books in my usual corner booth. As expected, the Frederick Douglass book [25] began with *Narrative* of the *Life,* which he wrote in 1845, but it also contained a number of his most prominent essays and speeches including,

- The Church and Prejudice, 1848

- We Have Decided to Stay, 1848

- The Meaning of the 4th of July for the Negro, 1852

- Fighting Rebels with Only One Hand, 1861

- What the Black Man Wants, 1865

- An Appeal to Congress for Impartial Suffrage, 1867

- The Color Line, 1881

- John Brown, 1881

- My Escape from Slavery, 1881

- The Race Problem, 1890

Every article captured my interest and I was eager to read them all, but for now I would limit my reading to Mordecai's book marks and the sections he highlighted. His first reference was from the July 4th, speech that I knew well, and quoted a number of times when covering stories on the subject of race relations. The most obvious quote, the one most people know, was marked as I expected, but the qualifying comments in the same speech tampered his rhetoric in a way I had not previously noticed.

"I say with a sad sense of disparity between us. I am not included within the pale of this glorious anniversary... the blessings in which you, this day, rejoice, are not enjoyed in common. The rich inheritance of justice, liberty, prosperity and independence, bequeathed by your fathers, is shared by you, not by me. The sunlight that brought light and healing to you, has brought stripes and death to me. This Fourth of July is yours, not mine. You may rejoice, I must mourn." (page 159)

"I will in the name of humanity which is outraged, in the name of liberty which is fettered, in the name of the constitution and the Bible which are disregarded and trampled upon, dare to call in question and to denounce, with all the emphasis I can command, everything that serves to perpetuate slavery—the great sin and shame of America! I will not equivocate; I will not excuse; I will use the severest language I can command and yet not one word shall escape from me that any man, whose judgment is not blinded by prejudice, or who is not at heart a slaveholder, shall not confess to be right and just." (page 160)

Those comments by Douglass I had heard before. They ring as loudly today as they did when Frederick Douglass first uttered them. But hidden in the speech were also words of hope and a belief that slavery and oppression are unnatural and would ultimately be vanquished. He was able to look beyond the reality of the moment, convinced that the Declaration's affirmation of equality for all would one day come to fruition.

"I have said that the Declaration of Independence is the ringbolt to the chain of your nation's destiny; so, indeed, I regard it.

The principles contained in that instrument are saving principles. (page 156)

"Allow me to say, in conclusion, notwithstanding the dark picture I have this day presented, of the state of the nation, I do not despair of this country. There are forces in operation which must inevitably work for the downfall of slavery." (page 173)

Frederick Douglass grew more optimistic as he observed the terrible price paid by white men during the Civil War to end slavery and establish a unified and free nation. Douglass, for his part, continued to speak out on the issue of race and equality.

"Aside from the curious contrast to himself, the white child feels nothing on the first sight of a colored man. Curiosity is the only feeling... the color is innocent enough, but the things with which it is coupled make it hated. Slavery, ignorance, stupidity, servility, poverty, dependence, are undesirable conditions. When these cease to be coupled with color, there will be no color line drawn." (page 202)

Near the end of his life, as evidenced in the highlighting of Mordecai's marker, Frederick Douglass came to believe it was only a matter of time before slavery and sanctioned prejudice would be overcome by God and the godly people of America. Of course, that does not mean sinful individuals who oppose God's standards of love and acceptance will discontinue all displays of prejudice. As the Good Book says in Romans 3:11–12, "There is no one that does only good and avoids all evil."

"I have seen darkness gradually disappearing and the light gradually increasing. One by one, I have seen obstacles removed, errors corrected, prejudices softened, proscriptions relinquished, and my people advancing in all the elements that go to make up the sum of general welfare. And I remember that God reigns in eternity, and that whatever delays, whatever disappointments and discouragements may come, truth, justice, liberty, and humanity will ultimately prevail." (page 255)

The Springsteen autobiography was the next book I opened while sipping coffee undisturbed in my corner booth. Of course, I knew his music: *Born in the USA, Glory Days, Hungry Heart, Thunder Road, The Streets of Philadelphia* and the song that made him a mega star: *Born to Run*.

Biographies of famous musicians are especially interesting to me. The love of music is universal, bringing fame, fortune and larger than life experiences to the best of the best. I've read my share including Frank Sinatra, Ray Charles, Nat King Cole, Michael Jackson, Billy Joel, Eric Clapton, and all the Beatles: Paul, John, Ringo, and George. A friend had read Springsteen's book and highly recommended it, but I had not picked it up yet. I once saw the E-Street Band play in Chicago and was struck by the diversity of his group: long hair, short hair, women, white and black musicians in equal number. I especially remember the chemistry Springsteen had with his phenomenal sax player, Clarence Clemons, who like many of the other E-Street bandmates had a reputation all his own.

The book, *Bruce Springsteen, Born to Run* [26] was written by his own hand and, according to the book jacket, took seven years to write. Bruce was 67 years old when it was completed in 2016. By the size of it, over 500 pages long, I expected the narrative to be detailed, and was not disappointed. Bruce was a down and out Jersey boy, born to working class parents who abandoned the East Coast to start over in California when he was nineteen years old. He stayed behind, hoping to make a life playing music with his friends in the Jersey bars up and down the coast.

Mordecai had marked four different sections in the book, all of them pertaining to the question of race. The first Post-it note directed me to a chapter Bruce entitled, The Big Bang (Have You Heard the News). In Springsteen's opinion, a huge step towards racial equality was taken on September 9, 1956, when it was announced, "Ladies and gentlemen...

Elvis Presley." Seventy million Americans tuned in. Bruce said, "THE
BARRICADES HAVE BEEN STORMED!!! THE REVOLUTION
HAS BEEN TELEVISED!!" (His emphasis, not mine.)

"He (Elvis) was a singer, a guitar player who loved black musical
culture, recognized its artistry, its mastery, its power, and yearned
for intimacy with it." (page 41)

"I don't know what his thoughts were on race. I don't know
whether he thought about the broader implications of his actions.
I do know that this is what he did: lived a life he was driven to
live and brought forth the truth that was within him and the
possibilities within us." (page 41)

The rest of Mordecai's bookmarks focused on the relationship between
Springsteen and Clarence Clemons, the man he called C. As Springsteen
tells it, "Previous to *Born to Run*, Clarence was just the very large black
saxophonist in my band." After *Born to Run*, it was hard to imagine one
without the other. The combination of race, size, style, and instruments
created a dynamic no one anticipated. The whole was greater than the
sum of the parts. Like bacon and eggs, mac and cheese, biscuits and gravy,
cookies and milk, chips and salsa, red beans and rice... they needed each
other, fed off each other, inspired each other. It wasn't easy, but both men
remained committed to mutual respect and brotherly love despite racial
and cultural differences.

"He (Clarence) struggled living in the predominantly white
world of our band. At that point, the E Street band was half black
and half white; the loss of Davey Sancious and Boom Carter deeply
affected him. For a long time he was alone. I was white. We had as
deep a relationship as I can imagine, but we lived in the real world,
where we'd experienced that nothing, not all the love in God's
heaven, obliterates race." (page 244)

The next note highlighted a song Springsteen wrote to honor the memory of Amadou Diallo, an African immigrant who was shot by undercover police officers outside his apartment in New York City. As the story goes, it was just before 1:00 AM when Amadou returned from grabbing a bite to eat. The police drove by, and believing he resembled the description of a serial rapist from the area, they ordered him to stop. But without uniforms, Amadou feared for his life and ran up the steps to his apartment door. When he stopped at the door and reached for his keys, one of the officers yelled, "Gun!" and four policemen unleased 41 shots, 19 of which struck Amadou, killing him instantly.

> "I wanted to write something new for our New York engagement at Madison Square Garden... to underscore the danger and deadly confusion of roaming the inner-city streets in black skin that still existed in late twentieth-century America."

The song was called, *American Skin*. Despite the best of motives, the *song was not* always well received, not *in* all circles. Some took it as an unprovoked attack *on* the law enforcement officers who, right *or* wrong, felt justified in their action.

> "I just wanted to help people see the other guy's point of view. The idea was: here is what systematic racial injustice, fear and paranoia do to our children, our loved ones, ourselves. Here's the price in blood... I was saddened that the song was still so misunderstood by good men toeing the blue line. On the other hand, I also encountered men and women who showed me their badge, thanked me and said they understood what I was saying." (page 436)

The last section of Springsteen's book Mordecai chose to highlight dealt with the death of C.

> "My great concern (2009) was Clarence's physical condition. This is something I had watched deteriorate for a long time...

Clarence was always the last band member off the stage. As I held up that big body night after night and we slowly made it down the stairs, he often whispered, 'Thanks for letting me be here."

"Clarence's stroke was massive, shutting the lights out of an entire side of his brain... Victoria (C.'s wife), spoke to him and told him I was there... a week passed; C.'s condition continued to worsen and all that could be done had been done... His wife, his sons, his brother, his nephews, myself, Max and Garry prepared to say our goodbyes. I strummed my guitar gently to Land Of Hope And Dreams, and then something inexplicable happened. Something great and timeless and beautiful and confounding just disappeared. Something was gone... gone for good... Clarence's great body became still." (page 473)

"Clarence was elemental in my life and losing him was like losing the rain." (page 475)

Wow. Mordecai had shared more through our mutual love of books than if we had sat down over coffee in a prolonged discussion of race. I had been upset when he did not make himself available, but in fact, the readings he highlighted for my benefit prepared me for my task better than a two-hour interview ever could. And there was still one more book to consider, *The Invisible Thread*.[27]

During all my years reporting stories for the *St. Louis Herald*, the issue of inner city blight and the circumstance of those who lived there was a given. I grew tired of reporting on accidental and not-so-accidental shootings, drug use, gang violence, car jackings, and homelessness. Those stories were so common we became immune to the tragedy measured in people's lives. It's hard to think in terms of individuals when the same heartbreaks with different names cross your desk week in and week out. Laura Schroff's book changed that. She got up-close with one individual who opened her eyes and the eyes of America to the very personal reality of it all.

Mordecai evidently wanted me to see how the issue of race and deprivation affects flesh and blood people and holds power even over those who attempt to look away. Laura can't fully explain why she got deeply involved with a young black kid from the streets of New York City. She knew first-hand the pain of a dysfunctional home. She had watched her own family be destroyed by an alcoholic, abusive father. But in her mind, it was more than empathy for a fellow innocent.

"It's something I call an invisible thread. It is, as the old Chinese proverb tells us, something that connects two people who are destined to meet, regardless of time and place and circumstance. Some legends call it the red string of fate; others, the thread of destiny. It is, I believe, what brought Maurice and me to the same stretch of sidewalk in a vast teeming city- just two people out of eight million, somehow connected, somehow meant to be friends." (page 6)

Their first encounter occurred as Laura walked to her office along a crowded New York street. At first, she passed by Maurice without notice, having grown accustomed to the ever-present commotion and din of people going about their business. But something caused her to turn around and walk back. Perhaps it was that invisible thread tugging on her heart. He of course was begging for money, but for whatever reason she was not in a check-the-box kind of mood. Instead, if he was truly hungry, she offered to buy him anything he wanted at a nearby McDonalds. It was just the first of the next 150 Mondays that they would share a meal together.

"He wasn't looking for anyone's sympathy. He was only looking to survive." (page 26)
"Sometimes we talked about the future, both his and mine. I remember once telling him he needed to be a "straight arrow" and explaining what that meant: he needed to think about the right thing to do, pick the right course of action, then stay on that course no matter what." (page 151)
"Everything I ever gave to Maurice, he gave back to me tenfold.

Every meal, every shirt, every bike or toothbrush, was matched by Maurice with more genuine appreciation than I have ever known... If love is the greatest gift of all—and I believe it is—then the greatest privilege of all is to be able to love someone... to this day my relationship with him is the relationship I am most proud of in my life." (page 220)

Over the years, many people have told me how lucky Maurice was to have met me, but my response is always, 'No, I was lucky to have met him.' Maurice, you have brought so much joy into my life and showed me in many ways the true meaning of friendship, and for that all I can say is, 'Thank you.' with all my heart." (page 233)

It was a lot to internalize. How could I possibly say all that needs to be said on the question of race, including corporate and personal responsibility, in four short columns? The quotations Mordecai shared ran the gamut from emancipation to contemporary interaction between black and white America in the 21ˢᵗ Century.

I definitely needed to revisit the work I had already done on the subject and had just a week to finish it. The words of Mordecai to Queen Esther in the Bible were ringing in my ears.

"For if you remain silent at this time, relief and deliverance for the Jews will arise from another place. ...And who knows, perhaps you have come to your position for such a time as this?" (Esther 4:14)

Like Laura Schroff, I needed to give up the notion of doing everything perfectly and just wade in. She had no idea how things would turn out when she first met Maurice, but that didn't stop her from turning around and walking back to ask a grungy street urchin, "Are you hungry?"

Outcomes are above our pay grade and maybe that's okay. We are not called to solve the world's problems but we can be faithful within our sphere of influence. Doing for one what you wish you could do for all, is a good place to start.

St. Louis Herald

Created Equal

By: **James King**

Our nation's founding document boldly declares, "All men are created equal, that they are endowed by their Creator with certain unalienable rights, that among these are life, liberty and the pursuit of happiness."

Is that just another way of saying, "On opening day of the season all teams are tied for first place"? It begins that way, but it doesn't stay that way... not for long. Eventually some teams win and some lose. In the end, survival of the fittest has its say. Eventually, inequality, not equality reigns. It's the natural way of things. So say the evolutionists.

Is that how it works in life? Initially, every person's race, gender, creed, marital status, sexual orientation, and national identity are considered equally valid. But it doesn't stay that way... not for long. The natural way of things, also known as "the survival of the fittest," will have its say. Some will win and some will lose.

Thankfully, the Founding Fathers didn't base their Declaration on evolutionary theory. America was established on belief in an almighty Creator who has endowed all people with certain "unalienable rights." The word "unalienable," is rarely used today. It means, "rights that cannot be alienated, or separated" from a person without violating the almighty Creator's intention. Really? Equality may be every person's right but, it's not every person's reality.

How ironic that the author of The Declaration of Independence was a slave owner when he wrote those words and remained a slave owner until the day he died. It sounds good in theory, but doesn't prove true in practice... does it? Slavery is not dead. There are twenty to thirty million people living in slavery at this very moment.

Does the evolutionist's Declaration of Natural Selection supersede America's Declaration of Independence established on, "The Laws of Nature and Nature's God?" Were the Founding Fathers wrong? And if not, why is our nation's reality so different from the principles they fought and died for? Who hijacked America's unalienable rights? Why is racism and prejudice epidemic across the world?

Equality rings true. TRUTH BE TOLD believes racial equality and equal opportunity are how things ought to be, despite how things actually are. TRUTH BE TOLD believes the principle of racial, ethnic, and gender equality *IS SELF-EVIDENT.* But the current state of equality and equal opportunity in America falls woefully short of the Founding Fathers' Declaration. Who's to blame and what can be done about it?

Some people want to blame the Creator. He's the author of distinctions among people. In the beginning God made people male and female. Gender was his idea. And if the Bible is to be believed, God created racial distinction too. According to the Bible, He confused the world's language to force the dispersion of its people which led to the creation of distinctive cultures. The aging process is also God's idea. *"For dust you are, and to dust you shall return."* He could

have made the world genderless, racially homogeneous, and ageless if he wanted. Procreation could have taken a gender-free form. But that was not His choice. As the prophet observed, *"Our days come to seventy years, or eighty, if our strength endures, and yet the best of them are but trouble and sorrow, for they quickly pass and we fly away."*

What was He thinking? Why did He do it? And can anything be done to rectify the situation?

The oft repeated line declares, *"From the beginning it was not so."* In the beginning, there was no prejudice, no inequality, no racism, and no hierarchical distinction between genders either. The book of beginnings states, *"God saw all that He had made, and behold it was good. And there was evening and there was morning the sixth day."* All people were created equal and their right to life, liberty and the pursuit of happiness was unalienable. It was all good. What happened?

Something broke. Good broke bad.

If we believe the "experts," the professors and scientists that the educated elite looks to for answers, the world and those who live it are the result of evolution, not the result of an almighty Creator. Therefore, according to the experts, race, culture, gender and social status have "evolved" to define our present reality.

According to evolutionary theory,

change occurs naturally over time. Survival of the fittest explains why those at the top of the "food-chain" exercise power, accumulate wealth, and enjoy privileged status over the rest. The fittest have evolved beyond their peers and therefore rightfully assume an elevated place in the world, evolutionists say. It is the "natural" way of things, evolutionists say.

Certain segments of society dominate other segments of society because they have achieved superiority. Dominance is the logical outcome of evolution. If you accept their theory, inequality is not an unfortunate condition based on arrogance, but the result of natural selection. Survival of the fittest naturally determines who rules over whom, evolutionists say. According to evolution: racism, poverty, misogyny and national supremacy exist because certain races, genders, and cultures have evolved to become superior to those less capable and less evolved.

The Law of Natural Selection is the means by which society as a whole advances. Evolutionists contend it appears unfair only to those who are inferior. Dominance of the fittest is the very definition of fairness, evolutionists say. Those who are stronger and intellectually superior deservedly rule over the weak and less capable. They've earned it. Evolutionists contend, nothing could be fairer than that.

From the evolutionist's point of view, America's Founding Fathers are the foolish ones. Equality based on the laws of nature and nature's God, rather than national selection is absurd to them. Believing that all people have been endowed by an almighty Creator with certain unalienable rights is the height of nonsense. Evolutionists argue the world was not created; it evolved. God had nothing to do with it, they say.

TRUTH BE TOLD believes there are many educated and uneducated people, maybe even the majority, who still resonate to the words of The Declaration of Independence just as it's written. Many who put faith in an almighty Creator are highly-educated, reasonably-minded, and successful people who believe in the origins of life as described in The Declaration of Independence. Creationists believe equality among the races, genders, and various cultures has been established by an almighty Creator the evolutionists deny.

The theory promoted by the evolutionists, not the Founding Fathers, is absurd to those who believe in a Creator of nature and nature's laws. Evolutionists can't have it both ways. Those who subscribe to evolution and survival of the fittest, must by their perspective of life, deny that all people have a natural right to equality, life, liberty and the pursuit of happiness. The two theories are irreconcilable.

Not everyone who believes in a creator is a Bible thumping fundamentalist. They simply believe every house has a builder and the Creator of all things is God. They don't claim to comprehend everything about the nature and ways of God. Some Creationists question and disagree with various teachings of the Bible. Some accept Jesus as their Savior and some do not, but they nonetheless believe, *"in the beginning God created the heaven and the earth."* They concede much about Creation and creation's God are beyond human comprehension, and they are okay with that.

TRUTH BE TOLD has yet to meet anyone who believes their smart phone evolved by natural selection over time without the assistance of a creator. It is silly to even suggest such a thing. TRUTH BE TOLD contends it is equally silly to advocate the universe with its infinite mysteries and complexity occurred by chance without the assistance of a creator. TRUTH BE TOLD is willing to,

"Hold these truths to be self-evident, that all men are created equal, that they are endowed by their creator with certain unalienable rights, that among these are life, liberty and the pursuit of happiness."

TRUTH BE TOLD is a strong advocate for racial equality and equal opportunity under the authority of an almighty Creator and nature's laws. TBT is eager to do its part to help our nation achieve the full potential of its Founding Father's famous words. ∎

St. Louis Herald

Racial Distinction

By: **James King**

How did you learn about racial distinction in America? I was a slow learner, not by choice, but by exposure. I have no recollection of knowing a person of color until high school. I was born and raised in an Indiana farm town of several thousand people. My hometown was as white as the snow that covered it every winter. I knew more about class distinction. My family was poor. Living on the wrong side of the tracks was not just a figure of speech to me. It was my reality.

My friends grew up to become farmers, truck drivers, drove heavy equipment in the quarries, worked on the line at a factory, got drafted, or joined the military. Many moved away. In the 1960's the evening news kept busy tracking the Vietnam war and the attempts of Martin Luther King Jr. to integrate schools, buses, restaurants, and the rest of society. The TV antenna protruding from the peak of our house received only two stations unless dad scaled the ladder to alter its direction so he could watch a Cub's game from Chicago. Watching him crabwalk the two-story roofline was as much fun as watching the game.

I don't recall much talk about civil rights. I do recall my dad laughing while watching Archie Bunker and Meathead argue about race, work, and gender. Hearing Dad laugh at Archie amused me. Although he would never admit it, they had a lot in common. Dad was a World War II Veteran and a shop steward for the UAW at the International Harvester plant in a nearby city. He worked shoulder to shoulder with racial minorities as part of his job. I never heard any racist comments in our home or from the sizeable contingent of Caucasian aunts, uncles, and church friends that were always around. It was more of a… "live and let live, albeit segregated," kind of an understanding on both sides of the race equation. There were no whites-only drinking fountains or restrooms. No whites-only signs anywhere in my hometown that I recall. It was more a culture of segregation by racial choice. I grew up assuming segregation was standard operating procedure on both sides of the color divide in the 1960's. We know now it was not right, but neither was it intentionally evil at its root.

We rarely missed church or Sunday school as kids. Our all-white congregation supported missionaries to Africa and taught us children to sing, "Jesus loves the little children. All the children of the world. Red and yellow, black and white; they are precious in His sight. Jesus loves the little children of the world." I recall one of the colorful pictures on the flip chart showed Jesus surrounded by little children. He was a decidedly white Jesus, surrounded by blonde-haired, blue-eyed, boys and girls… kids like us.

Things changed when I entered high school. Financially supported by family friends, I was enrolled in a college-prep school in the city where dad worked for International Harvester. My classmates were mostly upper middle class and white, but there were a number of affluent black families who wanted

their sons and daughters to have the same opportunities as the upper middle-class white families. I was a kid without a country. I was neither affluent nor black. We shared classes, played sports, and ate in the same cafeteria, but outside of school we went our own way… just like our parents.

I was recruited to play basketball in a small Christian college in Texas. That school too was mostly white with a few black students from the local community sprinkled in. I was assigned a dorm room with a black student-athlete from Alabama, named Jerome Jones. The dean of students made the assignment because he thought a "northern boy" would be less likely than a southern boy to object to sharing a room with a black student. He was well intentioned, but the logic of his decision amused us both. Discrimination, in all its forms, was not only a southern thing.

As Booker T. Washington, founder of Tuskegee Institute and one of the wisest men I've been privileged to study, famously said, "It became apparent at once, if we were to make any permanent impression upon those who had come to us for training, we must do something besides teach them mere books… We needed to teach them to study actual things instead of mere books alone."

The year I spent sharing a dorm room with Jerome was as

significant to my education as any class I attended. He taught me about Motown, The Jackson Five, dashikis, how to use a hair pick, and the purpose of Afro-sheen. He was equally curious about my love of hunting, jean jackets, country music, and ice hockey. But mostly we learned that our racial, cultural, and regional differences didn't define us. All who share the human condition and need love, acceptance, and someone to believe in them.

My adult life was increasingly more integrated, as were the schools our sons attended and the sports teams on which they competed. Some of that was the result of living in a larger, more diverse city and some to the credit of the civil rights movement. Integration and equality are a work in progress. There are neighborhoods and small towns still as racially segregated as my hometown was in the 1960's, but there is hope for better.

It causes me to wonder about the origins of race and the purpose it serves in the world. Some contend, perhaps even the majority of people, that racial and ethnic identity are the natural result of geographic isolation, resulting in distinctive skin tones, hair textures, facial features and physical structure.

TRUTH BE TOLD believes the theory of geographical isolation flies in the face of observable fact. The descendants of European settlers have lived in South Africa for more than 250 years but still give birth to blond-haired, blue-eyed babies every bit as Caucasian as their ancestors.

The first recorded African's brought to North America were "twenty negroes" who came to Jamestown, Virginia, as indentured servants in August of 1619, four-hundred years ago. Interracial propagation has altered the complexion of many but the climate of the Northern Hemisphere has had no impact. The geographic proximity of people to the equator has no effect on anyone's racial status, not even a little.

Those who accept creation as explained in Genesis must wrestle with the belief that all people are descendants of one man and one woman whom God himself created. They must explain how God's original plan got altered along the way. We know the story of gender's creation, when Eve was formed from the rib of Adam. Comedians have had a field day with that narrative, but it doesn't explain the origin of race. That part of the story occurs later in the Biblical narrative.

The Book of Genesis describes a time and place when God, for the good of mankind and his creation, intervened in the lives of Adam's descendants to create linguistic, cultural and racial distinction. Until that intervention, there was only one race, one language, one culture, one people.

If you accept the Genesis explanation in chapter eleven, racial diversity began at a place called Babel, a word that means, "confusion." As the author explains it, Adam's descendants refused God's directive to disperse across the earth. Lockstep unity is a powerful force for good or for evil. To mitigate the potential for evil, God created confusion and division among the people. Through the historic event of Babel, God introduced a natural check and balance into the human condition. Unchecked ambition put humanity on the path to unlimited evil. The world has glimpsed the result of that outcome in the atrocities of the Nazis, Pol Pot, Idi Amin, Mao Zedong, Kim Jong Il and the genocide perpetrated in Uganda, Rhodesia and Bosnia. God intervened, creating diversity of race, language, and culture as a restraint to the consequence of unbridled power.

If God is all-knowing and equally aware of the future as He is the past, He was not surprised by mankind's disobedience. We must conclude the intervention at Babel was always a part of God's plan even though it was not a part of his original creation. Not unlike the creation of Eve, the first woman, which took place only after Adam realized, "it is not good to be alone." For the human race to appreciate the value of diversity, God allowed them to first experience the destructive potential of unlimited evil without it.

The effect of evil holds a powerful attraction to many. Scary movies remain some of the most profitable ever made.

The top twenty horror movies have returned well over $100 million in profits to their producers. The top three have earned over $300 million including, 1.) Stephen King's *It*, the story of a demented clown called Pennywise. 2.) *The Sixth Sense*, the story of a nine-year-old boy referred to a psychiatrist because he sees dead people. 3.) *The Exorcist*, the story of a demon-possessed twelve year-old-girl. That controversial movie is still setting box office records, earning $450 million since its release in 1973. Its content was initially considered so graphic and obscene it was banned in several American cities and entirely in Great Britain until 1999.

The popularity of shows like *Stranger Things* by Netflix, demonstrates the continuous appeal of the horror genre. The series has received 31 Primetime Emmy Award nominations, including Outstanding Drama Series, and four Golden Globe Award nominations, and it won the Screen Actors Guild Award for Outstanding Performance by an Ensemble in a Drama Series in 2016.

What's the attraction? Stephen King, the undisputed champion of the books behind the movies, believes people enjoy such stories because no one is completely sane, some of us are just better at hiding it than others. Horror films are popular, he conjectures, because they provide a relatively safe way to enjoy the gore and adrenaline rush that comes from watching brutality in all its forms.

TRUTH BE TOLD doesn't know if Stephen King's theory is correct but is thankful God has placed limits on the expression of evil through the creation of diversity.

In the midst of the atrocities of America's Civil War, the poet Henry W. Longfellow, whose wife lost her life in a tragic accident and whose son was wounded and imprisoned by the enemy, nearly lost all faith in God. In the depth of his grief, he wrote,

> And in despair, I bowed my head:
> "There is no peace on earth," I said.

"For hate is strong, and mocks the song
    Of peace on earth, good will to men."

But Longfellow's faith in God did not allow him to permanently give up all hope. After a dark period of great anguish, he continued...

> "God is not dead, nor doth He sleep;
>   The wrong shall fail, the right prevail,
>   With peace on earth, good will to men."

TRUTH BE TOLD, believes that despite the insane capacity of people to brutally oppress, enslave, and massacre their fellow human beings, God has placed limits on evil.

Diversity of race, culture, and thought is God's way of keeping evil in check. People of good will, empowered by God's help, will ultimately rise up and destroy those who perpetuate evil. They always have, and they always will. ∎

St. Louis Herald

Minority Status

By: **James King**

I grew up watching Captain Kangaroo in the Treasure House with Mr. Green Jeans. They were surrounded by a host of interesting characters: Grandfather Clock, Bunny Rabbit, Mr. Moose, The Dancing Bear and of course the Captain's magic drawing board. It all looks a little hokey now... not just a little hokey, a lot hokey. It would probably still make kids laugh, but not for the right reasons.

My own sons grew up watching the Muppets. The magic of Jim Henson's creation has stood the test of time. Those characters were cool: Kermit the Frog, Miss Piggy, Animal, Scooter, Gonzo, The Swedish Chef among others. And who could forget the curmodgeons Sattler and Waldorf, sitting in their box seat overlooking the stage, providing critical commentary and insulting the guest hosts?

Sattler: Does this show constitute cruelty to animals?

Waldorf: Not unless they are watching it.

Sattler: Do you think this show is educational?

Waldorf: Yes. It'll drive people to read books!

It was not all fun and games. The main characters, Miss. Piggy and Kermit, touched on serious topics too. Take for example Kermit's theme song, *It's Not Easy Being Green*.

In his song, Kermit expresses frustration over the color of his skin and wonders why he wasn't assigned a more vibrant and attractive tone. Afterall, he laments, green is the color of so many common things like grass and leaves. Why could he not have been born red, orange, or have sparkles so people would notice? He envies something he is not.

What kid hasn't wondered why he was born into a certain family at a certain time and place, in a certain country and a certain race?

It's not easy being born black in America. It would be easier to be born white, or Asian or something cool like a Native American. Unfortunately, a child might be tempted to think black is the color of slavery. Black is the color of poverty, of gangs, public housing, and a hundred other negative things people of prejudice associate with black skin color.

But Kermit's theme song didn't end with lament. Not at all. He started thinking about all the cool things that are green.

Green, he realized is not so bad. Lots of neat things are green, the color of Spring, the ocean, tall trees and mountains when seen from a distance. In the end, he not only makes peace with his skin color, he embraces it and realizes that green is awesome.

In the 1960's people began saying, "Black is beautiful." They were right. A professional golfer of Mexican heritage was inspired by their demonstration of racial pride and encouraged the same attitude among his people saying, "If black is beautiful, brown is cute!" Lee Trevino was also right.

Black is the color of heroes: Frederick Douglass, Booker T. Washington, Harriet Tubman, Rosa Parks, Martin Luther King Jr.,

Michael Jordan, Michael Jackson, Aretha Franklin, Nat King Cole, Ray Charles, B.B. King, Louie Armstrong, Wynton Marsalis, Marvin Gaye, Cicely Tyson, Diana Ross, Jackie Robinson, Thurgood Marshall, Clarence Thomas, Ben Carson, Colin Powell, John Lewis, Jessie Owens, Maya Angelou, Barak Obama, Muhammed Ali, Jackie Robinson, Lester Holt, Hank Aaron, Joe Lewis, Arthur Ashe, Serena & Venus Williams, Oprah Winfrey, Tiger Woods, George Washington Carver, The Tuskegee Airmen, and the famous 54th Massachusetts Regiment of the Civil War. It is impossible to list all the incredible people that are black and the amazing things they have accomplished.

But why single out black heroes? What makes them worthy of mention, any more than heroes of any other race? Why stir the pot? Booker T. Washington, explained it this way:

"I have learned that success is to be measured not so much by the position that one has reached in life as by the obstacles which he has overcome while trying to succeed. Looked at from this standpoint, I almost reach the conclusion that often the Negro boy's birth and connection with an unpopular race is an advantage, so far as real life is concerned. With few exceptions, the Negro youth must work harder and must perform better than a white youth in order to secure recognition. But out of the hard and unusual struggle through which he is compelled to pass, he gets a strength, a confidence, that one misses whose pathway is comparatively smooth by reason of birth and race." [28]

In our previous editorial, TBT described how God established racial diversity as a check and balance against evil. That is reason enough, but it is not the only reason to sing the praises of diversity.

TBT has seen racial and cultural diversity expressed in the most positive ways. We've witnessed people helping each other without regard for race, creed, or culture. We've observed diverse racial groups relishing a shared love of music, regardless of the artist's color, singing lyrics about emotions and struggles common to them all. We have stood shoulder to shoulder with men and women of every race cheering for each other's children on a soccer field, baseball diamond, or neighborhood playground. We've all glimpsed examples of Dr. King's dream come true, "...that future day when children will live in a nation where they are not judged by the color of their skin, but by the content of their character."

America's not perfect, but it's a better country now than when Dr. King delivered his famous speech. Nothing this side of heaven will ever be perfect, but inequality presents an invaluable opportunity, not an impossible obstacle.

TBT, like you, has witnessed racist and ethnic hatred expressed in the most destructive ways by broken people of every race, creed, and culture. We've all seen graffiti scrawled on homes, places of worship, and public buildings, using the most vulgar language and symbols as weapons of hate against strangers. We've witnessed marches and rallies conducted to divide and destroy racial harmony. Human nature, it seems, is prone to distrust and disrespect those who are different. Instead of allowing displays of prejudice to discourage us, we can use them to inspire greater courage, unity and compassion for those who suffer.

Diversity provides opportunity to make the world and the lives of others better. TBT recognizes there are more positive than negative outcomes as a result of diversity.

- Diversity makes the world a more interesting place to live. I love the wide variety of birds that come to our feeder each winter as it hangs near the woods behind our house. They are distinct in color, habits, size, and preferences. Their diversity is always noticed and always beautiful.
- Diversity provides opportunity to serve others and help those who need a hand and an expression of kindness. As Booker T. Washington

observed, *"How often I wanted to say to white students that they lift themselves up in proportion as they help to lift up others, and the more unfortunate the race, and the lower in the scale of civilization, the more does one raise one's self by giving the assistance."* [29]

- Diversity also provides the opportunity for us to be encouraged by love, acceptance and help from others. In the song, *Have You Never Been Mellow*, Olivia Newton John asked if we ever experienced the power of letting someone else show their strength in response to our need? There is a definite blessing in letting other people be a blessing to you.

- Diversity provides opportunity for every person to play a significant role doing something important. A trip to the grocery store can become a mission of compassion, instead of a meaningless but necessary chore. I watch with interest how my wife takes time to get acquainted with the person working the check-out counter. They aren't working minimum wage jobs because they enjoy the long hours and low salary. She makes friends with clerks at grocery stores, fast-food restaurants, and coffee shops. If time permits, she asks about their family, their school, and their plans for an approaching holiday. And not always, but sometimes she will even tip those who have no expectation of such, just to see them smile. She is on a first name basis with a half-dozen such employees. Their faces brighten when they see her enter their line.

- For people of faith, diversity provides an opportunity to experience God's blessing. There is a Scripture that states, *"Do not merely listen to the word, and so deceive yourselves. Do what it says. Anyone who listens to the word but does not do what it says is like someone who looks at his face in a mirror and, after looking at himself, goes away and immediately forgets what he looks like. But whoever looks intently into the perfect law that gives freedom and continues in it—not forgetting what they have heard, but doing it—they will be blessed in what they do."* [30]

- Diversity gives everyone opportunity to make meaningful change. The next editorial in this series will expand on the concept of personal responsibility, but it must be said, every act of kindness matters. The ripple effect is real. While others wait for the next Supreme Court decision, the next law to pass, the next great leader to emerge, we can effect change one person at a time.

- Most people can identify an individual who significantly impacted their life: a teacher, a grandmother, a neighbor, a friend. Helping one person inspires them to help another, who helps another who helps another and another, and before long real change has happened.

TRUTH BE TOLD believes a diverse world is a better world. Imagine a world without color... the multi-faceted hues of the sun rising and setting, the brilliance of autumn, the beauty of a wheat field dancing in the breeze, a mist floating over the purple mountains' majesty. A world without color would be a dull world. Paul Simon got it right. Once you've experienced Kodachrome, *"...everything looks worse in black and white."*

In the same way, diversity makes the world more interesting. It creates opportunities for people to extend God's love to, and receive love from, those different from themselves. Do people mistreat and stereotype others on the basis of race? Absolutely! They always have and always will. It is the inherent nature of people. Parents don't have to teach their children how to be selfish and throw a tantrum. No, that comes naturally. They must teach their children self-control and kindness.

TRUTH BE TOLD believes the blessings of diversity outweigh the harm caused by prejudice. Diversity, no matter what form it takes: race, creed, gender, age, or culture, provides opportunity for personal growth and to make a difference in things that matter. Everyone is equally positioned to show love, demonstrate respect, and encourage those different from themselves. We are equally blessed to be a blessing.

If everyone looked the same, thought the same, believed the same, and acted the same we would lose the human distinctive. Robots are programmed for predictability; people are not.

God knew what he was doing. People grow through the process of listening, observing, and learning from perspectives different from their own. It is through giving that we receive, ...giving love, giving respect, giving opportunity, giving honor. It is counterintuitive but it is true. Truth is often counter-intuitive.

- The less desperate you are for something, the more likely you are to get it.
- The less choices you have, the easier it is to make a decision.
- The less you argue, the more you are able to convince.
- The less you know about something, the more time it takes to explain it.
- The less secure a person is, the more likely they are to bully others.

Henry Ford said, "If there is one secret of success, it lies in the ability to get the other person's point of view and see things from that person's angle as well as from your own." He also warned, "If you always do what you have always done you will always get what you always got."

TRUTH BE TOLD believes Henry Ford was a wise man. ▪

St. Louis Herald

Man in the Mirror

By: **James King**

I enjoy watching Social Media posts of toddlers singing their hearts out from their car seat behind mom and dad. It speaks "volumes" about the influence of music and parental choices in a child's life.

It's one thing when toddlers embrace the music of their parents, it's another when an older child does the same. Our boys are children of the 80's. Due to the nature of my work, we've lived in various cities, hours removed from grandparents. Can you say, "road trips?" We wore out more than a few cassette tapes driving to and from holiday get-togethers.

The Rockers of the era influenced our jams: Springsteen - *Born to Run* and *Glory Days*, Billy Joel - *Innocent Man, Only the Good Die Young* and

It's Still Rock and Roll to Me, Jim Croce had some fun hits – *Big Bad Leroy Brown* and *Don't Mess Around with Jim*, Prince – *Purple Rain* and *Little Red Corvette*, Elton John – *Rocket Man, I'm Still Standing* and *Don't Go Breaking My Heart*. But one artist stood out above all the others, the King of Pop, Michael Jackson. He transcended the generational divide between the front and back seat of our '86 Chevy Blazer.

My college roommate had introduced me to The Jackson Five: *It's Your Thing, I'll Be There, ABC, and I Want You Back*. Our boys knew none of those songs, but they completely embraced MJ's solo career as did everyone else, young and old alike. His music unified the races with, *Thriller, Beat It, Billy Jean, Black or White, Smooth Criminal and Bad*. One of our favorite family photos is of our youngest son rocking a red and black "Thriller Jacket" wearing a single white studded glove while striking an MJ pose. It wasn't even Halloween. It was his preferred ensemble for an entire year.

The MTV music era launched in 1981. A year later, Quincy Jones and Michael Jackson released their music video of the mega-hit *Thriller*. It was an Elvis-and-the-Beatles-appear-on-the-Ed-Sullivan-Show, moment in time. Over a million copies of the *Thriller* VHS video were sold, making it the best-selling video of all time. It transformed the pop music industry.

Before *Thriller*, MTV was limited to video broadcasts of bands playing their hits. After *Thriller*, music videos became mini-movies. MJ took music videos to still another level with the release of *Man in the Mirror*. Jackson is not featured in any part of the film. The focus is entirely on the victims of prejudice and hatred: the poor, the homeless, the starving, victims of war, victims of bigotry, Jewish oppression, racism, assassinations, Kent State, bombs dropping, nuclear fallout, tragic accidents, and brutality of every kind.

Man in the Mirror was an indictment of humanity's cruelty to his fellow man, but it was more than that. It was also, and especially, a call to personal responsibility. Although Michael's image is noticeably absent, his guilt and shame are on full display.

In the song Michael acknowledges he had been the victim of selfish love. His comment is insightful. He realized that selfishness on his part not only robs others of potential rescue, it also has a substantial negative impact on those able to make a difference. They are robbed of the joy, satisfaction and sense of purpose that is the natural outcome of a generous spirit.

The song describes Michael's growing awareness of his own responsibility and his plans to make a change. It was time for Michael (and the rest of us) to have a serious discussion with ourselves about misplace priorities. It's a song about making personal change. Just because mistakes have been made, doesn't mean all hope is lost. The present time is the perfect time to make a change. It's true what they say, "One more step in the wrong direction won't get you any nearer your destination."

Some argue racial prejudice is a blight too massive to be affected by any one person. It's not even a local or national crisis, it's global. Their attitude suggests we should collectively shrug our shoulders and accept injustice as a tragic but unavoidable fact of life, just make peace with it.

It's a good thing Christians in Holland, France and Poland didn't feel that way during WWII. Many of them were shot or sent to concentration camps for hiding Jews from the Nazi's.

No one told Oskar and Emilie

Schindler it was foolish to risk their lives to save the Jews. Together they spared 1,200 people by declaring them essential workers in their factory. A Polish Christian named Irena Sendler smuggled 2,500 babies out the Warsaw ghetto to other Polish families who protected them. Corrie ten Boom's family, Georges Loinger, Johan von Hulst, Varian Fry, Nicholas Winton and hundreds of others saved thousands more.

What difference can one person make?

A young woman, born in a country most Americans could not find on a map, is an excellent example. She has one of the most recognized faces and names in the entire world, not because of her beauty, athletic prowess, or political standing but by virtue of her compassion.

Anjeze Bojaxhiu's father died when she was eight years old. Sponsored by the Catholic Church, she was sent to Ireland at the age of eighteen to learn English and become a teacher. After 20 years of teaching, she felt called by God to leave the security of her profession to live and work among the poor in Calcutta, India. With no financial backing, she begged for food and support on the streets. Her example was so compelling; others donated to the cause and joined in her mission.

Her dedication was recognized worldwide. Mother Teresa, the name she chose for herself, was awarded the Nobel Peace Prize in 1979. She refused all financial awards and banquets associated with the honor, requesting the money be used to help the poor. Today more than 5,000 sisters have joined the order she founded, managing 600 missions in 120 different countries established to assist those dying of HIV, leprosy and tuberculosis. They also run soup kitchens, dispensaries, health clinics, orphanages and schools.

You don't have to become a lesser version of Mother Teresa to have a significant impact. Laura Schroff, a successful advertising executive made the effort to befriend a street kid in New York City. Her story is an example of the impact anyone can have through intentional kindness. It began when an 11-year-old street urchin begged her for change. Instead of doing the easy thing by handing him a dollar, Laura bought that boy lunch and took the time to get to know more about Maurice. With few exceptions, they continued meeting for lunch every Monday for the next 150 Mondays. She even invited him to her apartment, introduced him to her door-man, taught him to shop, cook, set a table, study, made school lunches for him, and befriended Maurice for the next three decades.

It wasn't a one-way relationship as most would suppose. Laura got as much out of her friendship with Maurice as she gave.

"Over the years, many people have

told me how lucky Maurice was to have met me, but my response was always, 'No, I was lucky to have met him.' Maurice has brought so much joy into my life and showed me in many ways the true meaning of friendship, and for that all I can say is, 'Thank you,' with all my heart." [31]

Maurice was raised by the streets. His parents were drug addicts, in and out of jail, doing whatever they could to survive. He barely knew his father. Apart from Laura, his grandmother, also an addict, was the only halfway stable person in his life. Schroff's friendship made the difference. Maurice was able to avoid the drugs, gangs and violence that consumed his world. He obtained his GED, got a job, married a good woman and is raising a remarkable family of seven children. He runs his own business, rehabbing properties in the city and serves as a mentor to other street kids.

Maurice wrote,

"When I look back on everything that's happened, I realize that if I hadn't met you, I would not be the man I am today. I am eternally grateful for the love and care that you've shown me through the years.

You've taught me how to dream, how to trust people, how to be a productive member of society, and most of all, how to be a good man and a great father." [32]

No one should under-estimate the power of personal influence and encouragement. In a speech given on the necessity of ending slavery, Frederick Douglass got a laugh when he quoted an English boy who said,

"I rule mamma, and mamma rules papa, and papa rules the people, and the people rule England." [33]

The concept of, "Doing for one, what you wish you could do for all," is a powerful formula that can change the world.

There is an old hymn my mother loved that says it best.

Let none hear you idly saying, "There is nothing I can do," While the multitudes are dying And the master calls for you. Take the task he gives you gladly; Let His work your pleasure be. Answer quickly when He calls you, "Here am I. Send me, send me!"

Maybe it's time to have a talk with the man in the mirror. Maybe it's past time. ■

*"If I have the gift of prophecy and can fathom all mysteries
and all knowledge, and if I have a faith that can move
mountains, but do not have love, I am nothing."*
—The Bible, 1 Corinthians 13:2

CHAPTER 9

The Invitation

The invitation came in the usual monarch-sized envelope. I handed it and the rest of our mail to Sarah, wondering out loud what was up with the Adams? I speculated it was probably another birth announcement. Their kids are fully engaged in the grandchild production business. George made no mention of it on the golf course, but that was to be expected. After the third or fourth grandchild, the hoopla and constant new-baby updates hit their stride and become more marathon than sprint.

I refilled my coffee cup and walked down the hall to the office. I intended to spend an hour checking responses to TRUTH BE TOLD, and afterward taking notes for the next column. TBT was different than my work experience. As a reporter, editors assigned stories based on workload and topic. Back then, my day was spent conducting interviews and gathering pertinent information. Some assignments involved more footwork than others, but most were OADs (one-and-done) gigs. A few stories required multiple columns as they unfolded, with a follow-up a week or two later to put a bow on it, but even those were fact-based, not opinion driven.

TRUTH BE TOLD was a different animal. By the time the columns were published, deadlines had me focusing on the next topic. Monitoring responses to an earlier post was a necessary but frustrating distraction. Production meetings, although few and far between, were equally disruptive. The team couldn't assess reactions or propose tweaks until the columns went public. I understood that. But I couldn't wait for their feedback before pressing on. It was a Catch-22. I believed it would all work out and eventually become routine, but for now it was wearisome.

Before I got very far into my morning, Sarah appeared at the door, fanning herself with the invitation from the Adams. She smiled in a "you-are-going-to-want-to-hear-this," posture.

"Guess what George and Elizabeth are hosting?"

"I have no idea. Another christening? An anniversary of some occasion? A bar-mitzvah? Knighthood? A Tupperware party—do people even have those anymore?"

Instead of answering, Sarah read the card in quasi-dramatic fashion.

Together with their parents
Paul David Adams
&
Bradley Charles Kelly
Invite you to a celebration of their love and marriage.
Saturday, June 19th, 2021.
Four o'clock in the afternoon
The Rainbow Ballroom, Astoria Hotel
St. Louis, Missouri
Cocktails, Dinner, & Dancing to Follow

"Really? I knew George and Elizabeth had two sons and a daughter, but I didn't know Paul was gay."

It shouldn't have come as a huge surprise. George talked a lot about his namesake, George Jr., and his work as a Federal Marshal and their daughter

Patti and her four kids, but he never had much to say about Paul. I knew he lived in the Central West-End and worked as an architect but that was about it. It bothered George that Paul no longer joined them for weekend worship and his politics were left of center, but he never told me he was gay.

"I'm sure Paul's lifestyle has been hard for them, given George's standing in their church," Sarah offered.

"No doubt. It bothers me that I didn't pick up on it. As much as we share, we never had that discussion. I hope George knows I would gladly serve as his sounding board and be supportive. Most people never stop loving their kids no matter what choices they make."

There must have been a thousand clues I missed, especially when we discussed the invitation to write TRUTH BE TOLD, and the issues I would be addressing. He had been encouraging and thought the column's concept was an excellent idea. I can only imagine how difficult this has been for him as a conservative Christian. Everyone loves their kids unconditionally, but that doesn't mean they agree with their life choices. I doubt my parents were always thrilled by my decisions as a teenager or even as an adult. It goes with the territory.

"George and Elizabeth must be conflicted," Sarah suggested. "But it's not unusual to have one of your children or siblings embrace a gay lifestyle these days. I read an article in *Upward Magazine* about famous people whose children are active in the LGBTQ lifestyle. It's more common than I would have guessed: Dick Cheney, Barbara Streisand, Alec Baldwin, Magic Johnson, Isaiah Thomas, Vanna White, Johnny Depp... even Marie Osmond's daughter, and I'm pretty sure the Osmonds are fairly conservative Mormons. They all gladly agreed to be interviewed and photographed with their children and were supportive and proud of their accomplishments. People are more open about life-choices today than a generation ago. That's gotta be a good thing."

Sarah could see I was deep in thought. "What are you thinking?"

"I was thinking about how George might feel about the next series. I should talk to him before I release it for publication. I doubt it will have any effect on my conclusions, but his insight as a conservative Christian whose son is involved in a same-sex relationship might be helpful."

I recalled George quoting a passage from the Bible that urged Christians to "speak the truth in love." That's the attitude I want for TRUTH BE TOLD. It's not only *what I say*, it's also about, *how I say what I say* that matters. People can agree to disagree, but everyone needs to make the effort to be respectful of each other. I've long advocated, "Love without truth is not true love, and truth without love has no effect."

"Talking it over with George might be good for both of you," Sarah replied.

"I don't think it's the kind of thing you discuss between a wayward shot off the tee box and a recovery wedge from the rough. We need to sit down for breakfast without the rest of the foursome chiming in."

"Good idea. But I wouldn't wait long. The wedding will be here before you know it, and your deadline is just around the corner. His perspective as a father, a Christian, and a friend will be insightful. Your next series could be ten times more controversial than the ones on self-evident truth and race."

I took Sarah's advice and arranged to meet George for breakfast the following Monday. It was usual for us to engage in serious discussions from time to time. He had become my unofficial public-opinion-guru. George had a knack for discernment but never in a negative way. When I invited him to meet, he didn't press for an explanation and I didn't offer any. I just said I had some thoughts to run by him, which was true.

As usual, George arrived early and was waiting when I walked in.

"Always good to see you, brother," I said in greeting. "After all the times I've taken your money on the course I wasn't sure you'd show up!"

"I assumed you are buying. It will square our accounts," George laughed.

"Thanks for agreeing to meet. After publishing a few TBT columns, I need your honest feedback."

"You always know where I stand, Jim. As I told you the other day, 'We are singing from the same hymnal.'"

"True, but a five-minute conversation on a tee box is different from a serious conversation over coffee."

George had wisely chosen a corner booth far from the ears and eyes of the curious public. After years of writing stories for *The Herald* my face and name were more well-known than I cared to admit. It never ceased to surprise me that complete strangers felt a connection between us because of stories I'd written which they had read. They thought they "knew" me, and therefore I must somehow also "know" them. It never crossed their mind we had never met, and I didn't know them from the south-end of a north-bound mule. Unlike many of my colleagues, I was uncomfortable with my public image. George understood that, thus the corner table. After ordering, our conversation picked up where we left off.

"Seriously Jim," George began, "you have a gift. Your journalistic experience has perfectly prepared you for this opportunity. I'm sure you've received more than your share of criticism, but don't let that discourage you from taking a stand. A courageous truth-advocate is needed now more than ever. There are probably more who agree with you than disagree. Those who disagree just tend to be more vocal," he said with a smile. "You should take it as a compliment. You are stirring the pot, which according to my understanding, is your primary purpose anyway. Apathy is your enemy, not controversy."

"I hear you, George. Criticism is nothing new. No one lasts long in this business if they're easily offended. The key for me has always been remaining open to feedback good or bad. I never considered it a compliment when people said I must have a thick skin. I want to remain sensitive but not allow my feelings to distort my objectivity. No father enjoys correcting his child. He does it because he wants what's best for them. Popularity is not the goal. Love requires a truth-teller to say hard things sometimes."

"It does. That's what makes your editorials so effective. You have empathy for people and tell your stories with compassion. But compassion hasn't kept you from being straightforward when it comes to the truth. Your column on Racial Distinction is a good example. You pointed out the hypocrisy of those who promote racial equality while simultaneously advocating the theory of evolution. You didn't hesitate to say the two are incompatible. Either you subscribe to the survival of the fittest or believe all people are created equal. You can't have it both ways. Hitler justified the superiority of the Aryan race and the genocide of inferiors based on the survival of the fittest. In his distorted way of thinking, he was making the world a better place by improving the genetic pool. That article was concise and on point."

"Thanks, George. Of course, not everyone agrees with us," I said with a smile.

"Truth has an edge to it. People recognize it when they hear it, even when it aggravates them."

"On a different subject," I shifted gears to the issue at hand. "Sarah and I got your invitation to Paul's wedding. Thanks so much for including us. It's a significant event in Paul's life. Sarah and I want to be as supportive as possible to you and Elizabeth."

"Thanks. I know it's not something we've ever discussed. Obviously, Liz and I have known about Paul's lifestyle for a while. We don't see eye-to-eye on the matter, but we've made peace with it. He's our son and we love him. It's been a struggle for us, and for him too I'm sure. His partner Brad is a good guy. It's not a lifestyle we prefer for him, but it's not the unforgiveable sin either."

"It's a timely issue, George, and one of the reasons I wanted to talk with you. I don't want to meddle, but I could benefit from your insight as a Christian and a father. I'm about to release a series of articles on sexuality, gender, and marriage… third-rail-type stuff," I smiled. "No journalist who cares a lick about his future would dare touch those subjects, but they didn't hire me to avoid tough issues. What did you mean when you said, 'Your son's lifestyle is not the unforgiveable sin.' Is there such a thing?"

"There's a story in the Bible about how Jacob once wrestled with the Lord all night. I know how he must have felt. I've been wrestling with God over this matter for the last six years. The unforgiveable sin is mentioned in the gospels of Matthew and Mark. Jesus said, *I tell you, every kind of sin and slander can be forgiven, but blasphemy against the Spirit will not be forgiven.*'"[34]

"What does that mean? What's blasphemy against the Spirit?"

"Denial of God pure and simple. The Bible says, *'No one can say, 'Jesus is Lord,' without the Holy Spirit.'*[35] Rejection of the Holy Spirit is in reality a denial of Jesus, and faith in him is our only hope of salvation. If we reject the Savior, we reject God's offer of redemption. God wants everyone to be saved, no matter how imperfect their life, but he won't force Himself on anyone."

I had to interrupt. "George, I don't want to be insensitive, but doesn't the Bible consider homosexuality a sin?" I knew George would be candid about the matter and would have studied the issue thoroughly.

"It does. It even calls homosexuality a sin that can keep people from inheriting the kingdom of God.[36] That is my greatest concern for Paul, but it's not homosexuality per se that leads to death. Sin is sin. Anyone who lives outside God's saving grace lives in jeopardy of eternal death. It's the nature of homosexuality that's so dangerous. People who choose that life are tempted to reject the Christian Church and the Bible that calls their decision a sin. Their separation from the Christian Church, by personal choice or in response to the rejection of misguided believers, can lead LGBTQ people on a path away from Jesus, a person's only hope of salvation.

What most Christians refuse to recognize is the same passages that condemn homosexuality also condemns sexual immorality, idolatry, hatred, jealousy, rage, selfish ambition... even argumentative people, and drunkenness. In other words, anyone and everyone who defends their sinful choices and rejects the Bible and the Savior puts their relationship with God in jeopardy. The unforgiveable sin is a rejection of the faith; it does not single out a particular sin or lifestyle. It is the consequence of the sin, not the sin itself that places eternity in jeopardy."

George had done his homework.

"George," I asked, "can you send me a list of those references? Obviously, I can't quote chapters and verses from the Bible in my editorials, but it helps me better understand the reasons Christians and the LGBTQ community are so often at odds with each other. From my observation, Christians mostly treat the LGBTQ community like lepers."

"Hard to argue with you. Christians definitely condemn some sins more strongly than others. I haven't heard much criticism or many sermons challenging alcohol abuse, selfish ambition, quarrelsome people, or divorce. The last time I checked, most people want their children to be ambitious, selfish or otherwise," I said with a smile. "There is something about human nature that's more threatened by some behaviors than others."

"What advice can you offer for the articles I'm about to publish?"

"Just do what you do. Don't be afraid to speak the truth in love. Be your compassionate self and remind people to be kind to each other. I want to make one more observation if I may?"

"Hey, that's why I'm here. There's a big difference between opinions shaped by experience and those formed by a reporter from a theoretical point of view."

"I believe many Christians and nonbelievers have a common misunderstanding of God's expectations. Too many in both camps equate Christian faithfulness with doing good and avoiding wrong. Christians can be intolerant of nonbelievers and nonbelievers are quick to return the favor. Jesus was the opposite of intolerant. His actions and words emphasized love and concern for believers and nonbelievers alike. He was consistently critical of the religious elites while taking time to embrace nonbelievers even to the consternation and confusion of his own disciples. Today's Christian leaders often advocate a misplaced emphasis on religious rules. They heap expectations of perfection on people that they can't achieve themselves. Jesus called such leaders white-washed tombs who look good on the outside, but on the inside are filled with decay. Blind guides giving advice to people living in darkness. He didn't tell his disciples, 'People will know us by our obedience to religious rules.' He told them, *'People will know us by our love.'* [37]

George was on a roll and not done yet.

"Don't get me wrong. God has rules, but He didn't provide the ten commandments to judge our faithfulness. The law shows us our sin and our need for a Savior. It reminds us that no one is good enough. God doesn't grade on a curve. Nothing short of perfection is good enough, and no one is perfect except those who are made perfect through the complete forgiveness of their sin. Jesus endured the judgment our sins deserved when He died on the cross. The price was paid in full. God's commandments are provided to reveal our sin and need for a Savior, and to provide moral guidance for life choices. God's expectations are a roadmap to the best life has to offer."

George's stream of thought had me jotting notes as fast as I could write. His explanation made sense. As parents of two sons, Sarah and I never established house rules to test the loyalty of our kids. Our rules were there to discourage self-destructive behavior and encourage choices that would benefit them in the future. When discipline was required, it was not meted out to make them pay for their mistakes, but to discourage behavior detrimental to their life. It made sense to think of God in terms of a parent/child relationship.

It was noteworthy to hear George compare judgmental Christian attitudes to the attitudes of nonbelievers. His explanation that many in both camps equate faithfulness to good behavior based on rules, echoed my experience. George obviously believed faithful behavior according to God's standard should be motivated by God's love freely given, not an attempt to win God's love by obedience to rules.

Personally, I often found it difficult to distinguish families who lived by stringent rules, from those who achieved results inspired by love. The outward results looked the same, with one significant difference, motivation. Rule-based families achieve results by rewarding good behavior and punishing bad. Sarah and I preferred our sons' behavior be motivated by their response to our love and concern for them. Not always, but often, both approaches raise obedient children, but it wasn't mere obedience we were after. We wanted a life-long loving relationship with our sons. George thought of God the same way. Those who belong to rules-based religions work hard at obedience, but George believed God was more interested in fostering good behavior motivated by love.

I've heard him say a thousand times, "There are only two religions in the world, Jim. Those that teach what you must do to please God, and the true Christian faith that teaches what God has done out of love to make you pleasing."

I always enjoyed playing golf with George. As I listened this morning, I began to understand why. His attitude towards life and golf was different than most. He embraced the good and the bad with the same optimism based on love of the game and his love of life. His faith instilled a perspective on life that made him easy to be around.

I thanked George for his time and insight and promised we'd see them at the wedding.

The meeting with George had been helpful. His parental perspective provided the balance I was striving to achieve in my column. Right or wrong, a good parent never stops loving their child. Neither do they stop caring about what is good, better or best for them. Whether people accepted or rejected my conclusions, I wanted to communicate a gracious attitude towards the subject and a sincere desire to be helpful.

I don't believe perfect objectivity exists. Everyone must confront their own bias formed over time by their family of origin, personal experiences, faith, education, and the basic human need to be accepted. The sooner we acknowledge our own prejudices the better our chance of discerning right from wrong.

I didn't need or expect my readers to agree with all my conclusions, but I wanted them to question their own. We were not publishing TBT to gain groupies. We were attempting to establish firm footing on the basis of ancient and self-evident truth in the swamp of popular opinion.

An old saying has it right, *"Faithful are the wounds of a friend, but deceitful are the kisses of an enemy."*[38] The truth may hurt for a moment, but its purpose is life. Flattering rhetoric, on the other hand, is practiced by those who don't have your best interest at heart.

"I prefer to believe that people are good and honest and respect me enough to tell me the truth. It's not easy to find those people all the time, but they're out there."

—Ellen DeGeneres

CHAPTER 10

The Wedding

S arah and I were looking forward to Paul's wedding for all the right reasons.

We've known George and Elizabeth for ten years and enjoy sharing an occasional dinner at the club in addition to my regular outings with him on the course. Over the years we've discussed the trials and tribulations of parenting, grand-parenting, home maintenance, religious and political perspectives and the adjustments dictated by retirement. When you strip away the details of life's blessings and challenges, family and friendships matter most.

I was curious about the details of the wedding and how it would play out. During my years at *The Herald*, I routinely came in contact with people of the LGBTQ community but not often on a personal level. Sarah and I were genuinely happy Paul had found a partner in life, but at the same time realized the LGBTQ lifestyle was not the happy-go-lucky, ho-hum, nothing-to-see-here norm that Hollywood, politicians and television made it out to be.

The belief that same sex relationships are aberrant, if you use the actual definition of the word, "a departure from the norm", should offend no one. From my research, I knew that less than 5% of the US population identified as members of the LGBTQ community.

According to The Williams Institute Study, only 4.5% of the US adult population over the age of 18, self-identify as a member of the LGBTQ community. [39] Of those who identified with the lifestyle, 42% were male and 58% female. The statistics differ by state. The District of Columbia has the highest percentage of people, 9.8% who voluntarily declare that status. The next highest percentage is Oregon with 5.6%. The lowest percentage of citizens in the LGBTQ lifestyle are found in North Dakota representing just 2.7% of the population. I'm not suggesting members of the LGBTQ community are in any way inferior or lesser people, but neither is their lifestyle as common as the media suggests.

In my travels around the world, it was not unusual for people to give Americans a double-take as we walked past them on the street or in a crowded restaurant. I was never offended by the fact I represented a culture unknown and "foreign" to them. Their reaction to my clothes, my skin color, my habits, my language, my diet, and preferences was often noticeable. I grew used to it and after a while, hardly noticed. Of course, people of other countries and cultures hold various opinions about Americans; some admire us, some resent us, many are curious, but most are too busy struggling with the day-to-day issues of their own lives to even care. After a quick glance my way, they typically went back to the business at hand. It's not a perfect analogy but I suppose being a member of the LGBTQ community in a 95% heterosexual culture must feel like that. Some people will be immediately supportive, others offended, many curious, but most have bigger fish to fry than to concern themselves with someone else's life choices.

I once attended a memorial service for a colleague who died of aids when that plague was dominating the news, afflicting mostly intravenous drug users and the homosexual community. Like every other funeral for loved ones who died much too young, the emotions of his family and friends was a heartbreaking testament to the power of love. The cause of death and sexual orientation of the deceased diminished none of the suffering endured by his family and friends that gathered to honor one of their own.

True love erases the lines of separation strangers draw based on race, creed, gender, or sexual preference. Right or wrong, love is blind to such things. At the same time, those who attended his memorial were in some respects unique from attendees at other funerals. The largest number of mourners were composed of single, well-dressed men sporting red ribbons of solidarity, but the emotions, the eulogies, even the message of the presiding minister was not much different from other memorials I have attended. Love is the great equalizer.

By the time we arrived at the Astoria there was already a steady line of cars entering the parking garage. Signs were posted directing wedding guests to park on the third level, the same as the Rainbow Ballroom. My eye was drawn to the bumper stickers we passed as we walked towards the entrance. Being obsessively observant was a hazard of my profession, like fishermen notice ripples near a snag or hunters scan tree lines as they drive down a country highway. Sarah shook her head and smiled. "Once a reporter, always a reporter."

The types of cars and the messages they displayed were an early indication of the attitudes of those gathered for the celebration. These did not disappoint: "Turn Left at The Next Election," "RESIST" (The "I" was replaced by a raised fist.) "Well Behaved Women Seldom Make History," "Keep Your Theology Off My Biology." My kind of people. Freethinkers. Nonconformists. Our politics and social perspectives certainly differed, but these were intentional people. Not all the messages were antagonistic. One displayed a pink heart with the words, "Be Kind." Another simply said, "Better Together."

The room was two-thirds full, and guests were already taking their seats. George and Elizabeth were standing next to the Kellys welcoming everyone as they entered. An ensemble of four musicians played right of center where Paul and Bradley were gathered with their close friends. It was an inclusive group of diverse people with a wide variety of race, gender, attire and age represented. My eye was drawn to a distinguished looking older gentleman talking quietly to a few people across the room from our seats. There wasn't time to greet him, but Mordecai noticed our entrance and gave a nod in my direction as we found our way to our chairs. I couldn't help but wonder about his connection to Paul and Bradley.

The service itself was usual except for the secular tone of the ceremony. Poems were read in the place of Scripture, the ensemble-backed soloist sang songs made famous by Sinatra rather than the Christian standards. The music was pleasant and felt appropriate for a wedding: *All or Nothing At All, Come Rain Or Come Shine,* and *All My Tomorrows.* Hearing those familiar songs in this setting drew my attention to the lyrics and gave a different flavor to their meaning. Love is an incredible thing no matter what form it takes between a parent and a child, soldiers on a battlefield, a husband and wife, or people of the same gender. Sinatra's words from *All or Nothing At All* captures the human need for intimacy in life. He suggests, if a relationship lacks complete transparency and vulnerability, you are just as well off alone.

A well-dressed man in a three-piece suit, a longtime friend of Paul's, served in the stead of clergy. His message was simple, based on an Old Testament Scripture,

> "Two are better than one, because they have a good return for their labor: If either of them falls down, one can help the other up. But pity anyone who falls and has no one to help them up. Also, if two lie down together, they will keep warm. But how can one keep warm alone? Though one may be overpowered, two can defend themselves." [40]

He made reference to the love that existed between King David and King Saul's son Jonathan, although his text was from Ecclesiastes, the words of Solomon. Apparently, the Bible says several times that David loved Jonathan as much as he loved himself. When Jonathan was killed alongside his father in a battle against the Philistines, David was crushed by the news as revealed in his response,

> "How the mighty have fallen in battle! Jonathan lies slain on your heights. I grieve for you, Jonathan my brother; you were very dear to me. Your love for me was wonderful, more wonderful than that of women."[41]

I was unfamiliar with that reference and made a note to discuss its meaning with George. The quotation was short and used only in passing. The speaker resisted the temptation to make the ceremony a defense of same sex marriage, choosing to focus his thoughts on the importance of love and the need for everyone, married or single to form lasting and significant relationships with other people. His mention of God was generic with no specific reference to Christ or the Christian faith, but there was clearly an emphasis on God's created intention for intimacy between people. In place of a unity candle, Paul and Bradley poured colorful sand from two different containers into a large clear vase forming a unique pattern that was immediately sealed with hot wax, signifying the joining of their lives into one shared life of different gifts and qualities. After the requisite hug, kiss, and pronouncement of marriage, everyone was invited to join the newlyweds in a celebratory toast at an open bar in the back of the room.

I took Sarah's hand and made a beeline for Mordecai. He explained how he had been "inadvertently" teamed-up by a starter with Bradley and his father on a public golf course a couple of months ago. (I couldn't help but silently question his use of the word, "inadvertently.") Evidently, it didn't take long for Mordecai to realize father and son were discussing Bradley's decision to marry Paul, and the ramifications it would have for his life and the rest of their family.

Mordecai explained how he became the unofficial "therapist, negotiator and referee" for the rest of their round and afterward was invited by Brad's father to discuss the matter with his wife. Like the Adams, they were struggling to understand their son's lifestyle, which after the marriage would become more publicly known. In gratitude for his counsel and by virtue of his charm, the Kelly's invited Mordecai to attend the ceremony.

Sarah played waitress while Mordecai and I took our conversation to a table further removed from the celebration. There was something about Mordecai's tendency to show up when least expected. I was either under surveillance by the CIA, or he was one of those *"strangers unaware,"*[42]...the name George gave angels working undercover. I started the conversation.

"I'm surprised to see you here, Mordecai. Odd, how just a few months ago we were complete strangers and now our paths cross on a regular basis."

"Life is like that. Like the good book says, *'Who can fathom the mysteries of God? Who can probe the depth of the Almighty?'* [43] I've learned to embrace and enjoy the mystery of things. You might want to try that James," he said with a curious smile.

"What counsel did you share with the Kelly's that helped them make peace with Brad and Paul's lifestyle? Are same-sex relationships acceptable in God's eyes? I was under the impression the Bible opposed homosexuality."

"There's a difference between God's design and man's decisions. I'm not one who believes God has a specific path predetermined for us to walk, and it's our job to stay the course. He gives humans free will to make their own decisions. Without free will we'd be no different than a computer programmed to function the same way day in and day out. Our choices, good bad, right, or wrong, don't change the way God feels about us. A parent loves the wayward child as much as the one who never strays."

"So are Brad and Paul wayward children? Or is the lifestyle they've chosen an acceptable option in the scheme of right and wrong?"

"There is a Scripture that says,

'Judge nothing before it's time, but wait until the Lord comes, who will bring to light the things hidden in secret and disclose the motives of each man's heart.' [44] And another says, 'Let no debt remain outstanding, except the continuing debt to love one another, for whoever loves others has fulfilled the law. The commandments,

'You shall not commit adultery,' 'You shall not murder,' 'You shall not steal,' 'You shall not covet,' and whatever other command there may be, are summed up in this one command: 'Love your neighbor as yourself.' Love does no harm to a neighbor. Therefore, love is the fulfillment of the law.' [45]

"What does that mean? I don't think you answered my question," I replied, engaging my best reporter skills to nail down a "yes or no" answer.

"You want things to be black or white, right, wrong, good or bad. The decisions people make are often out of sync with God's will, but our actions do not put us in or out of favor with God. He loves the sinner and the saint, James. And it's a good thing, since no one is without sin. Like any loving parent, (like the Kellys' and the Adams'), God has preferred values He wants His children to embrace, but life is messy. None of us do only right and avoid all wrong, but choices don't cause God to stop loving us. One of my favorite passages says, *All day long He holds out his hand to obstinate and disobedient people.*' [46] We give up on people. People even give up on themselves. But God doesn't give up on anyone. *'He wants everybody to be saved and come to the knowledge of the truth.'* [47]

"So, am I asking the wrong questions? If our standing with God is not defined by what's right and what's wrong, why should anyone care about His standards? Do our choices determine what He blesses or frustrates on earth and deepen or weaken our relationship with God?"

"James, 'There's no one who does only good and avoids all wrong.' [48] If God judged us like we judge each other and ourselves, no one would be worthy of His love and acceptance. God cares about our choices and wants only what is best for us and the world we live in, but it's grace that saves, not behavior." [49]

"It helps to think of God as a loving parent, I suppose. When I talk to George about Paul, I can see his frustration but more importantly, I can see how much he loves him and wants only what is best for his son."

"Right. For good reason Jesus taught his disciples to pray, 'Our Father, who is in heaven...'"

I changed the subject from discussing Paul and Bradley's relationship to a discussion of my assignment. "I'm about to publish a series of articles on sexuality, gender confusion, marriage, and this thing called love. It's an impossible assignment!"

"It's perfectly acceptable to advocate for what is true, right and best, but you can't ignore the human element. A good teacher understands God's directive, *'Speak the truth in love so we might grow in all aspects into Him who is the head, even Christ.'*[50] But I would personally add, "When in doubt, err on the side of love." Love is the fulfillment of the law. God who gave us right and wrong, also gave us the Savior, and for the same reason. Love. Both Law and the Gospel are given by God to His children out of love for them.

Sarah, who had been sitting quietly 'til now, brought the conversation to a close. "I can see why James wants your input before publishing his column. What confuses me is why James was chosen to address these complicated matters? Wouldn't it be better for someone like yourself, or an expert in the Bible to write TRUTH BE TOLD?"

"I think Jim is the perfect choice for the assignment. There are so-called experts who know the Bible but know little or nothing about people. The Bible says, 'God desires all people to be saved and come to the knowledge of the truth.'[51] Truth isn't all that's required. The art of knowing how to communicate the truth also matters. The prophets and apostles were not sent from heaven. They were real people with real lives living in real relationships that God used to tell His story. It is His way."

"I guess that makes sense, but it's nearly impossible to find the perfect balance between truth and love. No matter what position you take on these issues, some will criticize and attack. Jim's columns will always be considered too soft by some and too judgmental by others. He's truly a man in the middle, given an impossible task."

"No one is called to be successful, just faithful,"[52] Mordecai offered. "Don't underestimate the value of upset. It means people are being forced to think, and that's a good thing. Afflict the comfortable and comfort the afflicted. If you do that, you are doing a good thing. And with that, I need to keep moving. Sarah it was great to meet you. Jim has always spoken highly of your support. Jim, you're the right man for the job. Don't doubt that for a moment. You are asking all the right questions and are driven by a need to be helpful. No one expects more than that. God bless you both."

I stood to shake Mordecai's hand, but he pushed my reach aside, wrapping his arms around me in a strong embrace. There was an energy that passed between us that can only be described as other-worldly. It was what I needed for this assignment, not my spirit but God's spirit for the task ahead.

St. Louis Herald

What's Love Got to Do with It?

By: **James King**

Tina Turner's song, "What's Love Got to Do with It?" is a wake-up call for lovers. Tina's song is a vocal attempt to persuade her audience to recognize the difference between physical attraction and true love.

The song suggests that the physical attraction a potential lover communicates by a look, a touch, or a kiss, is not the same as love. Tina's soulful rendition suggests there would be a lot less heartache in the world if people understood the distinction. Love is powerful for good or for bad. Love can even be dangerous. She asks rhetorically if a heart is worth having if it can be broken. True love involves the heart, and Tina plans to protect hers.

Tina's attempt to dissuade people from falling in love was popular as a song but failed to convince people to give up on the concept. Perhaps that was not her true purpose. Maybe she was just trying to alert her fans to the danger of mistaking attraction for love. True love cuts both ways. It is the source of great pleasure and great pain.

Love, TRUTH BE TOLD believes, is the source of countless and often contradictory emotions: Joy, Sorrow, Laughter, Tears, Admiration, Heartache, Pride, Frustration, Sacrifice, Empathy, Inspiration, Sentiment, Jealousy, Desire, Honor, Sadness, Self-Denial, and Resentment…nearly every emotion, good, bad or otherwise, known to people of every race, creed, and culture.

Love refuses to be defined by words. It reveals itself in ways as unique as the heart it captures. Although it often tries, love can't hide. It's exposed by the action it prompts.

Love is the story of Sullivan

Ballou's letter to his precious wife and mother of his sons, hand-written from a civil war battlefield. Major Ballou answered President Lincoln's call to arms. Volunteering as a university-educated officer, he was third in command of the 2nd Rhode Island Infantry of the Union Army. Riding into battle at the front of his regiment, Ballou's leg was shattered and his horse killed by a confederate cannon during the First Battle of Bull Run. He died a week later of his wounds, but the tender letter he wrote to his wife lives on as his legacy of love.

"*My very dear Sarah: The indications are very strong that we shall move in a few days—perhaps tomorrow... Sarah, my love for you is deathless, it seems to bind me to you with mighty cables that nothing but Omnipotence could break; and yet my love of Country comes over me like a strong wind and bears me irresistibly on with all these chains to the battlefield.*

The memories of the blissful moments I have spent with you come creeping over me, and I feel most gratified to God and to you that I have enjoyed them so long. And hard it is for me to give them up and burn to ashes the hopes of future years, when God willing, we might still have lived and loved together and seen our sons grow up to honorable manhood around us.

My dear Sarah, never forget how much I love you, and when my last breath escapes me on the battlefield, it will whisper your name... But, O Sarah! If the dead can come back to this earth and flit unseen around those they loved, I shall always be near you; in the brightest day and in the darkest night—amidst your happiest scenes and gloomiest hours—always, always; and if there be a soft breeze upon your cheek, it shall be my breath; or the cool air fans your throbbing temple, it shall be my spirit passing by.

Sarah, I have unlimited confidence in your maternal care and your development of our sons' characters... O Sarah, I wait for you there! Come to me, and lead thither my children.

Sullivan"

Sarah was only 24 when Major Ballou died. She never remarried and lived the rest of her life under the care of her son, William. She died at the age of 80 in 1917, and is buried next to Sullivan in Swan Point Cemetery in Providence, Rhode Island.

Love is a dog named Hachiko, a golden-brown Akita, born in Japan in November of 1923.

He was brought to Tokyo by his owner Dr. Hideaburo Ueno, a professor of agriculture at the university. Every day he would follow his master to the train station at the nearby Shibuya junction. Hachi, as he was called, would find his way home but return to the platform every day at 4pm to greet the returning professor. This went on day after day, week after week for almost 2 years, until 1925. On that day in May, Professor Ueno suffered a cerebral hemorrhage while giving a lecture at the university, dying without returning to the Shibuya station.

Hachi was placed with new owners but escaped time after time to find his way to the familiar train station to await the return of his beloved professor. Realizing his master and wife no longer lived in their former house, Hachi began a 24-hour vigil at the station itself, eventually making friends with the staff and commuters who looked after him. Unrelenting, he kept constant vigil for the next 10 years.

A former student of Dr. Ueno's heard of the dog's loyalty while doing research on the rare Akita breed. He wrote an account of his faithfulness in an article published in the largest newspaper in Tokyo. Hachi became a national sensation and a symbol of loyalty and love that attracted crowds from across the city and even the world. The city erected a bronze statue of Hachi at the station even before his death in 1935. It remains a national landmark to this day. The loyal companion was cremated upon his death and his ashes interned next to his master. A second bronze statue also now adorns the University of Tokyo's campus depicting a happy reunion between Hachi and his beloved master.

The example of Hachi's love was so inspiring, a Japanese production company made his story into a movie in 1987. In 2009, an American production company bought the rights and with a budget of $16 million made a movie of their own, featuring Richard Gere as Professor Ueno. The movie returned many times its production costs at the box office, gathered a cult following, and is still producing royalties for its investors. Each year on March 3rd, the anniversary of Hachi's death, a ceremony of remembrance is conducted at the Shibuya station, attracting hundreds of people who gather to honor his devotion.

Love is the foundation of all great relationships, and relationships are the foundation of all that is most important.

- Love fills the eyes of parents with tears when asked about their baby in the NICU.
- Love chokes on words recounting the death of a loved one due to war, a car crash, or an overdose.
- Love mumbles bleacher prayers for a child competing on the field of play.
- Love drives through the night for Thanksgiving dinner.
- Love opens its gifts last on Christmas morning.
- Love sees only one person in a church packed with family and friends on its wedding day.
- Love sits quietly all night in the hospital room of its mom, dad, spouse or child.

- Love leaves home in the pouring rain to change a tire, retrieve a lost dog, or collect a forgotten homework assignment.
- Love works hard at a job it hates to provide for those it loves.
- Love gives with no expectation of return.
- Love waits for hours by the phone, fearing the worst but hoping for the best.
- Love wishes it could take the place of another.
- Love holds a sick child all night then goes to work without a mention.

The Bible says, *"Love is patient, love is kind. It does not envy, it does not boast, it is not proud. It does not dishonor others, it is not self-seeking, it is not easily angered, it keeps no record of wrongs. Love does not delight in evil but rejoices with the truth. It always protects, always trusts, always hopes, always perseveres."* [53]

Love fails as a noun but excels as a verb. Without action, love does not exist. Without love, all the money, power, influence and wisdom of the world serves no purpose. As the song says, until somebody loves you and cares for you, you are nobody.

You have heard it said, *"These three abide, 'Faith, Hope and Love,' but the greatest of all is love."* [54]

Go find yourself somebody to love. ∎

St. Louis Herald

Marriage: Till Death, Debt, or Divorce Do Us Part

By: **James King**

Truth never changes but has the power to change everything. People who ignore truth overestimate the importance of what they believe and underestimate the importance of the truth they choose to ignore.

The institution of marriage is undergoing radical change in America, but the human desire for the intimacy it provides will never change. The history of relationships begins with the phrase, *"It is not good for man to be alone."* [55] No matter how relationships change, that basic truth remains. Not everyone is meant for marriage, but everyone is meant to love and be loved. It is the key to a full, rich and satisfying life. Life without love is seeing a picture of a beautiful sunset rather than witnessing the grandeur yourself.

It doesn't compare. It might be trite but it's true, "A burden shared is a burden halved, and a joy shared is a joy multiplied."

The "institution" of marriage has taken many forms throughout history: arranged marriages, marriages to unite countries, marriages for financial security, marriages to produce an heir, marriages for companionship in old age, marriages of convenience, interracial marriages, generationally diverse marriages, and more recently, same-sex marriages.

Just when you think you understand the boundaries of acceptable and unacceptable behavior, someone moves the goalposts. Individuals don't set the standard, only their response to it. That includes relationships considered acceptable or unacceptable when it comes to marriage. The currents of change are strong. No one gets to steer the stream, only the set of their sail as they glide across its surface.

- Nearly half of the American population over the age of 18 is married. That percentage has declined by 8% in the last decade and is still falling.
- Americans are staying single longer. The median age for a first marriage has risen to 30 for men and 28 for women.
- Cohabitation outside of marriage is also on the rise. The number of Americans living with an unmarried partner reached 18 million in 2016, a whopping 29% increase in just the last decade. Roughly, half of those cohabitating were under the age of 35, but that choice is increasing fastest among those over the age of 50.
- The divorce rate has nearly tripled since 1990. Only half of all marriages are lifelong. Lack of communication, financial struggle, sexual incompatibility, abuse, and infidelity are the reasons given for dissolution, and in that order.
- Despite the trends, remarriage has lost none of its popularity. Forty percent of all marriages include a spouse who was married before, more common among men than women, 64% compared to 52%.
- Interracial marriages are also on the increase, roughly 17% of all newlyweds in 2018, compared to only 3% in 1967.

- Same-sex marriages are becoming more prevalent as support for legalization increases. 62% of Americans now approve verses 32% who remain opposed. 61% of all same-sex couples who live together are married.[56]

Historically marriage has been defined as a life-long commitment between one man and one woman. The majority of the world's religions and people of faith still hold to that view. But the majority of all Americans now favor the legalization of marriage between people of the same gender.

I recently attended a wedding for two men whose parents are both conservative Christians. Both parents oppose homosexuality based on their religious beliefs but were supportive and even happy that their grown children were in a loving, committed relationship.

Is it possible for the church and Christians to oppose same sex relationships while simultaneously accepting and loving those who are a part of the LBGTQ community? Likewise, can LBGTQ people simultaneously respect, accept, and love conservative Christians and members of faith communities who oppose homosexuality on the grounds of their religious belief? In our highly polarized culture, it's a lot to ask. I suspect some can but many never will …unless of course, it affects a member of their own family, and even then, nothing is guaranteed.

As an admittedly uninformed Christian, I was uncertain why people of faith were so opposed to same sex relationships. I was directed to Biblical references, (not just denominational positions), that oppose homosexuality as a sin against God's created intention for men and women. In those Scriptures, homosexuality is included in a list of sins that can put their salvation in jeopardy. Parents and friends who truly believe that, understandably oppose the homosexual lifestyle for those they love.

Such condemnation seemed extreme to me until I was shown in the Bible homosexuality is not the only sin singled out for warning. In the very same passages, the Bible includes sexual immorality of all kinds, idolatry (the sin of putting anything or anyone ahead of God), hatred, jealousy, rage, selfish ambition, even argumentative people and unrepentant alcoholics (drunkards) all fall under the same ban.[57]

Many Christians and nonbelievers have a common misunderstanding of God's expectations. Many in both camps equate Christian faithfulness with always doing right and avoiding all wrong. No one can meet that standard, and no one can adequately defend judgmental Christians who condemn certain sins more strongly than others. I haven't noticed the same kind of judgmental attitude by Christians against alcohol abuse, selfish ambition, quarrelsome people, divorced people and those that love to argue. There is something in human nature that is more threatened by some sins than others.

Jesus was the opposite of intolerant. His actions and words emphasized love and concern for believers and nonbelievers alike. He was critical of the religious elites who pretended to be free from sin, and simultaneously went out of His way to embrace nonbelievers and known sinners, even to the consternation and confusion of his own disciples.

When I questioned the clarity of those passages condemning homosexuality as a sin with the potential to damn, I was shown the only sin that damns is the sin of apostasy, denial of faith in Jesus who paid the price for all sin on the cross.

Homosexuality is one sin in the list of many behaviors that can lead a person to deny the Christian faith. Rather than exposing themselves to churches and Scriptures that condemn their lifestyle, those who participate in these behaviors are prone to reject the Christian faith and the Bible that opposes their lifestyle. The rejection of faith, according to Scripture, not any one sin more than another, puts salvation in jeopardy.

The argument of "nature verses nurture" always arises when it comes to sexual orientation. How can anyone be responsible for their sexual orientation if they were "born this way?" No one can explain with any degree of certainty, how human sexual orientation is determined. Apart from their sexual preference, the behaviors and choices of the LGBTQ community are not much different from heterosexuals. They share the same interest in sexual activity, neither more nor less. They are just as likely to form long lasting relationships, work for a living, shop, watch TV, vote and pay taxes.

Less than 5% of the American population identifies with the LGBTQ lifestyle, but when you include children, parents, grandparents, siblings, aunts, uncles, nieces and nephews to the equation, virtually every family is touched by the issue on a personal level.

Unfortunately, the lines of division appear to be drawn with permanent markers. Most are either for or against same sex relationships, and remain intolerant of anyone who disagrees with their personal perspective. On May 8, 2012, the citizens of North Carolina voted to ban gay marriage by a substantial margin of 61% to 31%. The next day, in a statement broadcast on national TV, President Obama said, "I think same-sex couples should be able to get married." To no one's surprise,

his statement was cheered by some and blasted by others.

The leaders of conservative faith communities continue to speak out against the legalization of same sex relationships. They contend it is not only an affront to their faith, but a danger to basic family values which they consider the foundation of a healthy society.

The First Amendment to the Constitution of the United States says,

"Congress shall make no law respecting an establishment of religion or prohibiting the free exercise thereof, or abridging the freedom of speech or of the press, or the right of the people peaceably to assemble and to petition the government for a redress of grievances."

Churches, pastors and ordinary citizens are entitled to their opinions, and they cannot be told their beliefs are forbidden. The Supreme Court made it clear that while laws cannot interfere with religious belief and opinions, laws can limit some religious practices, such as the practice of human sacrifice. To rule otherwise the court said, "Would permit every citizen to be a law unto himself... While the right to have religious beliefs is absolute, the freedom to act publicly on such beliefs is not absolute." (Reynolds vs. United States, 1878)

The phrase "Separation of Church and State," while not contained in the Bill of Rights, has its origin in a letter Thomas Jefferson wrote to the Danbury Baptist Association of Connecticut on January 1, 1802. It's a sound concept, based on a similar statement made by Jesus. *"Render unto Caesar the things that are Caesar's and unto God the things that are God's."*[58]

So where does that put marriage? Does the institution of marriage fall under the jurisdiction of the state or the Church? It depends. There are state laws involved: tax status, inheritance laws, and other legal implications. As it stands, marriages performed by spiritual leaders must be licensed by the state before the wedding and registered with the court afterwards. The approval and blessing of the Church is optional based on the belief of those being married.

A pastor I know would prefer the Church be removed from the equation all together. In his mind, it puts churches and pastors in a no-win situation. As a Christian, he is genuinely committed to love all people, as did Jesus. As a Christian pastor faithful to the Bible, he is also compelled to uphold God's truth, no matter how politically and culturally unacceptable it may be, just as Jesus did.

He would prefer that all weddings be conducted by the state, and afterward, people of faith may choose to come to the Church for God's blessing if they wish. He is of the opinion that approach would better maintain a proper separation between church and state and avoid the confusion created when a pastor acts as a servant of the court. As a spiritual leader, he wishes to retain the right to provide a blessing to those who sincerely seek God's favor and avoid conducting ceremonies for those who find God's standards troubling. In other words, "Return to Caesar what is Caesar's, and to God what is God's."

It sounds perfectly reasonable to me. ∎

St. Louis Herald

Gender: He, She, Us, and Them

By: **James King**

I was tempted to call this column, "What You Don't Know, You Don't Know." Many, perhaps even most of the world believes questions surrounding gender are not as complicated as people suggest. They are wrong. People who believe that, literally don't know what they don't know.

The more I studied the gender issue, the more I realized I was in over my head when it came to grasping the biological, moral and theological implications of the subject. I'm not alone in my confusion. Even the experts (biological and theological) don't agree and admit there is much they just don't know. In the end, perhaps that is the most honest explanation of what we know for certain about gender. We don't know what we don't know, and it's probably going to remain that way for the foreseeable future.

But why is it so complicated? The Bible says, "God created mankind in his own image, in the image of God He created them; male and female He created them." [59] Nothing about that seems difficult. God made only two genders, male and female, and together they reflect the image of God. But what does that mean? Men and women are differentiated chiefly but not exclusively, by their physical attributes. Does the passage suggest "the image of God" is best explained as a unification of both genders? Jesus told the woman he met at Jacob's well in Samaria, *"God is a spirit and his worshippers must worship Him in spirit and in truth."* [60] God is not limited by physical or even human characteristics, so the Image of God cannot be explained as a combination of genders.

Many theologians believe "the image of God," refers to the sinless nature of God. Humans were created like God "in the beginning" and as such were innocent, perfect, and without sin until that infamous moment when Satan tempted Eve who tempted Adam to eat the forbidden fruit. Humanity, male and female at that moment lost their innocence, (their perfection) and thus lost "God's image."

As additional evidence, theologians refer to King David who compared himself to nonbelievers who live only for this world. Unlike the godless, David looked forward to an eternal reunion with his God. *"But as for me, I will not be satisfied until I see your face and awake with Your likeness, O God."* [61] He looked forward to regaining the image of God, perfection restored by means of forgiveness.

Sin is the scourge that changed every aspect of God's creation. Earth and everything in it, including aspects of humanity's physical nature which no longer exists perfectly in every person as it did at creation "...in the beginning." *Paradise Lost,* is more than a book title. It describes the imperfection of a world changed by sin's arrival on earth. The fall of mankind into sin (as it is commonly called), was a watershed moment. From a Biblical perspective, earth's status should be considered BTF or ATF … Before the Fall, or After the Fall. When sin entered the world it brought with it disease, jealousy, inequality, hatred, birth abnormalities, impatience, despair, hunger, mental illness, everything that makes life difficult.

I thought about that when attending a funeral recently. It dawned on me that most of the Biblical references to heaven describe the absence of hardships more than they describe new blessings yet to be experienced on the other side. *"There will be no more death, or mourning or crying or pain, for the old order of things has passed away."* [62]

Immediately after sin's debut, God promised a Savior who would rescue those who put their faith in Him. He promised to restore what was lost and bring them home to a place called "paradise" …not unlike the paradise He created, "in the beginning."

The biological realities of our present-day, less-than-perfect-world were altered when sin entered the picture. Birth abnormalities are a reality of life. What was once true about gender is still mostly true, but not always true. This is where it gets biologically complicated.

Genes attached to human chromosomes are largely responsible for the determination of an individual's gender. Those who have XY chromosomes typically develop male testis. At seven weeks in utero, the testis send a shot of testosterone into the male brain that causes the body to develop male characteristics. It happens once more at birth and again at puberty to solidify the male gender. Those who have XX chromosomes typically develop ovaries. At seven weeks in utero, those ovaries secrete estrogen and progesterone that feminizes the female brain and cause her body to develop female characteristics. The biological process that determines gender is *almost always* predictable, but because the world is no longer perfect, not always.

Advanced scientific methods and tests have allowed scientists to discover there are individuals who are anatomically female but have XY chromosomes, and there are anatomically males who possessed XX chromosomes. Women born with this condition exhibit female genitalia but possess greater levels of testosterone than females with only XX chromosomes. Likewise, men with male genitalia but XX chromosomes will possess higher levels of estrogen than males with XY chromosomes. That reality is often the source of gender confusion in an individual. Their physiology may not match their gender identity, which is largely determined by the feminization or masculinization of their brain by means of hormone secretion.

Even when the XY and XX chromosomes match an individual's physical characteristics, there are other biological factors that can cause an imbalance resulting in greater than normal levels of testosterone in women or greater than normal estrogen levels in men. It may be true that in the beginning (before God's creative design was altered by sin), gender was always 100% male or 100% female, but it would be hard to make that biological case today.

Apart from these aberrations, the created concept of gender is ingenious. If you believe in the unlimited power and intelligence of God, He could have easily designed a different plan for procreation. But apart from reproduction, gender distinction is a blessing to the human race. Most who have worked in an all-male or all-female business would prefer the advantages of a gender-diverse environment. It may seem easier to work with people of the same gender, but the benefits of diversity provide unique perspectives and ultimately better outcomes.

The differences between the genders are more than physiological. As John Gray demonstrated in his best-selling book, *Men Are from Mars, Women Are from Venus*, there are emotional, social and focus distinctions between men and women. As the author acknowledges, his book makes broad generalizations, and there are degrees and exceptions in all individuals, nevertheless there are undeniable gender distinctives. He maintains that men, or Martians, as he refers to them,

"Value power, competency,

efficiency and achievement. They are always doing things to prove themselves and develop their power and skills. Their sense of self is defined through their ability to achieve results... They are more interested in "objects" and "things" rather than people and feelings. Even today on Earth, while women fantasize about romance, men fantasize about powerful cars, faster computers, gadgets, gizmos, and more powerful technology. Men are preoccupied with the "things" that can help them express power by creating results and achieving their goals." [63]

Remember, Gray is speaking in generalities and repeatedly cautions his readers to allow for variations between individuals, but has effectively demonstrated the gender difference between men and women. He contends,

"Venusians (as he refers to women in his book,) have different values. They value love, communication, beauty and relationships (more than Martians). They spend a lot of time supporting, helping and nurturing one another. Their sense of self-worth is defined through their feelings and the quality of their relationships. They experience fulfillment through sharing and relating... Instead of being goal oriented, women are relationship oriented; they are more concerned with expressing their goodness, love and caring... Because proving one's competence is not as important to Venusians, offering help

is not offensive and needing help is not a sign of weakness." [64]

In a perfect world, a clear distinction between male and female genders would be definitive. But it is wrong to condemn, demean, and reject those whose physiology is wired differently than the norm due to the consequence of their birth. They should be encouraged to pursue whatever therapies and treatments are available so they can better understand their physiological makeup and live free of any guilt or shame caused by their physical reality.

Christians are urged to love all people. Jesus did not shun those his culture called unclean. He interceded for them, touched them, and ministered to them, even when others attempted to push them in the shadows. He publicly demonstrated God's love for people the first-century culture rejected. Those who follow His example should do the same.

Jesus continued to uphold God's moral standards while extending God's love to prostitutes, lepers and known sinners. He did not condone sinful behavior while demonstrating acceptance to those enslaved by it. Nor did He condemn certain groups more than others. He opposed all forms of immorality and urged sinners to abandon behaviors that have the power to destroy a person's self-worth.

There is a difference between

those who are physically affected by the circumstances of their birth and those who practice immorality. The Bible does not condone nor excuse homosexuality and other immoral sins. It condemns homosexuality as a sin that is opposed to a person's created nature. But notice the same Scriptures condemn just as strongly all forms of sexual immorality, idolaters, thieves, slanderers, swindlers, the greedy, those with uncontrollable anger, the selfish, and those who love to argue. God calls all sinners (not only a select group) to abandon their sinful behavior for their own good and the good of others.

When discussing differences, words and definitions matter. During a recently televised broadcast, a news anchor described a group of voters as "returning citizens." It was a new term I hadn't heard before, and I wasn't sure who she was describing. I assumed it was a reference to people who had been living abroad or returning military personnel. It turned out to be a politically correct reference to ex-convicts and felons that had served prison time and were attempting to reenter society. The Florida legislature had voted to restore their voting privileges. Using new terminology was a well-meaning attempt on the part of the media to remove the stigma of their criminal past.

Language matters. When it comes to gender, I discovered a number of terms I thought I understood but didn't, and some I had never heard.

- Transgender: A person whose anatomy does not match their gender identity. They are also sometimes called nonbinary.
- Genderfluid or Genderqueer: These are folks who don't identify as either male or female. They may feel male one day and female another or even fluctuate during the day depending on the situation.
- Cisgender: A person whose anatomy and gender identity are the same. It comes from the Latin word: cis, which means "on this side," compared to Latin: trans, which means "on the other side."
- Gender-Expression: It is not a term that defines a specific gender. It describes the behavior of a person of one gender who prefers to dress in the style of the opposite gender.
- Lesbian: A woman who desires to have sexual relations with a person of her own gender. Men who prefer sex with other males are referred to by the generic term, homosexual.
- Bisexual: A person of a specific gender who is sexually attracted to both men and women.
- Queer: Until the 1990's it was considered a derogatory term for anyone who was not heterosexual. Today it

is more commonly used by political activists who refuse to be labeled by any one term. They are best described as noncompliant, nonconforming individuals.

TRUTH BE TOLD believes people have the right to be identified in whatever way they choose but considers any identity that focuses primarily on the sexual gender or sexual preferences of a person unfortunate. Individuals are more than their gender, or gender identity.

If I were asked to describe myself, I would say, "I'm a husband and father of two sons. I'm a university graduate with a degree in journalism and have been a reporter my entire working life. I enjoy golf, reading, travel, the theatre, concerts and any adventure that has the potential to expand my understanding of people and the world in which we live. I doubt I would say, "I'm a heterosexual." I *am a heterosexual*, but I'm so much more than that. I doubt I would make any reference at all to my sexual orientation to describe myself.

I would not want people to pigeonhole me by their perception of what it means to be a heterosexual. I believe the same standard should apply to transsexual, homosexual and bisexual people. The moment a person describes themselves as a lesbian, a transsexual woman or a homosexual man, they are abdicating their identity to others

who will make assumptions about them based on that person's understanding of their gender identity. It seems a grossly inaccurate way to describe the most important qualities of a person.

We are people of great diversity. As I wrote in a previous column called R-E-S-P-E-C-T, we may or may not agree with another person's lifestyle. We may not understand their biological nature, and on the basis of our faith perspective, may even believe their sexual orientations are aberrant and sinful. But all our interactions with other people should be conducted with *love*, and mutual respect.

I don't claim to be deeply spiritual, but as I understand God's nature, He would prefer to be described as the personification of love. *"God is love,"*[65] is the first passage most Christian children memorize. God has many more attributes than love. He is holy, just, omnipotent, eternal, almighty, gracious, omnipresent, omniscient and many other things. But *love* is how He primarily wants to be known. Once *love* is established between people, intelligent, compassionate, conversations can begin.

I've been to enough weddings to know the Bible says,

"If I speak in the tongues of men or of angels, but do not have love, I am only a resounding gong or a clanging cymbal. If I have the gift of prophecy and can fathom all mysteries and all

knowledge, and if I have a faith that can move mountains, but do not have love, I am nothing. If I give all I possess to the poor and give over my body to hardship that I may boast, but do not have love, I gain nothing."[66]

If that's God's advice on how to treat others, who am I to argue? ∎

St. Louis Herald

Sex Is Not a Four-Letter Word

By: **James King**

Some might argue s-e-x ought to be nothing more than a four-letter word, the kind young people and the less sophisticated use on the streets to describe human intimacy. They consider sex a basic physical need, nothing more and nothing less. That perception ignores the power of sexual intercourse to affirm or lessen a person's self-worth, especially among women.

Studies reveal sexual encounters are more a subjective and emotional experience for women than they are for men. It is not an exaggeration to say nearly half of all adult women have experienced unwanted sexual advances (and many of those, even sexual abuse) at some point in their life. It would be a mistake to suggest sex is merely a bodily function no different than eating, sleeping, or regular exercise. It is more than that.

Sexual intimacy done right is the ultimate expression of human connection. Done wrong, without mutual consent or adequate maturity, it has the power to emotionally cripple its victims. When experienced as designed by the Creator, it has the potential to cement a lifelong spiritual and emotional merger of two into one. Without a doubt, it is more than the consummation of a biological function.

Lust may lead to sex, but as a motive for intercourse, it fails to achieve sex's ultimate purpose, the joining of two hearts into one. Sex for the sake of sex is a poor substitute for intimacy. Those fortunate to experience the oneness of a sexual relationship within the bounds of love consider it the ultimate human experience, more important than money, power, or fame. Many wealthy and powerful celebrities envy those less fortunate who have found true love. Sexual intimacy experienced in a deeply loving relationship is hard to find and even harder to maintain in our sexually permissive culture.

It may be one of the greatest ironies of our time. In a rush for intimacy, people uncover their bodies but hide their hearts. They expose more but reveal less. They hide little but are less transparent. No wonder life-long, loving, intimate relationships are such a human rarity. Lovers, who exchange true intimacy, for the opportunity to get laid make a poor bargain. It's a high price to pay for momentary pleasure.

You've heard it said, "Women need to feel loved to have sex, and men need to have sex to feel loved." TRUTH BE TOLD submits that men and women are in pursuit of the same things whether they know it or not... true intimacy, something more profound that physical connection. Sex is both a means to that end, and an end to that means. When shared within the bounds of love it is a moment too profound for words.

What words are sufficient to do justice to the brilliance of a sun rise, the sweet smell of a Spring shower, a forest cloaked in autumn leaves, wheat stocks swaying in the breeze, the scent of a lilac, the flash of lightening in rolling clouds, or the peaceful beauty of a newborn asleep in its mother's arms? It is easier to describe what sexual intimacy isn't, than to describe what it is.

Vaughn Olson was the Literature and English teacher at Huntington County High School during my most formative years. It was Mr. Olson who introduced me to the power of words and the beauty of a well-turned phrase. He was one of those all too rare teachers who did what he loved and loved what he did. His classes were electric. He stirred our hearts and opened our minds through dramatic (and sometimes reenacted) recitations of great speeches, beautiful poetry and the vivid images created by well-written prose. When Robin Williams played the role of John Keating in *The Dead Poets Society*, I was reminded of Mr. Olson. His classes were always full, always interesting and never long enough.

It was Mr. Olson who introduced me to Robert Frost, Rudyard Kipling, Henry David Thoreau, Henry Wadsworth Longfellow, and many more. Our assignments were meaningful. It was one of only a hand-full of classes where students readily completed their assignments and eagerly shared them with each other. He took a special interest in my offerings and encouraged me throughout my university studies. He even followed my byline at *The Herald*, and sent feedback and wrote letters to the editor as a compliment from time to time. Who does that? His influence played an important role in my formation as a man, a husband, father and professional.

It was not a one-way street. He not only contributed to my work as a writer, he sometimes shared his own. One of his assignments required the class to write and original poem. He shared some of his own as an example to us. I have a file of his creations which includes a poem called, *Unrequited*, about the difference between infatuation and true love, the difference between the natural attraction of the sexes and true intimacy.

Unrequited

Intrigued and captivated
By feelings without substance.
A moth drawn precariously to the flame
Without reason or intention
Captive to a desperate longing
To connect to another,
prematurely…
Intrigued and captivated.

Confused and unsettled
Disguised as a liking, a love
That refuses to go unnoticed.
Compelled to assuage feelings
Masquerading as attraction
To another whose reality leaves us…
Confused and unsettled.

Older and wiser
Beholding with eyes
unclouded.
Feelings, as wonderful,

unreliable escorts
To things substantial and lasting.
Feelings feigning love and liking.
More is required and acquired by those…
Older and wiser.

Intrigued and captivated
Reason cannot explain it.
No heart can contain it.
True love consumes, blesses, and abides
Defying words, transcending feelings.
So long as life endures…
Intrigued and captivated.

Unrequited makes clear sexual attraction is not the same as love, but neither is it to be discarded as inappropriate within the bounds of love. Like poets must learn to use their pen and words, or a sculptor his mallet and chisel, lovers must learn to turn their sexual desires into a work of art. It is possible but not automatic.

Over the years many have turned the subject of sex into observations and surveys to be studied and analyzed. Sociologist, philosophers, poets, and songwriters have been doing it for centuries and have not yet run out of discoveries or ways to express them. For the purpose of our discussion, TRUTH BE TOLD will devote the rest of this column to sexual interaction between opposite genders, although everyone knows sex is not exclusive to male and female relationships, or for that matter, always a two-person affair.

Based on recent studies, as disclosed in medical journals and a wide variety of published physiological and psychological studies, it is commonly accepted that men have a higher libido than women. They are also more straightforward in their pursuit and in making their desires known. The female anatomy is designed to take pleasure in the physical aspects of sexual intercourse but is more subject to factors other than physical stimulation. Women derive greater benefit from the emotional and social expression of sexual interaction than their male counterparts.

Sexual satisfaction is typically experienced differently between men and women. It is said a woman's desire is prompted more by what happens between the ears than between the legs. In other words, women are more likely than men to be aroused by romance, the right setting, and the emotional connection she has with her partner. Studies reveal men are more visual in their orientation towards sexual attraction and as a result more quickly aroused and inclined to pursue casual sex than a woman. Prostitution, for example is still mostly a phenomenon of men seeking women, not something women are known to pursue.

Because sexual attraction is typically more emotional than physical for women, they are more apt than men to be open to same-sex relationships. They are also more likely to engage in bisexual relationships. Religious women on the other hand, are less inclined to hold permissive attitudes about sex than religious men. Women are also more commonly influenced than men by their peer group's attitudes towards what is appropriate or inappropriate sexually. Educated women are more accepting of sexual experimentation, while the degree of education among men seems to have little effect on their sexual opinions.

Women are more inclined to pursue intimacy, love and connection before entering a sexual relationship than men. Those things may be desired by men but are not considered essential before engaging in a sexual relationship. Some suggest the difference has to do with the fact women can become pregnant and ultimately bear the responsibility for the wellbeing of offspring. For this reason, either knowingly or instinctively, a woman is more likely to reserve sexual contact for partners she believes have the capacity to be loyal and committed to a long-term relationship.

Not all sex is created equal. Whether you subscribe to the

evolutionary development of humanity, or believe in God's creative hand, everyone can agree that sexual interaction is designed to be more than a method of procreation. There is intense pleasure in sex done right. Everyone involved in a loving relationship owes it to themselves and their partner to be aware not only of their own needs and desires, but also the needs, desires and preferences of their partner.

In sex, like most of life, it is in giving that we receive. ∎

*"Let me never fall into the vulgar mistake of dreaming
that I am persecuted whenever I am contradicted."*
—Ralph Waldo Emerson

CHAPTER 11

Be Careful What You Ask For

I doubt Brad knew what he was getting into when he recruited me to write the column. Even before my retirement, he floated the idea past *The Herald* owners to gain a foothold in the national market. Always interested in acquiring a new revenue stream, they agreed to a trial run. Everyone knows reporters have a limited shelf life after retirement. Out of sight, out of mind.

Brad was sure I was right for the job. I wasn't so sure, not initially. Like most people after a lifetime of work, I had other plans. There were places Sarah and I wanted to go, things we planned to do when we had the time and financial wherewithal to pursue them. I realized writing and op-ed would be less demanding than chasing breaking stories, but it would require a professional commitment just the same. My column could be written from anywhere as long as I hit my deadlines and met from time to time with the team. The money was tempting but not a deciding factor. I was more concerned about the weekly commitment and the column's purpose.

Brad indicated he was open to almost anything, but that was the problem. The column needed a focus. "Just keep it real and keep it interesting..." was Brad's mantra. I knew what *didn't* interest me. No disrespect, but I wasn't ready to become another Charles Kuralt, on-the-road-feel-good-columnist, no matter how popular or how much it paid. There were enough of those. The old-school reporting styles of Mike Royko and Charles Krauthammer were more to my liking. Their columns were diverse, sometimes humorous, always insightful, poignant, and sometimes political. I wasn't a political animal and had no desire to become one. Cable news networks had cornered that market. The one thing I knew for certain was I didn't want to be a poor imitation of anyone else.

If I was going to do this, three things were required:

1. The column had to capture and hold my interest and the interest of the public.

2. It had to be something significant, something worth my time and effort.

3. No matter if the public agreed or objected, the column needed to be well received. I wasn't interested if no one cared.

The question of purpose was answered the night I received my "prophetic call." I didn't mention my night visitor and subsequent "close encounters of the unusual kind" to Brad. That first visitation, my interaction with Mordecai and the other encounters convinced me there was much to discuss in my column if I had the courage. As I mentioned, Brad didn't have a specific focus for the column in mind, as long as I kept it interesting and controversial enough to hold the attention of the public. "Keep it real and keep it thought-provoking," was all he wanted. Whenever I heard him repeat his famous catch phrase, the thought "Be careful what you ask for," came to mind.

From the beginning, I had been candid about my intention. If I was going to do this, I planned to discuss the tough issues of our day, the ones no one with hopes for a long career would ever touch: Race, Gender, Sex, Marriage, Abortion, Life After Death, Money, Public Education, Unions vs. Right-To-Work, the Existence of God and whatever else kept people in a tizzy.

I was under no illusion that what I wrote would settle the issue, but maybe as a guy with no skin in the game (neither conservative nor liberal), I could tamp down the rhetoric. I was naïve enough to believe a well-written opinion might cause folks to question their presumptions long enough to consider a different perspective. People still believe in right and wrong, good, better, and best, but they can't agree on what is true. Has common sense left the building?

Challenging people to keep an open mind was nothing new. Think about it. Why would anyone buy a car when they owned a perfectly good horse? Why would any reasonable person believe they needed a phone in their pocket 24/7? Closer to home, the thought of eating raw oysters on the half-shell originally disgusted me, until I ate one. Changing opinions rarely happens overnight, but someone has to start the discussion. It is essential to progress.

I was convinced the four columns on Love, Gender, Marriage and Sex would make or break the column. No one was sure what to expect. As a group, the editorial staff never met in advance to discuss the issues or a point of view before I wrote the articles, but that didn't mean they didn't have opinions. They were a microcosm of public perception, and depending on their age, political bent, beliefs, and families of origin, were bound to have differing opinions. Brad did a good job of reminding everyone the paper's only concern should be the three R's of publishing... Relevance, Ratings and Revenue.

No one could question the *relevance* of TBT. The topics spoke for themselves. We had a corner on the market. No one else had the courage to ignite a firestorm of public opinion on the issues we were willing to address. They were too smart for that.

No one could question our *ratings*. They exceeded all expectations. Brad was right on that point, as long as we stirred public opinions, there was no such thing as a bad response. "Apathy," he liked to say, "not controversy was our enemy." Apathy was never a concern. These topics brought out the best and worst in people. The columns ignited unfiltered agreement and disagreement with TBT and each other.

Revenue was still fluid. We lost some accounts but gained others. Our sales team did a great job of reminding advertisers that exposure not popularity was the name of the game. We were exceeding all projections for readership and putting their company name and products in front of more people than we had promised. Advertising on TBT was good for business.

There was a difference of opinion on how to manage interaction on the threads. Should a representative from TBT ever respond, clarify or engage the responders, or stay out of the discussion all together? There was no industry standard, and even if there was, we were not inclined to follow the status quo. Some thought we should engage and some didn't. Those in favor argued responding in a limited fashion would keep TBT in touch with our readers. It would clarify our intention to provide a platform for a respectful exchange of opinions and ideologies. Those opposed to the idea, believed TBT should remain a catalyst, not an arbitrator. There was no right or wrong to the decision, but there was undoubtedly a good, better or best, outcome. Everyone was willing to do what seemed best.

The team suggested a trial to see what would happen. I was given the opportunity to respond to comments directly, but most didn't believe that was best. I agreed. My article should speak for itself. Brad also felt it would be best if a neutral party, maybe an intern, referred all comments and questions back to the main point of the editorial. He felt I might be tempted to widen the discussion or expound beyond the point of the original article. If a reader wanted to conjecture about the implications of the column or other issues, TBT should refuse the bait and stay on subject. Our respondent, like a good referee in a hotly contested athletic contest, should make sure the players compete fairly, not become a player, or determine the outcome of the game.

The last four TBT columns provided plenty of opportunity to test our decision. The column, *What's Love Got To Do With It,* was the least controversial of the four, but received more than its share of responses.

@fastforward: "Loved the column. Not only did it remind everyone of the enduring power of love, it spoke volumes on the tragedy of war. My heart goes out to all the Sarahs who have lost their beloved Sullivans."

@maggiemaybe: "Animals rule. The story of Hachiko is another testament to the unconditional love and faithfulness of man's best friend. Would to God more people could learn from Hachiko's example."

@TBT: "Thanks for all your responses. Both stories make the point, "Love cannot exist as a concept. It must be expressed in action. What action have you experienced that says LOVE to you?"

@homebrew: "Love is when my wife gets up early to share a cup of coffee and pack my lunch before I head out to work every morning."

@notevenonce: "Love is my husband starting my car and scraping the windshield on cold snowy mornings."

@UBcrazy: "Love is sitting up waiting for my teenage son to get home safely from a school activity or late date."

The column, *Gender: He, She, Us, and Them,* generated a lively exchange.

@Deuteronomy6.4: "It was helpful to be reminded the world is not the same today as it was before The Fall. Sin changed everything. But I'm still not certain that explains how Bruce Jenner became Caitlyn. I'm just saying."

@TBT: "@Deuteronomy6.4, TRUTH BE TOLD does not defend, or pass judgment on any one person or a given situation. We don't pretend to know the details of a person's life. But we believe a better understanding of the biological and theological concepts should help everyone become more tolerant of differences."

@manchild: "I'm more confused now than ever. Maybe that's the point. If experts can't agree on the cause of gender confusion, how can I be so certain?"

@wackjob: "You liberals are all alike. Things are more black and white than you are willing to accept. God made two genders, only two. If that's too confusing for you, drop your pants and take a long look in a mirror. Quit running cover for perverts."

@TBT: "You and everyone else are entitled to your opinions **@Wackjob**, but TBT believes it is helpful to know *why* others may disagree with you on the issue of gender. Anatomy isn't the only factor that determines a person's sexual persuasion. Be thankful it's not as confusing for you."

@badtattoo: "I learned more from this article than anything I have read on the subject of gender. Thanks for the objectivity."

@peachykeen: "How can anyone know the difference between immoral behavior and alternative lifestyles that are more biological than moral in origin? How can a person of faith know the difference?"

@TBT: "**@peachykeen**, thanks for the honesty of your question. We are attempting to share the truth as best we can discern it. It's not our job to pass judgment. The best anyone can do is attempt to understand, love and accept all people. TBT doesn't believe you must agree with someone to love them. That would put a lot of parents in a dilemma."

@sadsuzie: "You have heard the law that says, 'Love your neighbor' and hate your enemy. But I say, love your enemies! Pray for those who persecute you! In that way, you will be acting as true children of your Father in heaven. For He gives His sunlight to both the evil and the good, and He sends rain on the just and the unjust alike. If you love only those who love you, what reward is there for that? Even corrupt tax collectors do that much. If you are kind only to your friends, how are you different from anyone else? Even pagans do that." Matthew 5:43–47

By far, the most controversial columns were the two on the subject of Marriage and Sex. It came as no surprise to me or anyone on the TBT team. It was strange comfort that TBT was attacked from both the right and the left in reaction to those columns. As predicted, I had become an equal opportunity offender.

> **@sorrynotsorry:** "Make a decision already. Either you support same-sex marriage or you don't. I thought this column was called TRUTH BE TOLD not, REFUSE TO TAKE A STAND."

> **@TBT:** "Thanks for your response **@sorrynotsorry**. The position of TBT on the subject of marriage is that each person must decide for themselves what is right and wrong. Only God can judge the heart. Conservative believers should uphold and honor the values of their faith. Irreligious people who take a more liberal view of God's word will hold a different opinion. Is there room in your world for different viewpoints or is forced conformity your preference? And if so, who gets to decide?"

> **@sorrynotsorry:** "I'm well aware there are differences of opinion, but I expected a column called TRUTH BE TOLD to take a stand."

> **@TBT:** "Our stance is clear. 'Give to Caesar what belongs to Caesar and unto God what belongs to God.' Separation of church and state makes perfect sense to TBT. We encourage you to respectfully advocate for your perspective."

Many of the responses to the, Sex Is Not A Four-Letter Word column followed a predictable pattern. Apparently, more than a few people consider sex and love coequal, stand-alone options that may or may not coexist as a package deal.

> **@URsowrong:** "Sex is sex and love is love. Why confuse the two?"

> **@suspiciousmind:** "You can love someone passionately without great sex, and you can have passionate sex without great love."

> **@triggerfinger:** "If someone is in a loveless marriage, sex is going to become a problem. If someone is in a sexless marriage, love is going to become a problem too. What's a person to do?"

The reactions to Sex Is Not A Four-Letter Word came fast and furious. It was by far the most retweeted and shared column so far. The interaction was fascinating to track. Some sidebar exchanges took a life of their own without the need for any prompting from TBT. For the most part respondents were respectful, but several obscene and inappropriate posts had to be deleted by the site manager, a common occurrence in these types of columns. For the sake of clarification, TBT did enter the discussion of the "separate-but-equal, sex-and-love" dialogue.

@**TBT:** "There is no denying more and more people are engaged in casual sex, and sex outside of marriage and outside of committed loving relationships. TBT does not deny the pleasure sexual interaction can provide with or without love. TBT simply contends sexual interaction within the bounds of love has the potential for a much deeper and a more fulfilling relationship. Sex outside of marriage or a committed loving relationship is never impersonal. It has the potential to create relational conflict and leave one or both participants emotionally scarred and crippled."

@**ursowrong:** "I hear you. I simply believe separating sex and love makes better sense if we dump all the cultural and moral baggage people like you attach to sex. People who love each other should want their partners to enjoy good sex that may or may not include them. Insisting sex and love must coexist is the problem. Linking the two exponentially increases the potential for heartache."

@**TBT:** "We appreciate your thoughtful comments @**ursowrong**. From the observation of friends, family, and the testimony of relational experts, TBT believes casual sex apart from love is never emotionally neutral. There is something transcendent in a sexual encounter that is more than physical."

@**suspiciousmind:** "TBT's perspective may be ideal but it is impractical. Those days are long gone. Good riddance. You should be advocating sexual freedom not sexual bondage! Love whomever you want to love. Enjoy sex with whomever you want to enjoy sex. You only go around once in life."

@TBT: "**@suspiciousmind,** TBT does not apologize for promoting the ideal. We advocate for truth regardless of what is deemed politically correct. TBT believes there is right, wrong, good, better, and best outcomes in most things, sexual encounters included. You are free to disagree, but our assessment has stood the test of time."

In retrospect, it occurred to me, some of the greatest empires throughout history were weakened by moral decay from within long before they were vanquished by enemies from without. Those who advocate for the strength of life-long marriage and the family unit as the foundation of a healthy society are right.

Most, even those with strong religious convictions, don't insist morality should be forced on a free society, but neither do they believe they should remain silent about standards they endorse as morally preferable. Tolerance cuts both ways. Those who advocate for moral absolutes must accept their minority status in an increasingly permissive and amoral culture. ("Lights shining in the darkness," to quote a phrase.) Conversely, the irreligious and amoral must not only allow, but also defend the rights of those who advocate for morality with which they disagree.

The best decisions are rarely extreme decisions. The best decisions most often live in tension between two opposing, idealistic perspectives. Somewhere the Bible urges the faithful to, "Speak the truth in love." True love and absolute truth are not incompatible. It is entirely possible to love someone and speak critical truth into their life. Tough love based on truth, is an important aspect of true love.

From all I could ascertain, Brad, the marketing department and our website team were feeling pretty positive over the traction TRUTH BE TOLD was gaining. Sarah seemed proud of the column too and appreciated the fact I could work from home or wherever we traveled. Her only concern was the same caution expressed in the team meeting, "Not every column should be personally divisive." There are other things Americans debate

MAN IN THE MIDDLE

that are ripe for discussion: Life On Other Planets, Policing The World, Immigration, Environmentalism, Legalizing Marijuana, Social Media Etiquette, The Electoral College and The Keto Diet." Okay, The Keto Diet wasn't actually suggested, but I think it bears discussion.

The meeting was an encouragement to keep on keeping on. I agreed subject matter is as important (if not more important) than my ability to write an intriguing perspective. It is my job to stir the pot and get people talking *to each other* rather *than past each other*.

I began to wonder what my *other* "team of consultants" thought about the column thus far. Mordecai seemed adamant in his opinion that I was the right man for the job, but now that two months of columns had been published, I couldn't help but wonder if the man in white felt the same way.

Of course, I had no way of knowing when and how my divine recruiter would reconnect. If my off and on interactions with Mordecai had taught me anything it was that the God squad (as Sarah and I referred to them) were in charge of all appointments. My best course of action was for Sarah and me to enjoy life while awaiting further instructions.

Sarah had been bugging me to spend a month or two on the beach and that's what I intended to do. Spending a few weeks on the Gulf Coast, eating seafood, sunbathing, and playing golf surrounded by palm trees sounded good to me.

If the man upstairs wanted to talk, He'd have no trouble finding me.

*"The trouble with most of us is that we'd rather be
ruined by praise than saved by criticism."*

—Norman Vincent Peale

CHAPTER 12

Confirmation

S arah reserved a condo on the Alabama shore of the Gulf of Mexico
for two weeks beginning next Saturday. We both had things to
accomplish before heading South. I made plans to get the oil
changed and the tires rotated on the SUV while Sarah focused on the
groceries and beach supplies we would need for our hiatus. The condo was
only an eleven-hour drive from St. Louis. With no major airports nearby, it
made sense to drive rather than fly and rent a vehicle.

My go-to service station was across the street from my favorite coffee
shop, which explains why it was my favorite. I could drop the car for service
and enjoy a cup of coffee while reviewing my next project in a pleasant
setting. I brought along my journal to review the critiques and creative
suggestions The Herald's team had recommended for future TBT articles.

As I placed my order, a familiar voice greeted me from a corner table
surrounded by men. They were younger than the usual ROMEOs (Retired
Old Men Eating Out) you often encounter at such places. I scanned the
group of the twenty-and-thirty-year-old men, looking for a familiar face.

"James! James King! Imagine running into you here."

It was Sam Gooding, the landscape supervisor I met at the deli after attending morning worship at Reliance last Summer. I remembered immediately because that encounter seemed so bizarre, another in a long list of bizarre experiences following on the heels of my encounter with the man in white. It still seemed unlikely to meet a guy named Sam Gooding immediately after hearing a sermon about the GOOD SAMaritan.

Sitting next to Sam was the man whose truck he had asked me to jump-start as we were leaving the restaurant.

"Do you remember Henry? You were nice enough to help my crew jump start his truck that Sunday at the deli. Henry and I exchanged business cards and have been friends ever since."

"I do." I greeted Henry and asked no one in particular if their gathering was an impromptu or a regularly scheduled event?

"Funny you should ask, James," Sam replied. "We meet every Friday morning for coffee and conversation. We call our get-together "Truth or Consequence," he said with a chuckle. "It's a cross between a Bible Study and a current events discussion among friends. Why don't you join us? You could offer an insight or two that might be helpful," he said with an ironic chuckle.

Sam slid a copy of the study they were discussing across the table in my direction. It was a reprint of the TRUTH BE TOLD column entitled *"Marriage: Till Death, Debt Or Divorce Do Us Part."*

Sam explained, "Since you've been publishing TRUTH BE TOLD, we've been using it as the basis for our conversations. The column is a great discussion starter. As the facilitator I add a few Bible references to deepen the study, but as you can see for yourself, it's become a popular gathering. People need a safe place to make sense of all the noise coming from Washington, the evening news, and social media"

I was surprised and flattered to learn TRUTH BE TOLD was being used by their group as the basis for their weekly meetings.

"So what do you think," I asked no one in particular. "How do the TBT articles strike you? Are they helpful? Too opinionated? Too open-ended? My intention has always been to poke a finger in the eye of political correctness gone overboard. Common sense and moral certainty seem conspicuously absent from public discussion. I want TBT to be a catalyst for conversations among reasonable people who believe in right and wrong but struggle to know what constitutes truth."

Rather than speak for the group, Sam turned and asked for their response. Their answers varied but were more positive than critical. It was hardly surprising since everyone knew I was the author and probably wanted to avoid offending me. Even so, there were a few quasi-critical comments and suggestions.

"I wish you'd include more Scripture," the guy in Cargill coveralls and the camo ball cap offered. "I realize you are writing for the public who may not see eye-to-eye with the Bible's perspective, but it's always helpful to hear a word from the Lord. The passages Sam adds are always appreciated."

"It's obvious you try hard to be inclusive and gracious, even when taking a stance that runs contrary to public opinion. Your column on gender confusion opened my eyes to realize a person's sexual identity is not always a matter of personal choice. I didn't know there are biological factors that influence a person's sexual orientation. That was news to me. Of course those factors don't alter the Bible's opposition to homosexuality and same sex marriage, but your column encouraged me and probably a lot of others like me to be more tolerant of people I have judged as immoral."

"I for one, think TRUTH BE TOLD should be more direct. Sometimes when I finish reading what you've written I'm more confused than I was before considering your point of view. I prefer things to be more right or wrong, black or white. TRUTH BE TOLD in my opinion should be more emphatic."

"Respecting people and positions that disagree with my perspective is something I try to honor in TRUTH BE TOLD," I responded. "We live in a pluralistic society of different beliefs, cultures and perspectives. I think the conclusions I reach in TBT will be better received by those who disagree with me if I acknowledge those differences before coming down on one side or another. I don't expect everyone to agree with me. I don't even expect to change the opinions of those who have already made up their mind, but I want to create an appreciation for the complexity of an issue, and respect for others who disagree. I still believe truth has an edge to it. It needs no defense, just opportunity. Subconsciously people know it when they hear it. The fact that truth and common sense often provoke vehement opposition is evidence of its power. Truth is like that. It has the capacity to stir the conscience and hearts of those who wish it weren't true."

"Are you a Christian, Jim?"

The question came from Henry. It hit me like a splash of cold water to the face on a cold winter morning. People are usually more subtle when discussing politics, religion and personal preferences. The bluntness of Henry's challenge made me smile. Unexpected boldness was a strategy I'd used a thousand times as a reporter. "Did you kill that man?" "Did you embezzle the money?" "Do you deny the accusations against you?" The shock value of a direct question cannot be overstated. A person's reaction to an unexpectedly bold question reveals as much about them as the substance of their answer. It amused me to be on the receiving end.

"If you are looking for a 'Yes or No' answer, Henry, I'd have to say, 'Yes.' But your question deserves a more complete response. Before I accepted the assignment to write TRUTH BE TOLD, I was a Christian like some men are farmers, because their daddy was a farmer and his daddy and his daddy's daddy were all farmers. I was a Christian because that's how I was raised. I didn't know why I believed what I believed as a child, but that's not the case anymore.

"TRUTH BE TOLD has forced me to take a deeper look at the reasons for my faith. It would be fair to say until recently I took my beliefs for granted, but not anymore. I'm not only a Christian, I also believe the Bible is true and its truth is a powerful thing. The Book of Hebrews describes the Scripture's power as, *'Sharper than a two-edged sword, able to cut through self-deception and convict a person's heart and soul.'*[67] So while I don't think quoting the Bible in TRUTH BE TOLD would be an effective approach to challenge political correctness, I often draw on its truth as an important source in my research.

"If you are wondering, I believe that Jesus not only existed as a historic person, I believe He is also the Son of God, the Savior of the world, and my Savior. My faith has undergone a significant transformation since the days of my childhood, compared to the faith I profess now as an adult who has examined the evidence. My adult faith is based on the facts of the matter.

"Christianity is faith founded in history that can be examined. If the facts of the Bible's history can be proven true, it makes sense that the message of the Bible is likewise true and worthy of consideration. The Bible contains a narrative that took place over time from generation to generation. The facts of that narrative can be examined by means of other nations' parallel histories. The Bible's history has been confirmed by other extra-Biblical historic records again and again.

"There are also thousands of archaeological discoveries that have been uncovered in Egypt, Mesopotamia, and Israel during the last hundred years. Those discoveries overwhelmingly validate the people, places, and events of the Bible. Every other religion has established a moral standard of life that if achieved, results in a better well-deserved afterlife. Christianity is completely different. The Christian faith teaches what God has done through history to redeem people from their moral failures, which the Bible calls sin. His actions, not theirs, make them worthy of eternal life. It is not what the individual has done or is doing to please God that results in a Christian's eternal reward, but what God has done for all people through the promises He made and kept by sending the Messiah, Jesus. Faith in God's redemption through Jesus, not personal effort, is the key principle of the Christian faith.

"Within the pages of the Bible there also exists the collaboration of specific and complex prophecies that foretold verifiable events centuries before they occurred. Predictions made and fulfilled prove the veracity of the Bible. The prophecies concerning the birth of Jesus are a good example. Isaiah prophesied that the Messiah would come out of Galilee. Micah said he would be born in Bethlehem of Judea, while Hosea predicted the Messiah would come out of Egypt. Those promises placed side by side appear to be impossible and contradictory! The three prophecies on their face are irreconcilable. But history revealed Jesus' parents came from Nazareth (a village in Galilee where he was also raised), they traveled to Bethlehem where He was born, and were forced to flee to Egypt because of King Herod's attempt to murder the child which he considered a threat to his throne. After Herod's death, Jesus' family returned to Nazareth, fulfilling all the predictions in a way no one could have predicted. Those complex predictions were God's way of keeping anyone else from claiming the Messianic title and simultaneously verified the reliability of Scripture.

"I have also concluded that if the story of Jesus' life, death, and resurrection was a fraud perpetrated by His followers, it would be highly unlikely that His disciples, who were fisherman, tax collectors... uneducated men all, willingly endured torture and martyrdom rather than deny their fraud. Few have courage enough to die for the truth. No sane person would die to protect a lie. By their martyrdom, the disciples provided the ultimate validation of Jesus' death and resurrection. Torture and the threat of death did not persuade them to deny the truth of Jesus' life, death, resurrection, and purpose."

I realized suddenly that I had stopped talking and begun pontificating. My audience and a few other customers sipping coffee nearby had no choice but to listen and nod. It was not my usual style. I suddenly felt self-conscious and a bit awkward.

"Sorry for the sermon," I offered defensively, "but TRUTH BE TOLD has forced me to examine my beliefs in ways I had not anticipated. I know the majority of Americans question the authority of the Bible and abandoning the Bible as archaic nonsense has become the politically correct perspective. But rejection of the truth by the masses doesn't make truth any less true. Their perspective does, however, require me to advocate for the truth on the basis of reason, logic, and common sense. I'm okay with that, but I think it would be counterproductive for TBT to start quoting Biblical references."

Everyone was quiet and attentive, listening politely to my comments. I regretted rambling so long in my answer, but no one seemed offended. Henry was the first to comment.

"Don't apologize. I put you on the spot. It helps to know where you're coming from, James. I assumed you were a Christian from the perspective of your articles, but I couldn't discern the depth of your conviction from what I read."

"No worries, Henry. I'm not ashamed of my faith and mentioned my nominal Christian status in the very first article. I'm actually glad you sensed a degree of ambivalence in my writing. Every respectable journalist wants to remain objective. We are not without opinions on most topics, but as reporters we try hard to set aside our opinions in search of truth. I appreciate this morning's opportunity to hear the group's perspective on the column. What topics do you think TBT should tackle in future columns?"

A man I assumed to be part of Sam's crew was the first to respond.

"We were just talking about that before you sat down. There are some obvious issues under debate by our friends and families. Sanctity of life: abortion and euthanasia for a start."

"Everyone is talking about immigration, but no one seems to agree on how to handle it, even as Christians," another man offered. "I, for one, feel obligated to help those fleeing the gang and drug violence of Mexico and Central America. Most are simply trying to provide a better future for their families. My grandparents crossed the border 50 years ago with a green card and a dream. They never went back. Their children and grandchildren have all been born in America. I'm torn between helping illegals and being a good citizen. I think a lot of people are."

Henry added, "The columns you wrote on racism were helpful. Thanks for throwing rocks at that hornet's nest. I shared your articles with quite a few friends. We rarely agree with each other. TRUTH BE TOLD provided a basis for our discussion, instead of rehashing the same worn out arguments." He smiled, "Like it or not, it's easier to argue over the opinion of a stranger than challenge the opinion of a friend or family member."

Everyone laughed and agreed with Henry's sentiment. It gave me pause. I hadn't thought about TBT that way. My primary motive was to challenge the political correctness of the media, the elites, and the people of influence in our culture. Fostering mutual respect and understanding among families and friends was perhaps a more noble achievement. I began to realize I didn't need to drive every stake underground in a perfectly crafted, reasonable, and unassailable essay. I just needed to advocate for the truth as I saw it while respecting the right of others to disagree. The outcome was out of my control. At best, I was a catalyst for discussions too many people have been avoiding too long for fear of offense.

I thanked everyone for their time and toleration of my intrusion. I excused myself, explaining my need to get back to my original mission of auto maintenance that was waiting across the street.

"Hold up, Jim," Sam interjected. "Let me walk with you."

"No need Sam, I don't want to take you away from your meeting."

"No worries brother, we are done here." He turned to his group. "Same time next week guys. I'll send the discussion guide with a reminder on Thursday."

Everyone thanked me for the time we shared and began pushing back and suiting up for the day's activities. I was impressed. Despite their blue-collar appearance and work attire, these guys were taking time every week to discuss some pretty weighty issues from an informed perspective. My prejudice was showing. Just because a person doesn't don a suit, tie, polished leather shoes, and spend their day in front of a computer or sitting in the conference room of an office building, doesn't mean they lack intelligence and concern for what's right.

Sam put one hand on my shoulder as he pushed the door open with the other. "Thanks again Jim for joining us and sharing your thoughts with the guys. You treated us with respect and listened to our suggestions. I was impressed."

"It was my pleasure to hear first-hand from your group Sam. What's up? Is there something more you wanted to discuss?"

"There are a few of us that are concerned for you Jim. You need to know you are not alone on your mission. We know you have a team of analysts, an editor, and a marketing staff at The Herald, but pleasing them is not your mission. You've been asked to advocate for truth and like others before you, that can get pretty lonely."

As Sam talked, I began taking the measure of him through his words
and body language. It seemed like an awkward conversation for a stranger
to have with the writer of a syndicated column he barely knew. I couldn't
help but wonder if he was more than the supervisor of a landscape crew,
turned snow-plow and home decorating team for the holiday season.

"When you say, 'a few of us are concerned,' what does that mean, Sam?
Who are the few?"

"That doesn't matter Jim. I just want you to know we have your back
and encourage you to be strong and courageous in your writing. That
was the advice God gave to Joshua after the death of Moses, and one of
my favorite Old Testament moments. God told Joshua to be strong and
courageous and not turn to the right or the left of all that God said and He
would have success in all his endeavors. It was the same advice King David
gave from his deathbed to his son Solomon. He told the young king the key
to ultimate success was to be strong, courageous, and faithful to the Lord. I
believe God wants me to share that message with you this morning."

"I appreciate the support, but how do you know what God wants for
me, Sam?"

Sam smiled and laughed softly, his hand resting again on my shoulder
as he answered. "I'm on a first name basis with the Lord, Jim. You should
know that. He's taken a keen interest in you and wanted me to remind you
in a tangible way that you are not alone. He's got your back. That's all. The
more your column gains attention, the harder it will be for you to speak
the truth without compromise. He knows that too. There is an important
truth found in Paul's first letter to the Corinthians that says, "Unless the
trumpeter blows a clear sound, how will the soldiers know to get ready for
battle?" [68]

"That's what you are for us Jim. You are the man God has chosen to
remind the faithful to honor God's truth. Paul was referring to an Old
Testament analogy when a trumpet was used to prepare people for battle.
He was reminding Christians to speak the truth plainly and boldly. Nothing
more but nothing less. Truth is enough."

The hair was beginning to stand up on the back of my neck. I wanted to walk back to the coffee shop and continue the conversation with Sam. He was obviously more than he let on to be, but just as I was about to challenge his status, his crew pulled alongside the curb and swung open a door. He climbed in and with a wave of his hand was gone.

George's words drifted back to me. "Do not neglect being hospitable to strangers for in so doing many have entertained angels without knowing it." [69] George said that passage was from somewhere in the Book of Hebrews. I made a mental note to memorize its location. It had become a routine experience in my life.

I replayed Sam's words in my mind. "You are not alone in your mission. I know you have a team of analysts, an editor, and a marketing staff at the paper, but pleasing them is not your mission."

I watched Sam and his crew disappear around the corner, thinking about our conversation until a man approached me from the sidewalk to ask if I was okay, or should he call someone to help? I was stunned by his comment. I must have looked more than a bit confused. It brought me back to the reality of my morning errand.

The assignment to write TRUTH BE TOLD was quickly becoming the most interesting and challenging of my career. Sam was right about one thing, "You've been asked to advocate for the truth and that can get pretty lonely."

No one but Sarah would believe me if I explained everything I just experienced. I'm not sure even George would accept the idea of frequent angelic visits or that God had decided to use the likes of me to be his spokesman.

I had a hard time believing it myself.

"No one is useless in this world who lightens the burdens of another."
—*Charles Dickens*

CHAPTER 13

Walking in Memphis

Only people who've never had to climb on and off airplanes for business envy those who do. Staying in fancy hotels, ordering whatever you want from room service only sounds glamorous until it becomes necessary. I've done my share of traveling for business and know better. Traveling for pleasure is different.

Sarah and I always enjoyed escaping the demands of our crazy schedule in search of adventures near or far. Getaways might have consisted of a day or two enjoying a city before or after a conference, but an escape did not always have to be work related. Our St. Louis location made quick trips to the Lake of the Ozarks, Chicago, or Nashville, very doable. And although we had often driven *through* Memphis on the way to New Orleans or the Gulf Coast, we'd never spent any time there site-seeing. We made plans to change that.

Ralph Waldo Emerson famously said, "It's not the destination that matters, it's the journey." That man knew what he was talking about. Road trips provided the needed space to reflect on the past, reexamine priorities and plan for the future. Breaks from the daily grind and family responsibilities have always been important. Now, after Sarah's retirement and my release from the demands of reporting, getting away for a few weeks seemed especially appropriate and entirely possible.

The phrase, "God draws straight with a crooked line." always rang true in my life. It didn't matter whether I was chasing down a breaking story or impatiently waiting for the good Lord to answer an unanswered prayer, the solution always came in unexpected ways and unexpected times. Some say God is never late but seldom early. I can attest to the wisdom of that perspective.

Whenever a radio listener asks the financial guru Dave Ramsey, "How are you doing today, Dave?" He immediately answers, "Better than I deserve." That's how Sarah and I felt driving south to Memphis. Undoubtedly, we worked hard at our respective jobs, probably harder than most. We sacrificed, saved, and lived within our means, but there is still the undeniable element of blessing that explains our financial stability more than anything we did to make it happen. There is a Scripture that says,

> "The fastest runner doesn't always win the race, and the strongest warrior doesn't always win the battle. The wise sometimes go hungry, and the skillful are not necessarily wealthy. And those who are educated don't always lead successful lives. The outcome is often determined by chance, by being in the right place at the right time." [70]

When our boys were small, road trips were musical adventures, thanks to the invention of the radio cassette player. Our grown sons still know the lyrics, from the Beatles to Bruce Springsteen, and the soundtracks from *Footloose* and *Flash Dance*. Under Sarah's influence, there were also a few Christian artists we began to listen to although mainstream Christianity had not yet made peace with guitars, drums, and keyboards. Our Christian musical influence was limited to Sandi Patty, Steve Green, Amy Grant, Rich Mullins, and Twila Paris.

The "means" has changed but not the "end." The creation of the internet has made streaming services like Pandora and Spotify possible. It's now feasible to livestream our favorite music from a cell phone while traveling down the interstate, obtaining GPS directions, while answering hand-free phone calls all from the same device simultaneously. Technology is amazing.

Not long after we headed out, Sarah announced, "Okay, we need to get in a Memphis state of mind. What should we listen to? I read a list of artists who recorded at Sun Studios in Memphis. You choose: Johnny Cash, Elvis, Carl Perkins, Roy Orbison, Jerry Lee Lewis or Charlie Rich."

"Since we have tickets to see the stage production of *The Million Dollar Quartet*, let's listen to the soundtrack from that," I suggested.

The show is based on the historic night of December 4, 1956, when, for various reasons, Jerry Lee Lewis, Carl Perkins, Elvis Presley and Johnny Cash all showed up at the Sun Records Studio in Memphis at the same time. A jam session ensued which was wisely recorded by the sound engineer on duty. He even had the presence of mind to take a picture of the moment, which was published in newspapers around the world. In the picture, Elvis is seated at the piano surrounded by Lewis, Perkins and Cash. The engineer secretly recorded 17 different tracks from the impromptu jam, mostly gospel songs like *The Old Rugged Cross*, but also *Blue Moon*, and Elvis' current 1956 hit, *Don't Be Cruel*.

While enjoying the music, we discussed the plan for our three days in Memphis. "I'm excited to stay at the Peabody Hotel," Sarah said. "Did you know Andrew Johnson and William McKinley stayed there? And Jefferson Davis actually lived there after the Civil War and worked for an insurance agency. And I really want to see the duck parade."

"Duck parade?" I asked.

"Every day at 11:00 AM five Mallard ducks make their way from their penthouse coupe, onto the elevator, down to the lobby and into the fountain. Apparently, the owner of the hotel in the 1930's started the tradition after a duck hunting excursion. I'm sure some bourbon was involved," Sarah said with a laugh.

I chuckled with her. "After we watch the ducks, we can spend the afternoon on Beale Street. We absolutely need to find B.B. King's Blues Club and have a drink there."

Our second day included plans to visit the National Civil Rights Museum at the Lorraine Hotel, the site of Dr. Martin Luther King Jr.'s assassination on April 4th, 1968. Dr. King came to the city in support of a sanitation workers' strike that grabbed the nation's attention in the heyday of the Civil Rights movement.

The struggle for equality by descendants of slaves depicted there, was in sharp contrast to the city's Rock and Roll legacy and the party-like atmosphere on Beale Street. Memphis is a city of contrasts and diversity. All of it worthy of the time and effort it takes to visit.

"How profound to tour a place of such importance in the history of our country and our people," I mused as we left the memorial and headed for the Mason Temple Church.

"Agreed. To walk in places where an event happened makes it so real. Even though it's decades past, it's still vital to define who we are as Americans. I wonder how much of this history is taught in schools today?" asked Sarah. "I'm sure they teach lessons on slavery and the Civil War, but the tenacity of the Civil Rights movement and the courage of those who led it is inspiring on so many levels. Reminding people to stand for right and oppose wrong has implications for every generation."

We stopped at the Mason Temple Church of God (now simply called Mason Temple Church) where Dr. King made his now famous Mountain Top Speech. The Civil rights leader was assassinated the next day on the balcony of his hotel room at the Lorraine.

As we explored the church, I felt myself recalling the unrest of those days and glimpsed the responsibility King shouldered for the cause of equality. I took Sarah's hand and said, "Listen to this. Did King have a sense of his own death? The words are haunting." In barely a whisper I read her the words King uttered mere hours before his assassination.

"Well, I don't know what will happen now. We've got some difficult days ahead. But it really doesn't matter with me now, because I've been to the mountaintop. And I don't mind. Like anybody, I would like to live – a long life; longevity has its place. But I'm not concerned about that now. I just want to do God's will. And He's allowed me to go up to the mountain. And I've looked over. And I've seen the Promised Land. I may not get there with you. But I want you to know tonight, that we, as a people, will get to the Promised Land. So I'm happy tonight. I'm not worried about anything. I'm not fearing any man. Mine eyes have seen the glory of the coming of the Lord."

"Wow," Sarah sighed. "Makes me wonder how different things might be today if he had lived. One person can change history. It makes me wonder what difference your efforts writing TRUTH BE TOLD might make." She squeezed my hand.

"You're biased." I smiled and kissed her cheek. "What's next on the agenda?"

"We can't come to Memphis and not eat at Gus' Fried Chicken Diner," Sarah replied.

It seemed fitting to stop for a late lunch at the world-renown Gus' Diner on Front Street just two blocks south of Beale. We've had the pleasure of eating at many of the famous barbeque joints in St. Louis, Kansas City and Texas, and Gus' reminded me of those. It is not the uniqueness of the food that first captures my attention at places like that, but rather the integration of race, social status and the age of the patrons that gather in such well-known diners. The inclusive nature of the cultural heritage and social status of the patrons eating side by side always surprises me but seems so right. It is the living embodiment of Dr. King's dream of a better future when people would be judged for the quality of their character, not the color of their skin. Men in three-piece suits conduct business at simple tables next to workmen in coveralls. Black, White, Asian, Latino and people of all ages wait in line side-by-side, relaxed and eager to enjoy some "funky-fried" chicken.

Our experience in Memphis reinforced the truth that people are just people when it comes to our shared history, love of music, foods, and traditions. We may look different, come from different backgrounds, different zip codes, and different life experiences, but the human condition shares more in common than not. Gus' was only the tip of the iceberg when it came to culinary opportunity in Memphis. Sarah and I couldn't wait to explore a few of the world-famous Barbeque hot spots Memphis is so well known for. Diets be damned!

That night we listened to a live performance of Marc Cohn's song, *Walking in Memphis* as we drank a glass of wine in the Rum Boogie Café. Everyone in the restaurant knew the lyrics and sang along. *Walking in Memphis* has become for the city what Billy Joel's, *New York State of Mind* and Sinatra's *New York, New York,* has become for Manhattan. It was especially significant for Sarah and me since we had reservations to visit Graceland the next day.

In the song, Chon describes seeing the ghost of Elvis on the grounds of Graceland as he passed by the tourist and guards keeping watch. Everyone was too busy hovering around the King of Rock and Roll's nearby grave to notice. Elvis, according to the song, had more pressing business with a pretty young thing waiting for him in the famous Jungle Room.

The song captures the wonder and exhilaration of music fans like us who walk the streets of Memphis, impressed by the history and greatness of the legends who walked and played in the bars and jazz joints of Beale Street. The singer is so high on life from his personal pilgrimage to that sacred street, he finds it impossible to believe anyone can feel the power of the moment the way he feels it.

Graceland was fascinating for many reasons. Certainly the many display rooms garages and buildings containing Elvis' gold records, costumes, awards, classic car collection, motorcycles, even his personal airplanes, Priscilla's wedding dress and Elvis' wedding tuxedo were interesting enough, but I was more intrigued by the house itself and its eclectic furnishings.

"Now here's a rehab project," I commented as we entered the kitchen. "Harvest gold appliances haven't been in style for decades. If you put those things on the curb with a sign that says 'Free!' I'm pretty sure they would remain unclaimed for the rest of the week."

Sarah laughed. "I can remember when our house also featured a microwave sitting on a Formica countertop, although I doubt we would have ever installed green and purple carpet in our kitchen."

I had to suppress a chuckle when we entered the famous Jungle Room in the lower level of the mansion. How it achieved legendary status as a den of iniquity is beyond my comprehension. There were *"Do Not Touch,"* signs everywhere but they seemed unnecessary. If it were not for the room's historic connection to the King of Rock and Roll few would dare to even enter the room, let alone touch anything. It made me question the romantic reputation attributed to the space. I could only presume its status was achieved by the over consumption of alcohol and poor lighting. The walls, like the kitchen, were covered in wood paneling, except the brick waterfall that was described in the brochure as a maintenance nightmare ever since its construction. A hideous green shag, that a plaque said was installed to muffle sound for the benefit of private recording sessions, covered both the floor and the ceiling. A massive wooden and faux-fur couch was surrounded by an eclectic array of equally massive accent furniture and chairs. The end tables and a cumbersome wet bar were constructed of sawn tree trunks covered in thick lacquer.

At the end of the tour, Sarah and I were left in a contemplative mood. I mused, "It's hard to reconcile all this. Elvis sold 2.5 billion records and had 32 recordings that reached number one. People like Elton John are effusive in praise for him. Even the Smithsonian called him 'the greatest entertainer of the 20th century.' He had money and influence that allowed him any luxury and access to the latest technology. Still, happiness and contentment escaped his grasp."

Sarah agreed, "Such a sad story. He died alone at the age of 42, the victim of his own excess. There seems to be a fine line between success and insanity."

"It reminds me of a passage from my devotion the other day. Even ages ago, Solomon understood the tender balance required for a contented life."

"O God, I beg two favors from you;
let me have them before I die.
First, help me never to tell a lie.
Second, give me neither poverty nor riches!
Give me just enough to satisfy my needs.
For if I grow rich, I may deny you and say, "Who is the LORD?"
And if I am too poor, I may steal and thus insult God's holy name." [71]

"Give me neither poverty nor riches. Give me just enough to satisfy my needs." The writings of Solomon are called "Wisdom Literature" for a reason. There is nothing overtly wrong with ambition, success, and wealth, but they hold enormous potential to create substantial problems in a person's life. Sarah and I were blessed to have come from blue-collar families. Her dad was a mail carrier and my father worked on the assembly line at International Harvester. Neither of us could be accused of being raised by affluent families, but we always had enough.

When the time came to make our own way, we had to work for it, including college. We got the best paying jobs we could find during the summer and worked additional jobs while attending classes during the school term. Odd jobs posted on the university bulletin boards and the donation of plasma at the blood bank provided spending money for dates and fast food. Looking back, we never thought of ourselves as deprived. We grew up knowing that if we wanted something, we were going to have to work for it.

I don't recall envying those who received their tuition money and a healthy allowance from home every month. Good for them. I never felt lesser for it. As they say, a $10 watch tells time just as effectively as one costing $100, and an army surplus coat kept me just as warm (and looking a whole lot cooler) than a London Fog overcoat for ten times the money. We learned early-on to manage our expectations.

We were struggling to pay rent for an apartment, save money for our first house, keep our ten-year-old car running, and make ends meet while raising our children. Our sons were in no danger of being spoiled, simply because we lacked the means to accomplish it. We watched wealthy friends struggle to know how much was too much when it came to helping their children. I have always believed it must be harder to raise children when you have the means to solve their financial struggles. We learned blessings are not limited to good times and extravagance. We came to appreciate the advantage of struggle and hard work.

Sarah selected a contemporary Christian radio stream on Pandora as we made our way south from Memphis, headed toward the Gulf Coast. Christian music has come a long way since pipe organs were designated the only instrument worthy of sacred music. I'm not as devoted to Christian music as Sarah, but I have to admit JOY.FM in St. Louis now occupies one of the preset buttons on my truck radio.

Looking back, the story of Bart Millard, portrayed in the movie, *I Can Only Imagine,* was probably the turning point for me. His story is both painful and compelling. Bart's parents divorced when he was three years old. His mom remarried a couple of times and moved to another city, 6 hours away. His parents thought it was best to leave their sons together to be raised by their father. Bart's dad, who had been loving and kind early in his life, suffered a brain injury that caused him to become mean and abusive, especially towards Bart. He once beat him so badly, his father, out of remorse and fear, sent him away to live with his mother for Bart's own safety.

The two were reconciled when his dad was diagnosed with inoperable cancer during Bart's high-school years. Bart moved back to become his father's chief caregiver. By then his dad had found peace in what proved to be a sincere and deep conversion of faith. It took time, but Bart slowly realized his father had fundamentally changed.

Bart wrote the song *I Can Only Imagine* as a tribute to the peace his dad found before his death through faith in Jesus. The song crossed over musical genres to become a mainstream hit achieving Top 40 status on the Adult Contemporary pop charts, Country music's Top 40, and was named Christian song of the year, selling over 3 million recordings worldwide.

Bart and his band *Mercy Me* soon became more than a one hit wonder.

All of their music, written mostly by Bart, has that same kind of transparent honesty to it. Sarah convinced me to attend a *Mercy Me* concert just as the movie, *I Can Only Imagine* was hitting the theatres. The words and stories behind songs like, *Dear Younger Me, Even If.., Beautiful,* and *Shake* convinced me this guy was for real.

It didn't surprise me that Sarah's playlist was heavy on *Mercy Me* songs as we made our way out of Memphis towards Gulf Shores, Alabama. One of the songs that popped up on the playlist was called, *Happy Dance*. It's a call to stop and smell the roses, celebrating all that is good in life. I hadn't heard it before, but the lyrics struck me as an appropriate expression of the gratitude we were feeling as we headed toward the Gulf Coast.

I often say, "Life is hard even when life is good, and life isn't always good." No one is spared difficulty. Even mega-stars like Elvis face struggles and problems that can rob them of their happiness. Our visit to Graceland was a reminder that a person's attitude toward their circumstance is more important to achieving and maintaining a joyful life than their actual circumstance.

We were blessed, but the greater blessing is to realize just how blessed we were.

*"Learning is not attained by chance, it must be sought
for with ardor and attended to with diligence."*

—*Abigail Adams*

CHAPTER 14

Extending a Hand

Sarah's research in preparation for our vacation had definitely been worth the effort. The condo was perfect. It offered easy access to the beach, a clean gym with modern workout equipment, indoor and outdoor pools with access to two excellent golf courses. The view from our 10th floor unit was stunning. If it were not for the congested elevators and the party crowd, I could get used to Gulf coast living.

It was a two bedroom, two-bath condo with a nice-sized balcony off the master, perfect for early morning reading. The guest room was arranged as a combination office and bedroom. It checked all the boxes.

I'm observant by nature. When you spend your entire professional life as a beat reporter, it goes with the territory. It's not the kind of thing you can turn on and off. I'm not sure which came first. Did my inquisitive nature lead to my career choice, or did my career choice cause my inquisitive nature? Whether enjoying dinner in an upscale restaurant, playing golf with strangers, or sitting on the beach, curiosity always got the best of me. People's choices fascinate me: the clothes they wear, how they wear them, the degree of eye contact, the words they choose, and the effort to focus on themselves or others. As empty nesters recently retired, I enjoyed getting reacquainted with the intricacies of Sarah's nature. It was like dating again. After a lifetime of work and family distractions, we were both enjoying the opportunity to spend more time alone. The combination of Sarah's interests and priorities was what attracted and distinguished her to me from the beginning.

She was frugal by nature. No doubt, her modest upbringing played a role, but it was more than that. I've watched others from similar backgrounds embrace extravagance after achieving a degree of personal success. Not Sarah. She still loved to shop bargains, and although she sometimes shopped in upscale stores, she only bought items from their sale racks and bragged about the deals she found. She was just as happy shopping in discount stores, or even secondhand shops and wasn't embarrassed to admit it. She considered shopping for a needed item or an upcoming birthday an adventure, and the amount of savings she achieved often determined the measure of her success.

Sarah had no desire to drive a fancy car. We bought our first car together in college before we were even married. It was a four-year-old 1969 Chevy Malibu which we proceeded to drive into the ground for the next 5 years. We had racked up more than 200,000 miles when we sold it to purchase another preowned model. I actually saved the emblem off the grill as a reminder of how blessed we were by that car. The salt from winter roads had completely rusted out the floorboards before we parted ways. I screwed plywood panels to the floors to keep water from splashing on our feet when we drove in the rain. We never went anywhere without jumper cables. Our financial standing has improved substantially since then, but Sarah still prefers to buy a secondhand reliable car rather than suffer the new car depreciation. She likes a bargain.

She had the same attitude when it came to buying a house. As a real estate agent, she had access to the latest listings and watched them closely. It became a hobby and investment strategy for us. We would buy a fixer-upper, spend a couple of years making it the best house in the neighborhood, then sell it at a profit and start over. Sarah had an eye for design and over time, effort, trial and error, I developed better than average rehab skills. Not every wife would be willing to live on subfloors without a kitchen or a master bathroom for months, but it was something we could do together. We endured more than our share of good-natured ridicule from our friends, but it was an effective way to improve our financial status and supplement our retirement savings.

But what I especially enjoyed and observed in Sarah over the years was her compassion towards those who were financially less fortunate. She was a one-person social relief agency. Her parents were strong Christians who walked the talk when it came to helping the less fortunate. They were also tithers. I can still hear her father say, "Giving doesn't start, until you give your tithe. That doesn't belong to you anyway. It belongs to the Lord. After you give your tithe, the rest is yours to manage." The bumper sticker on his Ford Pinto said, "Tithe if you love Jesus. Anyone can honk."

I don't pretend to be that kind of Christian, but I didn't object to the concept of tithing, and have become convinced of its merits. We never were, see-you-in-church every Sunday Christians, but Sarah honored her father in designating ten percent of our income to charitable causes. She was careful about where our money went and what agencies we chose to support. She believed it was possible to actually harm those you tried to help by rewarding bad attitudes and making it profitable to be irresponsible. She took time to research the best ways to support the less fortunate. I trusted her judgment completely. We only worked closely with organizations that provided short-term assistance while counseling and training people to become self-sufficient. We subscribed to the principle of providing a hand up, not a handout.

We got involved with Habitat for Humanity about ten years ago, working alongside low income families to help them acquire decent housing. For an entire year, we worked with friends and like-minded strangers assisting a resident from a neglected neighborhood reopen an abandoned restaurant and quick-stop grocery store. There had not been an active store of any kind in that neighborhood for years. Others took notice.

A year after she opened her businesses, three more stores followed. That upstart shopping district is helping reestablish a viable neighborhood in a long-neglected part of the city. It was accomplished through the hard work and support of the greater community without government assistance. We still drive there from time to time for lunch and are grateful to have been a part of something important.

Along the way, we've learned contributing to worthwhile projects is more rewarding than merely adding dollars to our portfolio and stockpiling personal assets. I remember a passage my father-in-law loved to quote, a prayer of King David in the Old Testament.

"Deliver me, O Lord, from the men of this world,
whose portion is in this life only,
Who fill their bellies with Your treasure.
They are satisfied with children,
And desire to leave their abundance to their offspring.
But as for me, I shall not be satisfied until I behold Your face in
righteousness; When I see you face to face." [72]

Sarah was her father's daughter for sure.

But the attitude I most admire in Sarah is the way she conducts what I call, her one-on-one relief efforts. It's not always true, but often those working minimum-wage jobs at fast food joints or running the checkout counter at the local grocery are struggling to make ends meet. Some are immigrants, learning English as a second language; others are inner city moms and teenagers trying to better themselves and their families. Sarah pays attention and makes an effort to get acquainted. She asks innocent questions about the length of their shift, if they are required to work on an upcoming holiday, if they are in school or have a family of their own. More than once, I've watched them tear-up when she hands them an unexpected tip or walks around the counter and sticks a couple of twenties into their pocket or apron. Who tips check-out people?

Her one-on-one relief efforts are not limited to employees doing menial jobs. I've watched Sarah engage in conversations with fellow shoppers waiting to make a purchase in a check-out line. She notices those who are closely comparing the costs of their items to their cash on hand. Sometimes, to their surprise, she ends up paying for their entire purchase.

I once saw her strike up a conversation with a Hispanic man purchasing children's clothes just before Christmas. After a brief exchange, Sarah learned he was leaving later that day to drive from St. Louis to Mexico to celebrate Christmas with his family. He was working in the states to provide for their financial support. Before leaving he was purchasing a few last-minute gifts to brighten their celebration. By the look of his clothes and the way he was calculating the price of his items, he had little money to spare. Before he made the payment, Sarah covered the cost of his purchases and wished him, "Feliz Navidad." She considers helping strangers who are struggling financially her contribution to foreign relations and immigrant resettlement.

Helping through charitable organizations is important but helping people face-to-face in unexpected ways closes the gap between the haves and the have-nots in a personal and more powerful way. Sarah rarely gives money to people begging at an intersection or in front of a store. She prefers to help those trying to make it on their own. She calls it, "An expression of admiration and an encouragement of a healthy work ethic." Often, and to my frustration, she enters the longest check-out line, to maintain an ongoing conversation and get better acquainted with a particular checker, their family or life challenges. I've told her more than once, "If I wasn't your husband and knew what you are doing, I would accuse you of holding up the line!" I'm never surprised, when driving through a fast food check-out near our home, to hear one of the employees hand me my order and say, "Tell Ms. Sarah I said, 'Hi.'"

Our condo was less than ten miles south of Interstate #10, which runs 2,500 miles from Jacksonville, Florida, to Santa Monica, California, literally from sea to shining sea. For good reason they call it the homeless highway. It's not the only cross-continental interstate, but it is the only one that runs entirely along the southern border and rarely if ever experiences freezing temperatures. Sarah knew what to expect and had prepared two banker boxes full of what she calls, "Blessing Bags" which she intended to hand out to the homeless she anticipated encountering near our condo.

I shook my head and smiled as I watched her prepare for that aspect of our vacation. It was a natural extension of her desire to encourage and assist the less fortunate. She had given thought to each item she included in the gallon-size zip lock bags. Each bag contained three specific forms of assistance.

- Toiletries: Toothbrush/toothpaste, a bar of soap, a small bottle of shampoo, sunscreen, chap stick, band-aides, baby wipes, a washcloth and deodorant.

- Food items: Granola bars, trail mix, a fruit cup, a pack of gum, a candy bar that would not easily melt, a bag of peanuts, and a bottle of water.

- Realizing she could not anticipate all their needs, she included a $10 gift card to McDonald's, a mini-bag with 12 quarters for laundry, and a $5 bill, which she made sure was clearly visible from outside the plastic bag.

She told me the cost of each bag was slightly less than $25. She had prepared 40 of them in advance of our trip, for a grand total of $1,000. The condo rental was more than three times that amount, so to Sarah it seemed a reasonable contribution to help make the world a better place, one person at a time. She added, with a wink and a smile, not to worry if we ran out she had brought extra bags we could fill later. That wasn't my concern, but I think she already knew that. The note she included in each bag was equally important to her. It simply stated:

> *You are a child of God. You matter to Him and to your brothers and sisters in Christ. I hope this act of kindness reminds you of His love and encourages you today.*
>
> *Life knocks everyone down from time to time. I'm praying for your*

situation and the courage and effort it will take to achieve a better future.

God bless you.

The back of the card contained the Serenity Prayer, famously used by organizations that assist those trapped in various addictive behaviors. The connection between homelessness, drugs and alcohol has been well established. Although not true in every case, it is a major factor in the majority of situations.

THE SERENITY PRAYER

God grant me the serenity to accept the things I cannot change;
courage to change the things I can; and wisdom to know the difference.
Living one day at a time; Enjoying one moment at a time;
Accepting hardships as the pathway to peace;
Taking, as He did, this sinful world as it is, not as I would have it;
Trusting that He will make all things right if I surrender to His Will;
That I may be reasonably happy in this life and supremely happy with Him
forever in the next. Amen.

The bags were always well received. We didn't go out of our way to distribute them but didn't need to. On average, we pass out one or two of the Blessing Bags a day, sometimes two at a time. I'm sure everything they contained was appreciated, but the visible $5 bill and the McDonald's gift card always caught the attention of the recipient, often causing tears of appreciation. It struck me how little it takes to be considered generous by those who have nothing. Looking back on all that we did and enjoyed during our time away, the conversations and assistance we provided to complete strangers was the highlight of our vacation.

For Sarah, an important aspect of alleviating poverty was to avoid making people feel inferior. She contends providing money without encouragement and an effort to make a personal connection only reinforces their victim status and discourages personal initiative. She considers the personal connection the essential element that distinguishes a hand-up from a hand-out. She boiled it down to what she called the "Three R's of Assistance": Relief, Rahab, and Renewal.

Relief needs to be immediate. In the midst of a crisis, an immediate response is crucial. But, to Sarah's way of thinking, it must always be temporary, provided only as long as a person is unable to help themselves, and no longer. In St. Louis the cards she places in the Blessing Bags contain the phone numbers and addresses of agencies she trusts to help the down and out get back on their feet, secure housing, get a job, or obtain substance abuse counseling.

The second step towards recovery, "rehabilitation," should be offered immediately after providing relief. According to Sarah, the most successful interventions provide both. It is important whenever possible to connect people to agencies and organizations that can address the principle cause of their poverty. It takes time and effort to help people identify the root cause, but it's a necessary step in the rescue equation. The organizations Sarah selected to receive our financial support always connected the recipients to support groups that walked through the recovery process with those seeking help. That made sense to me.

For good reason they say, "A burden shared is a burden eased." Those who feel alone in their struggle can be easily overwhelmed. It diminishes a person's sense of isolation when they are supported by those who've overcome similar situations. When a victim of poverty is able to talk openly about past mistakes and bad choices in a safe setting, it removes their sense of shame and hopelessness. Regaining self-respect is a crucial part of their recovery.

The ultimate goal is the final step Sarah calls, "Renewal." When the impoverished are able to provide their own shelter and obtain work to support themselves and their families the healing process is achieved. It may not be their ultimate destination, but it's the launching pad to a better future. As patrons of helping agencies, we have been privileged to witness the testimonies of those who have overcome the streets and become self-sufficient. It is possible, "with a little help from a friend." Few things are more gratifying than making a positive difference in the life of another human being.

The most rewarding aspect of intervention is to see the effect it has on those who break the grip of poverty. They are transformed from victims to victors in ways that pay dividends in their future. Many stay connected to the agency that helped them and assist in rescuing others. They naturally want to give back to those who rescued them from the streets.

I credit Sarah for opening my eyes to helping others in personal ways, not only for the sake of the needy, but also to our benefit. It keeps us grateful, humble, and measured. I understand now why Sarah has no need for the best and latest in fashion, cars, and homes. Helping the less fortunate tempers the desire to compete with our friends and neighbors for status and material prosperity. Compared to the majority of the world, we are rich beyond measure.

We recently attended a dinner to raise awareness and support for the homeless and impoverished. In the center of each table there was a cardboard tent used to hold envelopes and pledge cards. It included a Scripture verse from 1 Timothy, chapter six.

"Teach those who are rich in this world not to be proud nor place their trust in money, which is so unreliable. Their trust should be in God, who richly gives us all we need for our enjoyment. Tell them to use their money to do good. They should be rich in good works and generous to those in need, always being ready to share with others. By doing this they will be storing up their treasure as a good foundation for the future so that they may experience life that is true life." [73]

I brought one of those cards home and placed it on the shelf behind my desk to serve as a constant reminder. Christian or not, the truth of that passage is hard to deny.

To be engaged in a cause and a mission greater than yourself keeps a person grounded. Our sense of personal importance was never enhanced by the acquisition of a new car, a better house or a winning golf score, nor was it diminished when we retired from our respective jobs. Those are not bad things and are perfectly worthy achievements but are not the most important nor the most satisfying accomplishments of anyone's life. The possession of things and the achievement of goals is not the ultimate purpose of life. There will always be others who own nicer things, achieve more, and receive greater recognition.

To recognize your blessings have been graciously given to achieve a purpose greater than yourself and to use those blessings to help others is the secret to a satisfying and fulfilling life... a "true life" the Bible calls it.

It really doesn't matter if you are rich or poor by the world's standards; everyone has equal opportunity to extend a hand to someone less fortunate. Some of the most generous people I have met, were neither wealthy nor influential. They were simply willing to share what they had with those who had less.

The advice Paul gave to Timothy bears repeating, "Tell them, by doing this they will be storing up their treasure as a good foundation for the future so that they may experience life that is true life." [74]

The Gratitude Factor

By: **James King**

Will Rogers famously said, *"There are three types of men. Those who learn by reading, those who learn by observation, and the vast majority who have to pee on an electric fence for themselves."* The key to *lifelong* happiness is a lesson best learned through experience, a lesson better caught than taught.

Most people presume happiness is achieved through circumstance, a healthy combination of money, significance, good health, and accomplishment. To a certain degree they are right, but happiness dependent upon *fleeting* conditions is, by definition, *fleeting*... here today and gone tomorrow.

The key to *lifelong* happiness has little to do with wealth, power, fame, health, or personal accomplishments. *The key to a happy and rewarding life is perspective, not acquisition or accomplishment.* Happiness is attained through a mindset of gratitude accompanied by contentment. I have known underprivileged people, suffering from poor health, undaunted by their struggle. Despite the difficulty of their circumstance, they embraced their future with contentment and optimism. Conversely, I've known wealthy people of good reputation and excellent health who wouldn't recognize happiness if it moved next door.

Happiness in life is in reach of all people. It's reserved for neither the poor nor the wealthy. Good health and financial security are advantageous, but they are no guarantee of happiness. Developing and maintaining an attitude of gratitude has more to do with happiness than the circumstance of a person's life.

Those who measure their

value through achievement and acquisition, find it harder to embrace a grateful mindset. It is difficult if not impossible to "feel grateful" for something you believe you've worked hard to accomplish. It seems illogical for successful people to credit God's blessing and good fortune for the accomplishments they have sacrificed and risked so much to achieve. Success, in their way of thinking, is no mystery. It has been hard won.

What factors contribute to an attitude of gratitude, and why is it the key to long-term happiness?

- Those raised in modest conditions are typically more aware and appreciative of their good fortune. Growing up poor provides a point of reference by which every future success can be compared.
- Those raised in privileged homes but expected to work in their youth are more likely to embrace gratitude than those who were raised in privilege with few or no expectations placed on them as a child.
- Those who volunteer to assist the less fortunate are also more likely to be grateful than those who don't. People with limited exposure to poverty have a tendency to compare themselves to those with greater rather than lesser resources than themselves.
- Those who place greater value

on love, relationships, and service to others, than on materialistic achievements, are also more likely to remain grateful for their good fortune.
- And finally, those whose friends demonstrate a balanced perspective on wealth and generosity are also more likely to maintain a grateful spirit.

Why is GRATITUDE so central to maintaining a healthy attitude in life? Its value can be demonstrated through a syllogism. A syllogism is a logical progression of thought that applies deductive reasoning to reach a conclusion established on two or more accepted truths. The Greek philosopher Aristotle first demonstrated the principle through a simple illustration.

- Knowing that all men are mortal.
- And knowing that Socrates is a man.
- We can validly conclude that Socrates is mortal.

The same principle can be used to demonstrate the power of gratitude in a person's life. Consider:

- Grateful people are by definition, more mindful of their good fortune.
- People mindful of their good fortune focus more on blessings than struggles.
- People who focus on blessings are more optimistic.
- Optimistic people are more courageous, expecting good

outcomes
- Courageous people are willing to risk more and attempt more in life.
- People who attempt more in life, achieve more.
- People who achieve more, enjoy greater blessings.
- Greater blessings lead to increased gratitude, which starts the cycle all over again.

Before the drug cartels made travel to Mexican border towns so dangerous, a Christian organization in our community made several trips there each year to build homes for the poorest of the poor. Our sons and their friends joined a number of those trips, eager to be part of something significant and to participate in the adventure of traveling to another country.

Young people are eager to engage with leaders and organizations that do more than just talk. They want to be involved in ways that make a difference in things that matter. The housing projects in Mexico checked all the boxes. Through their efforts, the organization provided a safe, dry, and debt-free home to people (even entire families) who were living in makeshift shelters of cardboard and plastic. The experience also taught young volunteers the importance of compassion, cooperation, and hard work.

The group leaders understood the significance of protecting the dignity of the families they chose

to help. They went out of their way to establish relationships, sharing meals with those who were chosen to_receive assistance. The children of the designated family and their friends were engaged by members of the crew who brought games to occupy them while the rest of the team constructed the new home with the assistance of local volunteers. At the completion of each home, the new owner was presented a Bible, a cross for their wall and the key to their new house. As a contributor to the cause, I've seen pictures of the recipients overwhelmed with gratitude, tears streaming down their faces, standing before their new one-room house.

That would be impressive enough, but more significant to me was the effect the housing projects had on the young volunteers, like our sons.

I remember one student named Laura who participated in several of those mission trips. Tragically, Laura died in a car accident a few months before graduating from high school. We attended her memorial with hundreds of her friends and family. During the service, Laura's mom shared an essay her daughter had written after her most recent mission trip. She wanted to share Laura's perspective with her high-school friends.

"My motives," Laura wrote, "for going to Mexico were pretty much the same as every other teenager along for the adventure. It provided a nice break from our summer routines. We were going to do some cool stuff on the way down and back too. But mostly, I wanted to hang out with some of my friends away from home.

We had been told the work would be hard and hot. I was prepared for that. I was also prepared to feel badly for the kids and the family we were going to help. We live in West St. Louis County, one of the nicest areas in the city. We have so much and they have so little. We were going to build a one-room house for them in a week. I couldn't imagine living like that. An entire family sleeping in one room. How could it get worse than that?

But the people we met in Mexico surprised me by how happy they were. They had so much less than the poorest Americans who came to help them. But they didn't complain. They worked hard for what little they had. They loved to sing as they worked. Their children also seemed happy, laughing and playing with sticks and an old soccer ball. Everything was special to them, even the peanut butter and jelly sandwiches we made for everyone. When we presented the keys to their home, a Spanish Bible and a cross to hang on their wall, the family was so thankful they cried and hugged us all. I have never been happier in my life.

I went to Mexico expecting to feel sorry for the people there. We had so much and they had so little. *But on my way home, I began to feel sorry for the kids growing up in West County. They never seemed happy with what they had and always wanted more. I have heard people say money doesn't make people happy, but I always thought they were lying. Now I know it is true. What makes a person happy is to be thankful for what you have, to love and be loved by others, and to act on your faith... not just worship on Sunday mornings and pray at bedtime and before your meals. I don't think I will ever be the same."*

Laura went to Mexico with the same expectations and values held by most American teenagers. She came back a changed person.

I asked her mom for a copy of the essay and even after twenty years, was able to easily locate it for this article. I'll never forget Laura or the profound insight she left as her legacy. I wonder if the teenagers who attended her memorial still remember her and the lesson she taught us? I hope so.

Gratitude for the blessings we enjoy, the love of family and friends, and the opportunity to do something important in life is the winning formula for happiness.

It's a game changer. ▪

St. Louis Herald

TRUTH BE TOLD   Edition 1, Column 14

The Haves and The Have Nots

By: **James King**

When you pick up a carry out order, do you tip the cashier?

For many years I never did. I considered a tip payment for service, and since I wasn't being served by a waiter, a tip wasn't justified. I have changed my mind on the subject.

One night I picked up a $10 pizza from a store near our home and while waiting watched the frantic pace of the people taking orders, making pies, cooking, slicing, boxing and serving customers who were not so patiently waiting for their pizza. I couldn't help but wonder how they kept their store open, paid their employees, and make pizzas for just $10? I concluded, to stay competitive, the company was probably paying their staff only the minimum wage required by law.

The man waiting on me was no kid. From what I could tell, most of the crew was closer to forty than twenty. Younger employees ran in to grab an insulated bag with a hot pie and delivery tag before rushing back to daddy's car to make their next delivery. No doubt, most of the carriers expected and received tips, but what about the people in the store working the assembly line? I added a $5 tip to my $10 bill. My theory of tipping no longer has anything to do with service; it's about gratitude, encouragement, and social justice.

It's time for THE HAVES to step up and step in to provide encouragement, support, and tangible expressions of concern for the HAVE NOTS. We've grown accustomed to maintaining our distance from one another.

THE HAVES often donate money and resources to their favorite charities, churches, temples, and social agencies rather than taking the time and making the effort to connect face-to-face with the HAVE NOTS. We justify our action as a more effective, better vetted, and better organized approach to provide help. But in doing so we fail to meet the greater need for one-on-one, heartfelt expressions of concern. The degree of support may be the same but the relational connection is not. The essential therapeutic benefit of one person helping another is lost by both the HAVES and the HAVE NOTS when it is achieved from a distance.

I encourage everyone to make an effort to get to know the names of the people who take your order at your favorite fast food stop, the cashier at your grocery, or local hardware store. Do business with the same cashier if possible to get to know them as individuals, even if their check-out line is longer. Do they live in your area, is this a second job for them, are they providing for a family, are they headed off to school, how many hours a week do they work?

Instead of trying to figure out the least amount of money you can spend at McDonalds, surprise the cashier with a tip. The seventy-year-old serving you breakfast or making change for your donuts at the local Quick Stop isn't standing on her feet all day because she's bored and doesn't like to sleep late. More than likely she's working to supplement her social security check and pay the rent.

How rich are you?

The answer to that question depends on how you define "rich," and who you compare yourself to. The average wage of a fulltime employee in America was $936/week in January, 2020. Men on average still make more than women, $53,444 annually compared to $43,836. Those lacking a high school diploma struggle the most, earning $30,992 compared to those with a high school diploma who pull down $38,844 on average. (PSA: These are the people who typically bring your food to the counter or check out your groceries.) The college-educated employee makes almost twice as much, earning on average $71,864 annually. Black people make less than whites and Hispanics average less than African Americans $39,312 annually compared to $37,024.

The Beatles said they didn't care a lot about money because money couldn't buy them love. It was an easy song for them to sing. They had plenty. I lean more towards the philosophy of the country singer Chris Janson's hit song on the subject called, *Buy Me a Boat*.

It's a fun song and an honest song too. The singer claims he is not rich but he'd like to be. He admits to envying those on the receiving end of large inheritances, or those who have bank accounts the size of Warren Buffet's.

He won't argue with those who say money can't buy a person happiness and love. He's a reasonable man, more than willing to manage his expectations. It may be true that money can't buy a person happiness, but it can buy a new boat and a shiny new truck to haul it to the water, he sings.

You get the feeling, the singer would be happy with that.

John Rockefeller, one of the world's all-time wealthiest people, a billionaire at the turn of the *last century*, was once asked, "How much is enough?" His answer speaks for most of us. "Just a little bit more." He is not alone.

No matter how much we make or what socio-economic level we occupy, most people say they would be perfectly satisfied if they just made about 10% more than they earn now. An employee making $40,000 believes he would have enough if he just made $45k. A college grad making $100k believes he would be perfectly satisfied if he just earned $10k more. It never works out that way. You can't outrun human nature. If you can't live on the money you make now, you will not be able to live within your means making 10% more, not for long. You will always want, "Just a little bit more." Different level, different devil, as they say.

The subject of money has captured the imagination of our greatest philosophers.

- Steve Martin – "I love money. I love everything about it. I bought some pretty good stuff. Got me a $300 pair of socks. Got a fur sink. An electric dog polisher. A gasoline powered turtleneck sweater. And of course, I bought some dumb stuff too."
- Will Rogers – "Too many people spend the money they earn to buy things they don't need to impress people they don't like."
- Benjamin Franklin – "Money never made a man happy yet, nor will it. The more he has, the more he wants. Instead of filling a vacuum, it makes one."
- Ralph Waldo Emerson – "Money often costs too much."

A friend once told me Jesus spoke more about money than he did on any other subject. That seemed odd to me at first, but it made perfect sense after I checked it out. He said,

"Where your treasure is your heart will be also... The eye is the lamp of the body. If your eyes are healthy, your whole body will be full of light. But if your eyes are unhealthy, your whole body will be full of darkness. If then the light within you is darkness, how great is that darkness! No one can serve two masters. Either you will hate the one and love the other, or you will be devoted to the one and despise the other. You cannot serve both God and money." [75]

Jesus' analogy makes sense. What

you *perceive* as important (the things that capture your eye), will determine your life's perspective. If your focus is right, your life will be full of light. If your focus is wrong, your life will be a dismal affair.

Apparently, God is not anti-money or even anti-rich people. Some of the great heroes of the Old Testament had more than their share of money. Abraham, Jacob, Judah, Job, David and Solomon were some of the richest people of their era. God may not be anti-money but He is very concerned about the destructive potential of money in the lives of those he loves.

Everyone has heard the Scripture, *"The love of money is the root of all evil."* [76] Notice, money is not the problem, it's *the love of money* that leads to all the trouble. Lots of good can be done with money. The same chapter that contains the warning about loving money too much continues by saying,

"Command those who are rich in this present world not to be arrogant nor to put their hope in wealth, which is so uncertain, but to put their hope in God, who richly provides us with everything for our enjoyment. Command them to do good, to be rich in good deeds, and to be generous and willing to share. In this way they will lay up treasure for themselves as a firm foundation for the coming age, so that they may take hold of the life that is truly life." [77]

Scholars claim that Solomon was the wisest man that ever lived. He was also one the richest. It didn't take him long to discover that relationships and love should be valued more than money. One of Solomon's proverbs reflects his discovery.

"There was a man all alone; he had neither son nor brother. There was no end to his toil but his eyes were never content with all his wealth. 'For whom am I toiling?' he asked. 'And why am I depriving myself of enjoyment? This is meaningless and miserable business!'" Two are better than one because they have a good return for their investment. If either of them falls down, one can help the other up. But pity anyone who falls and has no one to help them up." [78]

The degree of a person's wealth has little to do with their state of happiness. Not all people with money are rich and not all those with little or nothing are poor. Winston Churchill said, "We make a living by what we get, we make a life by what we give." A wise person knows a $20 department store watch keeps time as well as a $10,000 Rolex. A $10,000 used car will get you where you need to be as quickly as a $100,000 Tesla. There is nothing wrong with owning nice things so long as you realize the most important things in life are not things.

As the Beatles reminded us, money can't buy you love, but it can be used to demonstrate your love of the things that matter most. ▪

St. Louis Herald

Work Ethic

By: **James King**

It's the one question asked more often of successful people than any other. It's also the most frustrating and misguided. The question itself is based on a false assumption. The question? "What's the secret of your success?"

The question assumes there is just one thing, one tidbit of information able to propel anyone who knows the answer to the same success as the person they are questioning.

Thomas Edison, famously known for developing the long-lasting incandescent filament and directly or indirectly responsible for more than a thousand other original patents, offered his answer in no uncertain terms, "Genius is ninety-nine percent perspiration and one percent inspiration." In other words, there is no simple answer. Success almost always requires hard work. In Edison's way of thinking, too few are willing to invest the time and energy required to become successful.

"Opportunity," he said, "is missed by most people because it comes dressed in overalls and looks like work."

Edison himself was known to work incredibly long hours, especially if he believed the solution to a troublesome problem was eminent. He'd remain at the shop around the clock, taking catnaps or sleeping three or four hours on a work bench instead of going home. He was equally focused when it came to motivating his employees. He made bets, offered prizes, and played his phonograph loudly to keep everyone alert and energized. When the desired outcome was finally achieved, he might declare a holiday, or take the whole team fishing.

I'm not sure if it's found in the Bible or somewhere in the writings of Benjamin Franklin—the two are often confused, but somewhere it says, "If a person doesn't work, neither should he eat." [79] Not everyone has a choice. If you grew up poor, work wasn't an optional activity, not if you wanted to survive.

No doubt there were families poorer than ours in my hometown, but I didn't know any. Except for my first cousin being raised by a single mom, everyone in my school was better off financially. Dad made his living sanding floors before the advent of wall-to-wall carpet drove him out of business. Looking back, I now realize he was a better tradesman than a businessman. People all over town owed him money he'd never collect for jobs completed on their behalf. Our clothes were hand-me-downs from family friends or purchased for dimes at garage sales. With seven children to feed, everyone was expected to contribute, hoeing the garden, picking beans, mowing lawns, shoveling snow, working any job we could get.

I was ten years old when I landed my first paper route. It had been my older brother's, who passed it along to me when he secured a larger route for a better-paying paper. The money we earned was not our own. We turned it over to our mother so she could buy milk for the baby or purchase butcher scraps she added to the vegetable soup. Spending money was acquired by collecting soda bottles from ditches along country roads and returning them for the deposit at a gas station a mile from our house. We knew all the best ditches to scour. When I was old enough to land a job at the neighborhood dairy store, I thought my ship had come in. My starting salary was $.75/hour. I'd be rich in no time.

I'm not objecting. Unbeknownst to me at the time, I was receiving the best education money couldn't buy. Over the years I have worked alongside lots of talented people. I couldn't help but notice some of the best talent is wasted on people who never learned to work very hard. You can teach almost anything to an eager student, but you can't teach a person to be industrious. Either they are or they aren't.

I've had success in life mostly due to the tenacity born from the necessity of my childhood. I've worked with many smarter, more gifted, and better-educated colleagues who have not achieved as much. Our success as parents has sometimes frustrated me as the father of our two sons. Unlike our parents, we were able to provide for almost all their needs and many of their desires. In my opinion, it's harder to raise well-adjusted, hardworking, industrious children when the parents are able to meet most, if not all their needs. It must be nearly impossible for rich people to raise hard-working, industrious children. But unless they do, they will cripple them for life.

Raising well-adjusted hardworking children in a middle or upper class family is possible, and I believe we achieved that goal, but it required a good deal of intentional effort. We expected both of our sons to get jobs as soon as they were old enough. They weed-wacked ditches at the golf course, watered trees in the hot sun at a local nursery, de-tassled corn, cleaned up construction sites and operated a fork-lift in a warehouse for a trucking company. To my way of thinking, the dirtier the work the better.

I was sometimes able to secure an interview through relationships I had with the owners that hired them, but they had to take it from there. They were not coddled, nor did I want them to be. Their supervisors were not the owners I knew, and the crews they worked with often resented the presence of college-bound interlopers. It goes with the territory. There is something important learned when a young person works side-by-side and takes direction from people who grew up in less educated and less affluent circumstances than themselves. Looking back, I probably should have paid those companies for the education in life they provided for our sons.

In his classic autobiography *Up from Slavery*, Booker T. Washington describes how he established

Tuskegee Institute with the intention of educating the whole person. Each student was required to learn a trade in addition to participating in classroom instruction. Dr. Washington discovered early in life there was more to success than a good education.

"I learned what education was expected to do for an individual. Before going there (Hampton Institute) I had a good idea of the then rather prevalent thinking among our people, that to secure an education meant to have a good, easy time, free from all necessity for manual labor. At Hampton I not only learned that it was not a disgrace to labor, but learned to love labor, not alone for its financial value, but for labor's own sake and for the independence and self-reliance achieved through the ability to do something which the world wants done" [80]

I should admit that early in my career as a reporter for *The Herald*, my tenacious work ethic had as much to do with my insecurity as it did my training. I didn't know what I didn't know, and that drove me. I wrote and rewrote every article half-dozen times. I did more research and threw away three times the amount of information I could include in any story. Doing more than necessary is good training for people who are new at anything.

As I grew more confident and more experienced, I also became more efficient. I'm tempted to advise young reporters to work smarter not harder, but that would probably be a mistake. When you are starting out, it is nearly impossible to work too hard at anything. My only regret, looking back, is that during those years when I was working around the clock, my family was young and needed me the most. On the other hand, maybe the self-imposed demands of my work kept me from micromanaging our sons' lives and required them to figure some things out on their own. It was probably better for them than the helicopter parents I've noticed running interference for children, making it more difficult for them to stand on their own two feet.

I'm not advocating work-a-holism. In his autobiography Lee Iacocca commented,

"Over the years, many executives have said to me with pride: 'Boy, I worked so hard last year that I didn't take any vacation.' I always feel like responding, 'You dummy. You mean to tell me you can take responsibility for an eighty-million-dollar project, and you can't plan two weeks out of the year to have some fun?" [81]

Balance is important when walking a high-wire, riding a two-wheel bicycle, and in finding success in a demanding career. My job often required me to work weekends to cover a breaking news story. My wife was a realtor who worked when her clients were available, often on the weekends. We realized early on the futility of comparing the demands of our professions to other people's jobs. We did, however, always manage to schedule one entire day free from work each week. When it came time for vacations, we had our back-ups in place. If you don't take care of yourself, you only have yourself to blame.

I've never believed in the strict code of family first, friends second, and work last. It never works out exactly that way. There were times when a real estate contract had to be signed, a story had to be covered, or a trip had to be made, despite personal obligations. But we never allowed exceptions to become the norm.

Two years before his death, Thomas Edison was awarded the Congressional Medal of Honor at a special dinner held for the occasion at the White House. Over 500 guests attended the dinner, including President and Mrs. Hoover. Overcome with emotion and fatigue, the aged Edison faltered and had to be attended by the President's personal physician. After recovering sufficient strength in the home and under the care and attention of his dear friend Henry Ford, Edison announced, "I'm tired of all the glory. I want to get back to work."

When you do what you love and love what you do, work is its own reward. ∎

St. Louis Herald

Get Smart

By: **James King**

A friend and colleague once called our journalism degrees our "union card." He said, "It afforded us the right to work in our field but really didn't provide the necessary training or skills to succeed at our jobs."

It was hard to argue with his reasoning, more than half the graduates we hire don't like the work, or are so bad at it, they quit within two years. I've heard the same is true for teachers, accountants, engineers, and a host of other professions. It reminds me of comments I've heard repeatedly in documentaries about war. Battle-tested veterans didn't bother to learn the names of replacements until they survived a couple of battles. They considered it a waste of time and energy since the newbies probably wouldn't survive anyway.

A University degree doesn't necessarily prepare you for the real world. It won't teach you how to get along with people, take orders from a supervisor who may or may not be very good at what they do, or even provide the specific skills needed to accomplish the job you signed up for. The expertise needed to succeed is acquired through experience and the help of seasoned veterans... provided you survive. Many don't.

Not everyone quits or leaves a job they aren't cut out for, only the smart ones. The workplace is full of people who are willing to exchange happiness for a paycheck. They have so much time and money invested in their career they keep going to a job they hate to support a lifestyle they believe is worth their unhappiness.

Many high school graduates enroll in a four-year university because they've been taught it's the American thing to do. I grew up in a small agricultural town in Indiana. The high school there still taught shop, auto-repair, and typing because so few students were college-bound. A local business owner and friend of our family took an interest in my potential and offered to pay the tuition cost if my parents enrolled me in a private high school that provided what they called a "college-prep curriculum." Unlike my father, who worked in a factory, almost all my classmates' parents were college graduates and worked at white-collar jobs. When I enrolled in college four years later, it was still possible to earn enough money during the summer to pay for a year's tuition. The additional expense of room and board could be earned by taking part-time jobs during the school term. It's a different story today.

The average cost of a year's tuition at a state university in 2020 is approximately $10,000/annually, not including room and board. It is 80% more expensive than the less-popular community college choice, which costs an average of $3,500/annually. While the price of higher education is escalating, entry-level wages upon graduation are stagnating, creating a major ROI (Return On Investment) quandary. To pay the bills, students and their parents have turned to government sponsored and privately acquired student loans.

Consider the Class of 2019 for example. Sixty-nine percent of those enrolled assumed student loans and graduated with an average indebtedness of $29,000. Forty-five million borrowers in America now owe over $1.64 trillion in student loans. That's $587 billion more than the total credit card debt in the United States, and many of those loans have interest rates as high as 14%.

Many consider outstanding student loans one of America's greatest financial challenges. Politicians are soliciting votes proposing various remedies from complete loan forgiveness, to forgiveness-over-time in exchange for voluntary service upon graduation. Something has to be done. Ten percent of all student loans are 90 days or more delinquent. Forty-eight percent of borrowers that attended for-profit universities, 12% of those who attend State Universities, and 14% of those attending nonprofit colleges, default on their loans within 12 years. Student loan indebtedness is now increasing at a rate of $13 billion annually.

Enrolling in a university is no guarantee a student will complete their degree. Thirty percent of college freshman drop out after their first year, including my roommate and best friend. Of those that stay, only 2/3 ever receive a professional degree. More than half of those take six years to complete a four-year program. It quickly becomes an expensive proposition.

Mike Rowe believes he has a solution for the problem. You may not recognize Mike by name but you'd recognize his voice if you heard it. He has narrated programs for the *Discovery Channel, the National Geographic Channel, Deadliest Catch and Shark Week.* He is more famous for his hit show, *Dirty Jobs.* Mike suggests it is possible to acquire the skills most people need for a successful life at a community college or trade school at much less expense. He calls attempting to acquire a bachelor's degree by half of America's youth, "A big waste of time and money." As evidence, he points out 45% of recent college graduates are working at jobs that don't require a college education.

Mike argues,

"The flaw in our character is our insistence on separating blue-collar jobs from white-collar jobs and encouraging one form of education over another. I think a trillion dollars of student loans and a massive skills gap are precisely what happens to a society that actively promotes one form of education as the best course for most people. I think the stigma and stereotypes that keep so many people from pursuing a truly useful skill begin with the mistaken belief that a four-year degree is somehow superior to all other forms of learning. We are lending money we don't have to kids who can't pay it back to train them for jobs that no longer exist.

That's nuts."

The age-old argument promoting "higher education" as the fast track to a more affluent lifestyle has kept universities in business. On average, a college dropout earns 35% less ($21,000) than a college graduate. Those lacking a college degree are twice as likely to be unemployed than those with a college diploma. It's hard to debate those facts, but Mike isn't arguing against education and useful training. He's arguing against the insanity of a university degree for its own sake.

Other skilled jobs pay as well as a college graduate and provide an equally rewarding and secure lifestyle. Certified Plumbers, Electricians, IT Technicians, Nurses, Skilled Carpenters and Machinists earn in the neighborhood of $40/hour, or approximately $80k per year compared to the average $70k earned by a college graduate. And those are just the salaries of skilled employees working in the industry, not to mention the real possibility of working independently.

The man that services my home irrigation system has become a good friend. He charges less for a service call than the larger companies and does a better job. The only problem I have ever had using him is trying to get on his schedule, because his calendar is full of appointments and he enjoys taking a vacation now and then, even a recent tour of Europe. He is obviously making ends meet.

I recently rehabbed my son's bathroom, tearing out and replacing the tile and shower base along with other projects I am capable of performing. I knew enough to schedule a plumber a week in advance to replace the shower control valve behind the wall. It was over twenty years old, so why risk keeping it when the wall was already opened during reconstruction? The bill for two hours of work was $250, and that included a loyal customer discount. The same can be said for the skilled carpenter I hired to put the crown molding on the kitchen cabinets I replaced recently. All of those people are enjoying their life and making a good living. None of them have a college education, but all of them know more than me in their area of expertise and are training people to help manage their burgeoning business.

Mike Rowe doesn't feel he has the right to tell anyone what to do with their life, He just wishes people would make decisions best suited for themselves and not follow the herd mentality because, "It's the thing to do." He has said, "I wouldn't wish any specific thing on any specific person—it's none of my business. But the idea that a four-year degree is the only path to worthwhile knowledge is insane. It's insane. People with dirty jobs are happier than you think. As a group, they are the happiest people I know."

There is an old German proverb I heard years ago that applies, "Too soon old. Too late smart." A young man I know recently left a career he spent years studying to enter. It wasn't a rash decision. He had been working hard at it for more than a decade with a degree of success and future opportunities. Against the advice of many, he left it to pursue a career in a completely different field that provided greater independence and the potential of earning a good income, maybe even better than the job he was leaving.

He had every reason not to risk making the change: a good salary, benefits, and a young family that depended on his income with no assurance of success. His new venture provided no guaranteed salary and no company benefits. He would be entirely dependent on his own work ethic. Two years later, he is a happy man enjoying his freedom and earning a better income with greater earning potential than he had in the job he left. His decision took courage and a great deal of self-belief. It also took a willingness to make a change despite the opinion of nay-sayers and those who defend the status quo.

His courageous decision puts me in mind of another old proverb, *"One more step in the wrong direction won't get you nearer to your destination."* ▪

"Focusing is about saying No."

—*Steve Jobs*

CHAPTER 15

Playing It Safe

"Vacations must agree with you. You're driving the ball ten yards further and hitting it straighter than a Baptist preacher. If you ever learn to putt you'll be dangerous."

It was just George being George. It felt good to be back on my home course playing with my usual foursome. I enjoyed the time with Sarah on the Gulf Coast, but it's true what they say, "Absence makes the heart grow fonder." I missed our friends and the familiarity of St. Louis more than I expected.

"How are you feeling about the new gig?" It was Gary this time. He had always been curious about my work as a reporter, especially the human-interest features and the stories of the people I interviewed."

"It's different to be sure. As a beat reporter, I kept my opinions to myself. It seems odd now, even a little arrogant, to write an Op-Ed. on topics that people have strong opinions about. In my mind, facts still matter. I believe there are right, wrong, good, better, and best positions on most things. My column is designed to stimulate informed discussions on sensitive topics. I'm not a fan of political correctness. Perhaps you've noticed," I said with a wink and a smile. "I consider it my job to encourage people to rethink their opinions. There are always other informed perspectives different from our own. What you think about TRUTH BE TOLD is probably more important than how I feel about it. Do you think it's helpful, or am I just adding to the noise? Feel free to be critical."

He was quick with his response, "You were made for this, Jim. Your experience as a reporter is invaluable. You're aware of public opinion but don't mind poking the bear. To be honest, I'm a bit surprised by the column's conservative perspective. *The Herald* has had a tendency over the years to pull their putts to the left, if you know what I mean. People don't call it 'The St. Louis Daily Blues' for nothing. I'm surprised they've given you free reign. Hell, I'm surprised you believe the things you write. I always took you for a lib. The Preacher must be rubbing off on you!" Gary said with a laugh. "Even your golf game has gotten more conservative!"

Everyone but George saw the humor in Gary's comments. They loved giving George a hard time. They called him "The Preacher" because of his constant banter about his church, the Bible, or something morally askew in the news. They called me "Clark," a veiled reference to Clark Kent of Superman fame. If I managed to hit a great shot, they'd say, "Your cape is showing Clark," or something to that effect.

"Less talk, more golf please," was my usual response. "We're falling a hole behind."

George hadn't said anything about the TBT column since my return. The two of us hadn't had opportunity to discuss it privately and he was hesitant to share his opinion in an open debate with the other guys. I was eager to get his feedback after several months of publication. Other than Sarah, he more than anyone else, had urged me to accept the opportunity. I didn't have to wait long.

George played especially well all morning, making two unlikely birdies, barely missing two more that burned the edge of the cup from ten feet. It was great to see George string some good holes together. I lipped-out twice in a row from makeable range. George was quick to comment, "You know Jim, there is a difference between putting to make birdie and putting not to miss one." His point was not lost on me. I was playing it safe. Instead of making a confident stroke, I found myself punching the ball toward the hole, careful not to blow it past. There was something in George's tone that led me to believe he was talking about more than golf. As we walked to the next tee box, I thanked him for the tip.

"You're right, George. I've been playing it safe rather than making a confident stroke. I need to be gently firm. There are a hundred ways to mess up a score and that's one of them."

"It's not just true in golf, Jim," he added. "I never took you for a 'playing it safe,' kind of guy." Jim and Gary were in a hurry to drop their clubs at the bag room and head to the showers. As per usual, we bumped fists, wished each other well, and parted on the eighteenth green. George and I had a side-bet going so he walked with me to the snack bar to calculate the damage.

"What do you mean, 'You never took me for a playing-it-safe kind of guy?'" I had to ask. We grabbed a cold drink and sat down to double-check the scorecard and continue our conversation.

"I was talking about TRUTH BE TOLD." When George had an opinion, it didn't take much prompting to get him to share it. "Don't get me wrong, you're a gifted writer and I'm sure *The Herald* is pleased with the response it's getting. You've got people talking. I haven't disagreed with anything you've written. You have a knack for sharing an opinion on controversial issues in a clever way."

"But?" I added.

"But... I feel you're playing it safe. Putting to not miss rather than putting to score the birdie. You're close but holding back. Truth falls short when it focuses only on behavior and not motive. You're serving the cake but not sharing the recipe. I don't fault your conclusions. You've tackled some tough subjects. You've taken a stand on the hot topics of our day and your readers respect your candor, even when they disagree. Jesus said, 'What good does it do if a person gains the whole world and forfeits his soul, or what will a person sacrifice in exchange for their soul?' [82] You're providing answers but not the formula, the destination but not direction. You need to show your work, be willing to reveal the reason for the conclusions you offer."

"I hear what you're saying, but TRUTH BE TOLD isn't a Bible study. I'm not Franklin Graham, and I can't apologize for that. TRUTH BE TOLD is an issue-focused Op-Ed., not a sermon. Truth is truth is truth. It doesn't matter if you believe in Allah, Yahweh, Buddha, or Zeus. TRUTH BE TOLD is a non-partisan, spiritually inclusive, Fatherhood of God and brotherhood of man approach to life; no more, no less."

"And therein lies the problem as I see it." George was not backing down. "I'm not suggesting you change TRUTH BE TOLD'S approach, just finish your stroke, so to speak. TBT has obviously captured people's attention. It has the potential to make the world a kinder and better place. But don't be afraid to credit your source. Like you said, it's an Op-Ed. You have a right to express your opinion. People don't have to share your belief, but you should be transparent about it. You've been given a powerful platform to guide thousands, maybe millions to the source of ultimate truth.

"There have been other popular writers who were well-known and respected Christians. Norman Vincent Peale, Paul Harvey and Zig Ziglar were three of the most popular columnists in our nation. They are gone now, and no one has filled their shoes. Millions appreciated their business savvy and heeded their advice. They were open about their faith without jamming their beliefs down anyone's throat. I can honestly say, I never heard Zig give a speech when he didn't start or finish by sharing his personal testimony. It might have been just a closing statement or a recording offered at the door as people filed out. He didn't force his faith on anyone, but he didn't hide it either. The same is true for some well-known Christian athletes who have microphones shoved in their face at the end of competition. There is a Scripture that says,

If our faith in Christ is only for this life, we are more to be pitied than anyone in the world. [83]

Jesus wasn't sent to earth to offer good advice on how best to win friends and influence people. Offering sound relational advice and achieving success in life was part of His purpose, but it wasn't His primary purpose. He came to reconcile the world to their Creator and offer life that leads to eternal life. Paul called the truth about Jesus' true mission, 'A stumbling block to Jews and foolishness to Gentiles, but,' ...he added, 'to those whom God has called, both Jews and Gentiles, Christ is the power of God and the wisdom of God.' [84] Like TBT, Paul began many of his letters providing guidance on contested issues, but he didn't stop there. His purpose was greater than that." He finished his stroke and made the putt.

"I get it George, but it's just not possible, not in a weekly column distributed for public consumption by a nationally recognized news outlet in the business to make money, not save souls," I replied.

"I don't pretend to know how to do it, but then I'm not as gifted as you," George said with a smile. "I'm here as your faithful sounding board, not to figure out the hard stuff. But don't forget, you were called by God before you were hired by *The Herald*. TRUTH BE TOLD, in my opinion, is meant to be a means to a greater end. It was no coincidence you were offered the column at the same time you were recruited as God's spokesman. Your mission *is your higher purpose*, to be God's spokesman to this generation. I'll pray that the Lord provides the wisdom you need to figure it out. I refuse to believe you've been chosen by God to be the Ann Landers of our time. You have a more important purpose. While you consider it, I've made a list of some passages to help guide your deliberations. I didn't know what else to do. I believe there is power as well as truth in the Bible."

George slipped a list of a half-dozen neatly typed Scriptures across the table. I can't say I disagreed with anything he said, but it aggravated me to be challenged. He was right of course, I probably wouldn't be writing TBT, if it weren't for the man in white and my continuing encounters with the likes of Mordecai and Sam. No doubt, TRUTH BE TOLD was intended by God to be more than a continuation of my job as a reporter for *The Herald*. I was convinced of my calling to be His spokesman to a lost generation. It was obvious but confusing at the same time. George had given me a lot to think about.

I was truly a man in the middle. I believe most people realize there is something basically wrong with the political correctness that our mainstream media and politicians constantly advocate. I was blessed, (or cursed... somedays it is hard to tell the difference), to be in a position to do something about it. From what I could tell, many of the most popular churches have fallen into the same political correctness trap, overly concerned about offending anyone by teaching unvarnished truth. Truth has an edge to it. Edges are sharp. Sharp edges are bound to cut. Cuts hurt. You can't have it both ways. You can't be truthful without offending some people. You can't avoid offense if you speak the truth. But God's cuts are not life-threatening. They are life-saving. Of course, love must dominate every action, statement, and belief. Love, kindness, and compassion must always remain paramount, but not at the expense of the truth. Truth without love is not the whole truth. Love without truth is not true love.

"How much do I owe you?" George asked, returning to the business at hand.

"You actually won the round by a stroke. You played out of your mind and already paid for the cold drinks, so I'm the one in debt here today. I learn a lot from our time together on and off the course. I value your friendship more than you might suspect, especially the insight you offer for TBT. Your knowledge of the Scripture is invaluable. The courage of your candor makes what I do better. I've never forgotten what you told me, 'Wounds from a friend can be trusted but an enemy multiplies praise.'[85] You must be a good friend. You are always willing to wound me," I chuckled.

"I take no credit for my sometimes painful advice." George injected. "Solomon said it first, and it still rings true."

"No one at The Herald knows the greater purpose of TRUTH BE TOLD. If I told them I've been called by God to be His spokesman and TBT is my pulpit, I'd be sacked for sure. Thanks for keeping me from mission-drift. I still don't know how to pull it off, but your list of passages is a good place to start." And with that, we headed towards the locker room.

George had given me a lot to think about. I needed time to digest his comments and an opportunity to talk it over with Sarah. We've been on this road together for over a year. I trust her judgment. We are both pragmatists, but willing to believe my interactions with the likes of Mordecai, Sam, and all the other strange occurrences of recent months have not been accidental. I began this journey as a skeptic and have become a true believer. I hardly recognized myself.

I took a moment in the privacy of my car to glance at George's list of passages before leaving the parking lot. I liked giving ideas time to germinate, breathing room. I compare it to letting dough rise before baking it in the oven. I can't recall how many times I've faced a confusing situation by giving it serious thought before going to bed, only to wake with a clear understanding of what needed to be done.

- Mark 12:34 – *"When Jesus saw that the teacher of the law had answered wisely, he said to him, 'You are not far from the kingdom of God.'"*

- Mark 8:36–38 – *"What good is it for someone to gain the whole world, yet forfeit their soul? Or what can anyone give in exchange for their soul? If anyone is ashamed of me and my words in this adulterous and sinful generation, the Son of Man will be ashamed of them when he comes in his Father's glory with the holy angels."*

- Hebrews 11:6 – *"Without faith it is impossible to please God, because anyone who comes to him must believe that He exists and that He rewards those who earnestly seek him."*

- Revelation 3:14–16 – *"These are the words of the Amen, the faithful and true witness, the ruler of God's creation. I know your deeds, that you are neither cold nor hot. I wish you were either one or the other! So, because you are lukewarm—neither hot nor cold—I am about to spit you out of my mouth."*

- Matthew 7:21 – *"Not everyone who says to me, 'Lord, Lord,' will enter the kingdom of heaven, but only the one who does the will of my Father who is in heaven."*

- 1 Corinthians 2:2–5 – *"I resolved to know nothing while I was with*

*you except Jesus Christ and him crucified. I came to you in weakness
with great fear and trembling. My message and my preaching were
not with wise and persuasive words, but with a demonstration of the
Spirit's power, so that your faith might not rest on human wisdom,
but on God's power."*

- Ephesians 2:8–10 – *"It is by grace you have been saved, through
  faith—and this is not from yourselves, it is the gift of God—not by
  works, so that no one can boast. For we are God's handiwork, created
  in Christ Jesus to do good works, which God prepared in advance for
  us to do."*

I was eager to get home to highlight the main points of each passage
and let the thoughts sink in. But even now, as I made my way through
traffic, the first passage on the list had my mind churning. Jesus told the
teacher *he was not far* from the kingdom of God. George's earlier comment
came to mind. The teacher was partly right, but not completely right. A
miss is as good as a mile, like putting to not miss rather than making the
solid stroke to sink the birdie. Was Jesus saying respect for God and man is
nice but not enough? Is that what I was doing with TBT? Playing good but
not good enough? Leaving my putts short?

Sarah was busy potting flowers when I got home. Never a fan of daytime
TV, she preferred being outside and active. Like usual, she greeted me with
a kiss and a smile. We sat in the rocking chairs on the porch to catch up
and discuss our plans for the rest of the day. She had spent her morning
connecting by phone with our daughters-in-law, checking on their well-
being and the activities of our grandchildren. She had also made calls to
encourage friends who were going through rough patches and shared their
status with me.

"How was your game? Did your swing hold up? I'm sure the guys were
glad to see you back again."

"George beat me by a stroke, but I played well, better than before our
vacation. Playing often helps," I laughed. "I enjoyed our time in Memphis
and Alabama, but it felt good to get back on my home course. The fairways

and greens up North are so different compared to the South. Bermuda and Zoysia have nothing in common. I know my home course better for sure. I know which direction the greens break and where to hit the ball. I don't always hit it where I'm aiming, but at least I know where it's supposed to go."

"Did you get to talk to George? How are Elizabeth and he doing since the wedding? "

"They seem fine. They want to get together for dinner and hear about the things we saw and did in Memphis. George offered some great insight into my writing on TRUTH BE TOLD. Nothing especially negative, more a course-correction type of discussion."

"You're kidding, right? I think the column has been some of your best work ever."

"He compared it to timid putting, trying to not miss rather than sinking the birdie. It feels to him that I've been playing it safe with TBT."

"Playing it safe? Hardly. You've taken strong stands on every issue, positions I'm thought he'd be happy to see." I had to smile. I loved Sarah's instinctive rush to my defense.

"True, but he reminded me the purpose of TBT should be greater than exposing the errors of the politically correct culture. He said God didn't call me to be a poor imitation of Ann Landers, or something to that effect. You have to admire the courage of his convictions."

"What did he suggest you should do differently?"

"He said I'm serving the cake but not sharing the recipe, promoting the destination but withholding the directions," I smiled to recall his analogy. "He mentioned I was asked to be God's spokesman before *The Herald* recruited me, and that I shouldn't substitute the means for the message. It was hard to find fault with anything he said."

"That's what they call a true 'conundrum.' How can you possibly write an Op-Ed, distributed by a nationally syndicated publisher and advocate belief in God at the same time? You're not Franklin Graham after all."

"That's exactly what I said!" I laughed. George didn't offer a solution, but he didn't back down either. He said, 'I'm just here to give you advice, not figure out the hard stuff. That's why you get paid the big bucks.' It's like telling a dying man, 'You are in my thoughts and prayers.' A lot of good that does. He did provide a list of Scriptures he thought might be helpful. I'll start by studying those."

Sarah pulled her gloves on and headed back to her flowers. "You know what they say, 'God's work, done God's way, never lacks God's provision.'"

"Who says that?" I asked.

"I have no idea." Sarah replied with a kiss to my cheek. "It was something my dad always said when a situation seemed impossible."

The Scriptures George had typed reaffirmed his advice to be more explicit in expressing my beliefs from a Biblical perspective. I read each of the Scriptures and jotted down what I thought was its applicable truth.

1. **Mark 12.** Jesus didn't criticize the religious teacher for advocating anything wrong. It was more a sin of omission than of commission. The teacher considered loving God and loving one's neighbor as the sum total of all divine expectations. Jesus suggested he was "not far from the whole truth." That's kind of what George thought about TRUTH BE TOLD. Close but not close enough. Like a putt that comes up short.

2. **Mark 8.** Jesus said in the end it won't matter how wise, rich, and famous a person is if they don't acknowledge Him as their Savior. When it's all said and done and we stand before our Creator, God will acknowledge those who acknowledged the truth about Jesus.

3. **Hebrews 11.** Faith is required for something to be considered a good work in God's sight. *Why* you do something matters as much to God as *what* you do.

4. **Revelation 3.** God expects us to get off the fence. Refusing to take a stand for the whole truth is like lukewarm coffee and God prefers his hot.

5. **Matthew 7.** There are people who know Jesus but don't accept Him

as their Savior. Knowing and respecting Jesus as a good teacher and moral example is not enough.

6. **1 Corinthians 2.** Paul didn't take credit for his persuasive abilities. He considered himself inadequate for the task of convincing anyone of God's truth. He relied on God to do the convincing. That was a relief to me. It wasn't my job to change people's minds about God, just be courageous about my faith and expect God to do the rest.

7. **Ephesians 2.** We are saved to do good, not saved by doing good. God wants everyone to know the difference.

I knew what I had to do but wasn't sure how to go about it. It reminded me of a weekend human interest story I wrote years ago. I was asked to compare the influence of Stephen Covey, author of the best-selling book, *The Seven Habits of Highly Effective People*, to Norman Vincent Peale, the author of *The Power of Positive Thinking*. Both were men of faith. Covey was a devout Mormon and Peale was an ordained Christian pastor. It struck me that Covey's contemporaries were more complementary of his work than Peale's contemporaries were during his lifetime. Many Christian leaders thought Peale had sold out by swapping the gospel of Jesus for a more popular and politically correct message of optimistic thinking. It wasn't true but perception is reality.

I remembered a story Peale told in his autobiography about a time when he and Billy Graham shared the stage before a packed audience at Madison Square Garden. It amused Peale to recall that day in his book, *The True Joy of Positive Living*. I was such a fan of his thinking; I kept a copy of it on the bookshelf in my office.

"Once at a meeting in Madison Square Garden, when I sat next to Dr. Graham on the platform and looked out over a sea of faces in the packed arena, I turned to Billy in admiration and asked, 'Billy, how do you do it?' With that winsome smile of his, he replied, 'By practicing the power of positive thinking.' We both laughed, but each of us knew that the real answer was the power of Christ working in him." [86]

Peale's approach was intentional. He believed if he could help businessmen succeed at their jobs and life by sharing God's truth about human nature, they would naturally want to know the source of his wisdom. Their curiosity and thirst for advice would provide Peale the opportunity to share his Christian faith to a receptive audience rather than attempting to persuade skeptics against their will. I believe many contemporary Christian leaders and authors with public appeal are merely following in Peal's footsteps. They are cross-over artists, able to share their faith and God's wisdom about life and business at the same time.

My next three editorials were already assigned but the fourth was designated an "author's choice." Brad had asked me to write columns on the subjects of *Life, Liberty, and the Pursuit of Happiness*. I liked the concept for obvious reasons. Writing about our nation's founding principles was a natural lead into a discussion of their fundamental beliefs. It would provide an excellent reason to discuss the relevance of God in our nation. I made a note to call the fourth article in the series, *"Faith: The Assurance of Things Hoped for and the Conviction about Things Unseen."* That's how faith is defined in the Bible. [87]

I'm not sure how Brad will receive the idea, but I don't expect too much resistance. So long as my articles are interesting, provocative, and a reasonable discussion of a popular and challenging topic, he expected me to be controversial.

He liked to say, "I'm okay with controversy. It's apathy I can't stand."

We were about to see if he really meant it.

*"Everyone is entitled to their own opinion, but
they are not entitled to their own facts."*

—*Sen. Patrick Moynihan*

CHAPTER 16

Recalculating

I t's my job to check the garage, make sure doors are locked, and turn out
the lights before heading off for bed. I woke-up uneasy in the middle
of the night. Something didn't feel right. A glance towards the hallway
confirmed my suspicion. There was a light on in the living room. Sarah was
still fast asleep next to me. I have been known to leave a lamp on in the
study, but rarely.

I retrieved my 9mm. from its secure location and walked quietly towards
the light. If there was a burglar in the house, I wanted equal footing. If it
was nothing more than a forgotten lamp, no harm, no foul. I saw no need to
wake Sarah. I felt silly playing security guard and didn't want to alarm her.

When I reached the end of the hall and entered the living room, I
realized the light was coming from the fireplace. How could I have not
turned off the gas logs? My eyes were drawn to the easy chair next to the
casement windows that overlooked the back yard. It took a second, but I
recognized the sitting figure of our man in white. The lamp was off but there
was ample moonlight streaming through the glass. I felt the adrenaline

drain from my body as my heart slowed its rhythm. I had no intention of shooting anyone, not even a burglar if I could help it. The handgun was purely precautionary. I hadn't even chambered a round.

It took only an instant but seemed longer, as if everything was moving in slow motion. He spoke before I did.

"Fear not, James. I mean you no harm. We've met before."

I recognized his voice. "Who are you? Why are you here?" I asked instinctively.

"My name is not important. I am one who stands in the presence of the Lord. I've been sent by the Father to reassure you. Your work has not gone unnoticed. The Lord is pleased with all you've done and the spirit of your effort, speaking the truth in love. He is always near and willing to help."

I had prayed for this moment and didn't intend to let it slip away without some clarification. "I'm confused by the implication. What do you mean, 'My work has not gone unnoticed?' Am I..." But before I could finish, the man in white raised his hand asking for silence.

"It is not our place to question the Lord, James. The Father is pleased by your acceptance of those He has placed in your path. You have demonstrated a humble willingness to heed the counsel of the faithful.

"Your words have been courageous, and your column is helping people rethink some of life's most important values. The Lord is pleased. He desires all to be saved and come to the knowledge of His truth. God did not send his Son into the world to condemn the world but so that the world might be saved through Him. As moonlight enlightens the night, so His truth shines through the darkness. The greater the darkness, the more noticeable the light. Remember, James, it is only required that a servant be found faithful.

"Consider the Lord's counsel to the church in Ephesus. Stay focused on the mission you've been given. Do not waver or be afraid. He will walk by your side and provide the counsel you need. The Lord upholds His own.

"Jesus is the way, the truth, and the life; no one comes to the Father except through Him. It is written, 'Whoever calls on the name of the Lord will be saved. But how can they call on Him in whom they have not believed? And how can they believe in Him of whom they have not heard?

And how can they hear without a spokesman? How beautiful are the feet of those who bring the good news of salvation.'[88]

"The Father has not given you a spirit of timidity but rather a spirit of power, love, and self-discipline.[89] The Lord goes before you. Not everyone will listen. The enemy has deceived and blinded many. The road is wide that leads to destruction and the lost walk aimlessly down its path. Their path will be met with frustration designed to turn them back to the Lord. They will not find the peace they seek. As the prophet said, 'They buy food but remain hungry. They spend wages on things that cannot satisfy. The Lord has invited them to eat for free what is good and enjoy without cost the abundance he provides. His words are life and his wisdom true food.'[90]

"Attempting to ease their conscience, the lost seek teachers who will say what they want to hear. They exchange God's truth for lies, and His counsel for deception. Yet they are not beyond the Lord's reach. All day long, the Lord extends a hand of reconciliation to an obstinate and disobedient people.[91]

"Manage your expectations, James. Do not despair. Do not become discouraged. Your words will be challenged. They attacked the prophets who came before you. Read what the Scripture reveals about Elijah of old —how he appealed to God against Israel:

'Lord, they have killed your prophets and torn down your altars; I am the only one left, and they are trying to kill me?'[92]

"And what was God's answer to him?

'I have reserved for myself seven thousand who have not bowed the knee to Baal.'[93]

"So also today, there is a remnant chosen by grace as a testament to God's truth and a witness to the lost. They need the comfort and encouragement of God's wisdom. They need a spokesman to say openly what every heart knows to be true. God's truth is evident within them. The Lord has written it on their hearts.

"You are not alone in your mission. Wise counsel and encouragement surrounds you. The Lord goes before you. Your words will be empowered by His Spirit. Do not fear the ridicule of those who do not believe. They are blind guides speaking words without power. They oppose truth to their own destruction. Be encouraged by the example of Jesus who endured hostility by sinners against Himself, so that you do not grow weary or lose heart. *Fix your eyes on Jesus, the author and perfecter of faith, who for the joy before Him, endured the cross, despised its shame and is now seated at the right hand of the throne of God. Run with endurance the race set before you.*" [94]

And with those words, the man in white rose, turned, and passed effortlessly through the windows behind him, disappearing in the trees bordering our property. How? I have no idea.

As I sat there on the couch, next to the now empty chair, amazed and in awe of what I had just experienced I thought about the distinction between dreams and visions as described in the Bible. Which was this? How could I be sure? "A vision," the commentators say, "happens when you are awake, and dreams occur in your sleep." Was I awake or merely dreaming? How could I be sure?

The fireplace was still flickering, casting dancing shadows on the walls. I felt the heat of it spilling into the room where I stood. I reached through the wire mesh and turned off the feed. The logs glowed hot, but the flames gasped and died. Except for the faint moonlight, the room went mostly dark and silent. Light from the street crept through the transom above the front door, falling on the hardwood leading back to the bedroom. I knew for certain I was fully awake, more alert than ever.

My instincts kicked in. I needed a moment, time to jot down notes from the words I had just heard. My office was close to the bedroom where Sarah lay sleeping. I couldn't risk waking her before capturing the main points of what had been said. I grabbed a stool from under the kitchen counter, nudged on the dimmer switch, opened the tablet and began writing.

- The Lord will place others in my path to help and encourage me. (I knew that to be true.)

- Light overpowers darkness, no matter how great the darkness, no matter how faint the light.

- Consider the words of the Lord to the church in Ephesus. (Google it.)

- The Lord's primary mission is to save the world, not merely educate it.

- Don't be timid. Demonstrate strength with love and self-discipline.

- Manage your expectations. The prophets suffered rejection.

- Elijah was told thousands of faithful people still believed despite his frustrations. Secret believers exist in times of persecution.

- The fact God would go before me didn't mean I would be spared ridicule.

- Consider the example of Jesus and all He endured to not lose heart.

- Persevere. Don't give up.

The clock on the microwave glowed 3:30 am. If I returned to the bedroom, I risked waking Sarah. We would spend the rest of the night discussing what just happened and that wouldn't do either of us any good. I had spent the night on the couch before, when a project had me too restless to sleep. I turned out the lights, unfolded the quilt we kept there, and settled in to weigh the implications of my encounter.

I woke up several hours later to the sound of Sarah making coffee in the kitchen. I wasn't sure of the time, but the sun was up, and the birds were singing. I laid still for a moment, recalling the events of the night. I stirred as Sarah slid a fresh cup of coffee on the table next to the couch.

She was the first to speak. "One of those nights? I noticed you were AWOL about 4:30, and found you sleeping on the couch. I decided it was best to let you rest for a few more hours. I suppose confusion over TRUTH BE TOLD has your mind racing."

"What a night." I replied. "About 3:15, I noticed a light coming from the living room. I thought it might be a burglar. There's been a few break-ins in the neighborhood recently. I came out to investigate and encountered our man in white. The fireplace was burning and he was sitting in the chair by the windows. I tried to engage him in conversation, but he is not the conversing type. He said what he came to say, then walked straight through the plate glass into the woods behind the house."

"When you least expect it, I guess," Sarah commented. "What was so important he needed to make a house call? Did he seem pleased with TBT or disappointed?"

"I don't think he was disappointed. I didn't sense anything critical in his words. I felt encouraged and supported after he left. It was more like a father/son talk than a critical assessment. I made a list of his comments. It's on the counter."

Sarah moved to retrieve the tablet and returned to her seat. "What does, 'Consider the words of the Lord to the church of Ephesus mean?'"

"I have no idea, but it seemed important. I planned to check my Bible app. It must be significant."

"The rest of it is pretty straight forward. You had already decided to be more candid about your faith. We both sense God's desire to be known is more essential than helping people find success, get along, and live healthy lives. Those are all good things, but they won't save anyone. Have you decided how to do that yet?"

"That's the guidance I was seeking, but never got the chance to ask. It was a one-way conversation. I have some ideas but I'm not ready to spring them on Brad yet. I want to have my thoughts squared away. He knows I intend to write an editorial on faith. The refrain from Bob Dylan's song, *Gotta Serve Somebody*, keeps coming to mind. Everyone has a point of view and a philosophy they live by. I'm no different. It's worthy of an Op-Ed. I don't believe most people are aware of why they do what they do and believe what they believe."

Sarah continued, "Not everything on this list is uplifting. It says, 'You need to manage your expectations, and expect ridicule.'"

"Forewarned is forearmed," I shrugged.

"I do like the metaphor of light." She continued. "I never thought about it like that. No matter how dark the room, if you light a candle every eye is drawn to it, like truth surrounded by error, I suppose. That's worth remembering."

"What's your next move, baby?" she asked.

"Well for starters, I want to check out the reference to the church at Ephesus. After that I thought I might make a run to The Footnote to think it over."

"In hopes of seeing Mordecai, no doubt?"

"You're way ahead of me," I laughed.

"I was born at night, but not last night," Sarah said with a smile as she refilled my coffee cup. It was one of her favorite phrases. "The man in white said God will put people in your path to provide the guidance you need. A stop at The Footnote makes sense. I'll leave you to it. I need to run some errands this morning. I'll catch up with you later this afternoon."

I considered taking a quick shower but was too intrigued by the reference to the church at Ephesus. I needed time to think about it before drawing any conclusions. I headed to my office where I kept my newly acquired study Bible and a copy of Strong's Exhaustive Concordance. It didn't take long to locate the reference to the church in Ephesus from Revelation, chapter two.

"To the angel of the church in Ephesus write:
These are the words of Him who holds the seven stars in His right hand and walks among the seven golden lampstands. I know your deeds, your hard work and your perseverance. I know that you cannot tolerate wicked people, that you have tested those who claim to be apostles but are not and have found them false. You have persevered and have endured hardships for My name, and have not grown weary.

Yet I hold this against you: You have forsaken the love you had at first. Consider how far you have fallen! Repent and do the things you did at first. If you do not repent, I will come to you and remove your lampstand from its place. But you have this in your favor: You hate the practices of the Nicolaitans, which I also hate.

Whoever has ears, let them hear what the Spirit says to the churches. To the one who is victorious, I will give the right to eat from the tree of life, which is in the paradise of God." [95]

I circled the main thoughts for deeper consideration. (They were commended for their perseverance. They challenged false teachers. They didn't tolerate evil. They were committed to truth. Their sincerity was without question. And they were willing to suffer the consequence of their convictions.) It was important to note, something about the Christians in Ephesus had changed. The Christians there had been known for their compassion and love. In an earlier letter to them, Paul had written, *"I have heard of your faith in the Lord Jesus, and your love for all the saints."* [96] Perhaps the hardships they had suffered led to the loss of joy and compassion for others in their work. Stress can take the joy out of life and turn the best of us stoic. They were challenged to regain their spirit of love and compassion, even for those who caused them grief.

In closing, the Lord commends the Ephesians for opposing a group called the Nicolaitans. My study Bible identified the Nicolaitans as Gnostics and antinominalist. I laughed. Whatever that means? I had to google it.

The Nicolaitans were apparently a sect that opposed religious rules and any standards of morality, emphasizing the spiritual relationship of believers to the Lord is all that matters. From what I learned, the Nicolaitans practiced unrestrained indulgence, because according to their belief, Christ's sacrifice completely exonerated them from any consequence of sin. On the basis of their perspective, Nicolaitans believed Christians were free from all moral constraints, including The Ten Commandments which most Christians consider the summation of all applicable moral law.

A footnote directed me to compare their theological viewpoint with Paul's explanation in 1 Corinthians 10:23, 24.

"I have the right to do anything," you say. But not everything is beneficial. "I have the right to do anything—but not everything is constructive. No one should seek their own good, but the good of others." [97]

As I understood Paul's explanation, being free from sin, does not mean God's moral expectations are null and void. Our behavior, good, bad, or otherwise, does not contribute to our salvation, but it still matters. What was morally right or wrong before Jesus, after Jesus, and even today is still morally right or wrong. Doing what's right and rejecting what's wrong affects the quality of our life and our value to others.

By referring to the advice to the Ephesians, I believed the man in white was directing my attention to God's advice in Revelation, chapter two, for the sake of the column. God is obviously pleased with those who oppose wrong and challenge false teachers, even within the church. Truth exists for the benefit of humanity, to encourage the faithful and correct the misguided. The advice to the Ephesians reminds the faithful to focus on God's love and His desire to bring everyone to the knowledge of salvation. He urged the Ephesians to renew the love for others they had demonstrated in their past.

I appreciated the insight and was in full agreement. It gave me confidence to express strong opinions on controversial issues with an emphasis on love. I wanted to help, not hurt; to guide not judge. It's a tough balancing act, to speak the truth in love. It is what every good parent struggles to do correctly.

It was a welcomed reminder to be told I was not alone in my task. The Lord had surrounded me with the support of George, Mordecai, Sam, Sarah, and perhaps even my editor Brad, although unwittingly. I was reminded God would empower the truth of my words, like light piercing darkness. I was challenged to trust the power of truth, speak boldly with love and clarity, and anticipate (but not be discouraged by) criticism and rejection. The man in white's visit came at a good time, providing the encouragement and perspective I needed. I've heard it said, "God is never late, but seldom early." It seemed about right.

After showering, I grabbed a legal pad and headed to The Footnote. I was not surprised to find Mordecai sitting alone in the corner booth, nor did he seem surprised to see me.

"Great to see you Mordecai. I was hoping to find you here. Give me a moment to grab a cup of coffee. I need to run some things by you," I said, laying my binder on the table across from my friend.

"Take all the time you need, James. It's good to see you too."

"It's been too long," I suggested as I slid into the booth opposite my mentor.

"I hope you've been well," he responded. "I've been enjoying your column. I consider it a privilege to know the man behind the byline."

Mordecai had always been sincere in his praise and candid in his counsel. I expected no less. "Thanks for the encouragement, but I think there is more to be done. TRUTH BE TOLD has been a challenge to write but provides a great platform to question popular opinion. I don't expect everyone to agree with my point of view but it's getting noticed. The criticism has been less severe than I expected. I try to be gracious with my words, yet firm in my conviction."

"I agree that's the right approach. What makes you think there is more to be done?"

Mordecai's question seemed more probing than inquiring. "I've come to my conclusion based on conversations I've had with people I trust and my own sense of a greater purpose. A friend quoted something Jesus said that provided a lot of clarity. I wrote it down."

I opened the binder with my notes. "Jesus said, *'What good is it for someone to gain the whole world, yet forfeit their soul? Or what can anyone give in exchange for their soul?'* [98] He seems to suggest that possessing wisdom for this life falls short of God's greater purpose to provide wisdom that leads to eternal life. I know that's true, but am not sure what I can do about it through TRUTH BE TOLD.

Giving voice to my thoughts, Mordecai replied, "So you've believe it's beneficial to provide God's counsel for life issues through TRUTH BE TOLD, but think if you try to provide spiritual guidance, TBT will lose its influence among the very people you are trying to reach?"

"Exactly. I'm not writing TBT because I need the work, or for the sake of my reputation or popularity. I'm convinced God recruited me as His spokesman to advance His ultimate purpose of redemption. Otherwise I should just retire and enjoy my privacy."

"Can't you do both? Didn't the prophets and apostles do both?"

"I intend to write an Op-Ed. on the issue of faith." I replied. "It's a start and I'm sure it falls within the parameters we've established for the column. Dylan wrote a song years ago claiming everyone serves somebody. A column on the subject of faith would allow me to be honest about my own perspective and challenge my readers to consider theirs. But how can I make faith a part of every column?"

"Isn't that the challenge of every Christian teacher and every Christian individual? How can Christians engage real people about real issues and still maintain a friendship with skeptics and nonbelievers?"

Wow, I never thought about it like that. Mordecai was right. A pastor friend said he rarely discloses his profession to strangers when playing golf because it changes the conversation and often ends the relationship before it has a chance to get started. People assume preachers and faithful Christians are closed-minded and easily offended. And no one wants to be "preached at" while playing golf, or at any other time for that matter.

Mordecai continued, "If you crack that nut, TBT could be an example to Christians everywhere, and a powerful witness to those yet to believe."

I liked the way he said, "those yet to believe." It implies everyone can be gained for Christ if we break through their defenses and demonstrate the love God has for all people. "But how?" I asked. "How can I maintain my audience and not hide my faith?"

Mordecai had helped me boil my struggle down to one question.

"I suggest you do it with subtle honesty," he replied. "TBT is providing an important service as it is, but it can do more. Have you noticed the automatic signatures attached to most of business emails you receive? By means of their signature block, they identify their business and often even their purpose. Perhaps you could add a signature block to your column."

"What would you suggest?"

"It should be inviting and inclusive. It could be a famous quote, a favorite passage, or a phrase that defines your perspective without being offensive. As an author yourself, I suggest you refrain from quoting another author. It should be an original thought or a Scripture that advocates for faith without being judgmental."

"*The Herald* once hired a consultant to address the staff as part of our annual development conference," I recalled. "Among other things, we were asked to draft a personal mission statement. Mine was, '*Challenging the status quo for the sake of truth, justice and compassion.*'"

"It reminds me of a passage from the prophet Micah, chapter six," Mordecai added. 'The LORD has told you what is good, and what He requires of you: to do what is right, to love mercy, and to walk humbly with your God.'" [99]

"This has been helpful. I'm not sure what my editor will think of the idea, but I'm compelled to be more than the Ann Landers or Dear Abby of my generation. That's what a Christian friend called me the other day and it smarted a bit."

"He sounds like a good friend." Mordecai replied. "But don't dismiss the impact TRUTH BE TOLD is already enjoying. It will give you leverage when you meet with your editor," he said with a knowing smile.

"And by leverage, you are referring to corporate profits I assume?"

"Leverage? Profits? Purpose?" Mordecai smiled in response. "Why sacrifice one for the other? They seem to work nicely together. You achieve your purpose. *The Herald* achieves theirs, and your editor is happy. Everyone's happy. Sounds like a win/win/win proposition to me."

Time would tell.

"I don't feel very much like Pooh today," said Pooh. "There, there," said Piglet. "I'll bring you tea and honey until you do."
—A.A. Milne, Winnie-the-Pooh

CHAPTER 17

Unchained

I've always been a bit of a movie buff. The story-behind-the-story is what interests me most. It's not unusual for me to google an actor's profile, a movie detail, or a historic fact while live-streaming a movie at home. It drives Sarah crazy, especially when I search ahead for the outcome of a cliff-hanger while we're engaged in a dramatic series. I can't help myself. My reporter's curiosity demands an answer.

Well-known songs prompt the same aberrant behavior on my part. Take *Unchained Melody* for instance. It's a song that begs to be explained. Anyone who's heard the haunting 1965, Righteous Brothers rendition has it forever etched in their subconscious. The song has been covered by no fewer than 1,500 different artists and reached the top of the charts an unprecedented four different times by four different singers. The powerful feelings it evokes were employed in the 1990, blockbuster movie *Ghost* to illustrate the sensual relationship of the couple played by Patrick Swayze and Demi Moore.

The song is a powerful blend of lyric and melody no doubt. But why was it entitled, "*Unchained Melody?*" There is no mention of chains in the lyrics and it's not only a melody. Therein lies the story.

Unknown to most who love the ballad, it was the theme song for the little-known 1955 movie, *Unchained*. The movie tells the story of a man incarcerated in a medium-security prison for a minor offense. He couldn't bear being separated from his wife and son but refused to allow them to visit him in prison. He plans to escape, but a wiser inmate intervenes, keeping him from making his legal situation worse. The song, *Unchained Melody* was written to describe the depth of his longing caused by separation from his wife and son.

He describes his love as a consuming hunger that cannot be satisfied until they are reunited. Their forced separation is more than he can bear. It feels like time is standing still... moving so slowly. He is desperate for reassurance and prays that God would hasten the day his love would come to him.

In the movie, the prisoner accepts his sentence rather than risk the consequence of being recaptured and incurring an even longer sentence. I reached a similar conclusion about my situation relative to TRUTH BE TOLD.

As the famous prayer says, I planned to change the things that were within my control and accept with serenity the things that were beyond my control. The renewed commitment to my purpose compelled me to be more forthright about my faith, no matter how it might be received. I was willing to accept the consequence of my action. Let the chips fall where they may. I was committed to TBT but going forward it would have to be on my terms, even if it meant the end of the opportunity.

I was about to find out if Brad and our advertisers would support my decision.

I heard through the grapevine Brad was in a good mood. He had every reason to be. TRUTH BE TOLD had been sold as a concept based on the credibility of *The Herald* and my reputation as a reporter. Understandably, most of our initial advertisers had been local and regional businesses who knew of our work firsthand and trusted our reputation. As the column gained national traction, our sales team secured advertising from a growing number of Fortune 500 companies, significantly improving our profit margin. In the media business, ratings are everything and ours were through the roof. Evidently, there was a growing thirst for a perspective other than political correctness on the controversial issues of the day.

TRUTH BE TOLD was being quoted by other news outlets and mentioned a time or two on cable news shows that feasted on divergent perspectives. I'd been interviewed about my perspective on radio talk shows, a new and unexpected experience for me. Those went smoothly and everyone seemed pleased with our increased exposure. Free publicity is always good and pleased our advertisers. Things were looking up professionally. There was even talk of appearance as a regular contributor on a conservative cable network, but that was still under discussion. My buddies like to say I have a face made for radio, so I wasn't overly optimistic about that possibility.

I kept recalling the advice of Mordecai from our last meeting, "Don't dismiss the impact TRUTH BE TOLD is already enjoying. It will provide leverage when you meet with your editor." He believed, based on the popularity of the column, Brad would be inclined to trust my judgment and make every effort to keep me happy. We had worked together for years. Brad knew it was not in my nature to be difficult.

Mordecai's reference to Micah, chapter six, was also on my mind, "The LORD has told you what is good, and what He requires of you: to do what is right, to love mercy, and to walk humbly with your God." [100] I was convinced the Lord's blessing had as much to do with TBT's success as my writing skills. I wasn't the least bit tempted to let the column's success inflate my ego.

My only ambition was to be faithful to my purpose, providing a voice of reason in a world of compromise. I liked the emphasis on humility in the Micah passage. "Walking humbly" was not something often experienced in the cutthroat media business. The writers I admired most resisted the spotlight and were gratified solely by the acceptance of their work. Increased notoriety, increased income, and additional opportunities beyond TBT were not goals I was eager to pursue. "Been there done that…" as far as I was concerned.

I was not opposed to the profitability of TRUTH BE TOLD. Profits were the measure of success in every business and there was without a doubt a business side to publishing. Greater recognition led to increased syndication, which led to greater visibility, which led to greater influence. Writing is hard work. No one does it to be ignored.

Brad arrived at Mulligans before me for a change. He had a reputation for being late to meetings, so I took his punctuality as a positive sign. He was obviously pleased with TBT's success and considered our meeting significant.

He stood as I entered the restaurant and waved me over to his table. "How was your vacation? I'll bet taking off an entire month seemed strange after a lifetime of working day in and day out."

"It was great, but you're right," I replied. "Freedom to come and go as I please takes some getting used to. We spent the better part of a week in Memphis on our way to the coast. If you haven't been, you should go. Between Beale Street, the Peabody, Sun Studios, the Civil Rights Center, Graceland, and the world-famous restaurants, you can't go wrong."

"How was the weather on the coast? I'm sure you took your sticks with you."

"You know the coast. They have three seasons; hot, humid, and tropical depression. We didn't' experience any significant storms, but hot and humid were well represented. Everything was green and lush. There are some excellent golf courses there, for sure. Lots of bunkers, lakes, and healthy Bermuda grass to negotiate. It's a tough job, but someone has to do it."

"Speaking of tough jobs," Brad deftly shifted topics. "TRUTH BE TOLD is going gangbusters. Online publication is changing everything in the newspaper business. More than half of *The Herald*'s content is now viewed online. Can you believe that? Print subscriptions are way down, and the actual paper is getting smaller and smaller. We still do a good business with bundle drops at hotels, restaurants, and newsstands around the city, but if it were not for the midweek advertisements and the weekend subscriptions, I doubt it would pay to publish a daily anymore. It's hard to tell where it's all headed. There is still a business angle to pursue. Stores need to advertise, and people still want the in-depth reporting you'll never get from the sound bites that pass for the evening news. People want to be informed about the decisions of government officials, crime, local developments, the Cardinals and the Blues. It's a creative moment."

"You know what they say, 'When you are through changing, you are through.'"

"Sounds like a topic worthy of TBT," Brad suggested. "I've always been fascinated by the number of resilient people and businesses who for one reason or another stop being resilient. I've never understood why they become suddenly paralyzed by a setback, trauma, or loss, when in the past it would have been a mere bump in the road for them. So long as I have a say at *The Herald*, we will find ways to embrace change and stay profitable."

"Thanks for the suggestion. There is no shortage of worthy topics," I concurred. "From what you've told me, TRUTH BE TOLD seems to be holding its own. I assume the financial side of the column is showing a positive return? I confess I don't spend much time reading the threads, but I've noticed the Op-Eds. are attracting thousands of online replies each week."

"You don't know what you've been missing," Brad said with a smile. The team loves the threads and keeps a list of their favorite replies. I brought some of the latest along just for laughs."

@**soothsayer:** "Don't tell me gratitude is the key to success. The only key to success is sacrifice and hard work. If you wait around for someone to applaud your efforts, you are screwed."

@**peaceout:** "Here's a syllogism for you, 'Only idiots believe in syllogisms.' You believe in syllogisms. You're an idiot."

@**sadbuttrue:** "Money may not make you happy, but it sure helps."

Brad was obviously enjoying himself. "People never cease to amaze me. I especially enjoy the critical responses. You are good at rattling their cage. Like I always say, "I don't mind controversy. It's apathy I can't stand," he smiled. "Nevertheless, most of the comments have been surprisingly positive. I encourage you to be as controversial as you want. Don't hold back. Controversy sells more papers than convention. Here are a few more...

@**sowhat**: "I'm going to print this article and send it to my kids. Hard times provide perspective. There are always reasons to be grateful. Life is filled with possibilities."

@**yellowbrickroad**: "Loved the reference to Janson's song, *Buy Me a Boat*. I'm gonna make it my new ringtone!"

@**innuendo**: "Thanks for calling out white privilege. It's true that on average African Americans earn less than whites, and Hispanics less than African Americans. And I agree the amount of a person's wealth doesn't equate to the degree of their happiness."

@**John10.10**: "The most important things in life are not things. The sooner a person learns that, the happier they will be."

@**tiredofdogma**: "I subscribe to the Johnny Paycheck school of thought, '*Take This Job and Shove It*.' If you don't enjoy your job, no matter how much it pays, get the hell out."

@**DogGoneIt**: "'It's harder to raise well-adjusted, hardworking, industrious children when parents are wealthy.' Truer words were never spoken. I speak from experience."

"Your column on the cost and value of education in America is still drawing lots of comments. That topic hit a nerve for sure," Brad remarked, as he continued reading from his notes.

@**Underdog**: "If a free public education for children was considered a good thing 150 years ago, don't you think a free college education is the least we can do for young people today?"

"That comment got over 250 "thumbs up" in the thread," Brad noted.

@licketysplit: "When will America realize a typical four-year university degree has little or no value in the workplace? Businesses of every kind would do better by offering internships to train people for their needs. I don't care if it is teaching, electrical engineering, or coding. On the job training in the workplace is the best way to equip people for the task at hand. America's Universities are best at teaching kids how to drink, party and hook-up. Little more."

@tubesteak: "It's a question of supply and demand. Skilled electricians, plumbers, carpenters, roofers, truck drivers, computer technicians and electronic experts will always find work. Mike Rowe is right: a liberal arts degree is mostly a waste of time and money."

@stillwaiting: "So much for my degree in English Literature! 'You want fries with that order sir?'"

@offdutydude: "Loved, loved, loved the statement, 'Not everyone quits a job they aren't cut out for, only the smart ones.' I wish I had been told that ten years ago. TRUTH BE TOLD got it right!"

It was my turn to talk. "Brad, I need to ask you something. Did you mean it when you said, 'You want to encourage me to be more controversial.' And, 'Controversy sells more papers than convention'?"

"It seems to be working. I realize we all were a bit tentative initially," Brad replied. "No one was sure how a weekly Op-Ed. written to challenge the status quo would be received. There are obviously a lot of people, and I mean a lot of people who are fed up with clichés that have no connection to the harsh realities of life. TRUTH BE TOLD is tapping into that frustration. The pendulum seems to be swinging back to a more pragmatic, less idealistic perspective on life."

"You are the perfect man for this assignment Jim," Brad continued. "You have the right credentials but don't need the work, which gives you a free-wheeling attitude about what you write, no matter how popular or unpopular it might be."

"I'm glad to hear you say that because I feel I've been holding back. No worries, I always want to be gracious towards those who disagree with me and those who haven't given the subject much thought. But I'm not wired to walk the line. The longer I do this, the more adamant I feel about advocating more strongly for what is good, better, and best. These next few columns on Life, Liberty and the Pursuit of Happiness may be some of the most controversial I've submitted."

"I was thinking just the opposite," Brad countered. "Life, Liberty, and the Pursuit of Happiness are as American as baseball, apple pie and The Declaration of Independence. Who could possibly disagree with those values?"

"You'd be surprised," I laughed. "The subject of life, death, abortion and euthanasia are pretty controversial these days. Serious hot buttons. What qualifies as Liberty? When does one man's liberty become another man's imposition? Have you given much thought to what constitutes happiness? King Solomon had everything the world could offer: wine, women, riches, power and possessions. In the end, he considered it meaningless... all smoke, mirrors, and chasing after the wind. If you want controversy, I'm not in any danger of boring you on those topics."

"I hear you. I hear you. As long as you stick with positions that are self-evident, and make your case from a rational point of view, I'm okay with wherever you come down on those topics," Brad conceded. "We just can't go all Bible and preachy in the column, if you know what I mean."

"I both agree and disagree with you Brad. I agree, we need to resist quoting chapter and verse, but when it comes to what is morally right and morally wrong, I don't see myself straying far from what is Biblically true or false. I don't believe there is any difference between what is Biblically true and what is practically true. They are the same in my opinion."

I continued, "I also want the fourth column in the next series to focus on the subject of faith. I believe I can show that everyone takes positions on moral issues from the perspective of a personal belief system. It may not be Biblical faith, but their faith in democracy, socialism, pragmatism,

Hinduism, Buddhism, Islam, or even agnosticism determines their point of view on life's most important issues. I intend to be honest about my Christian perspective and I'm more than willing to acknowledge that mine is a minority opinion. Popular or not, I believe truth has an edge to it. People know it when they hear it."

"You've given me no reason to question your perspective so far, Jim. I've always known you to be a reasonable and gracious person, but to be honest I never took you for a religious guy until recently."

I appreciated the candor between us and felt a need to explain myself to Brad, but only to a point. This was not the time or the place to come clean on my angelic visitor or my many encounters with the likes of Mordecai and Sam.

"You're probably right Brad. Until I began writing TBT, my work for *The Herald* didn't involve expressing opinions on the stories I covered. In the past I was only interested in discovering the "who, what, where and how" of a story and the opinions of the people involved, but TBT is different. *My opinion is the story*. I still spend a good deal of time investigating the issue and weighing the opinions of the experts, but ultimately, I'm forced to come down on one side or the other. My examination of the issues has driven me back to my roots and the moral certainty I've rediscovered in my Christian faith."

"Are you a believer, Brad?" Wow. I can't believe I even went there, but I felt compelled to understand his perspective before I dropped my latest intention for TBT on him.

Brad didn't seem offended or hesitate in answering. "I was raised in the faith. My mom's dad was a Baptist preacher part time, so I got inoculated early in life. They say once you're inoculated there is little danger of catching the real thing, and I suppose that's what happened to me. My grandad married us, and our family gatherings early in life revolved around the church, but after my folks died, I've never been accused of being very religious. We celebrate the big three, Christmas, Easter and the 4th of July," he said with a smile. "I'm not offended by those who believe in Jesus nor those who don't. Live and let live. Like you wrote in your column, I believe

MAN IN THE MIDDLE

there is right and wrong, and most people know it when they see it. That's good enough for me."

"The reason I asked, is that I have a proposal to make about TRUTH BE TOLD," I continued. "Well, it's really not as much a proposal as a stated intention," I continued.

"I feel the need to be more transparent about my perspective since TBT is tackling some of the more controversial moral aspects of our culture. I don't intend to be offensive but I'm finding it increasingly difficult to separate my opinion from Biblical truth. I don't plan on changing anything about my approach to the column. I think it's solid, but I do want my byline to include a statement of my perspective."

"What do you have in mind?" I had Brad's attention.

"Do you remember when *The Herald* had the reporters and editorial departments go through a mission-writing exercise?"

"Yes, of course. It was my idea," Brad acknowledged.

"Well I'd like that statement to be included in my byline. I appreciated the exercise and benefitted from the experience. It helped me focus my professional perspective and would clarify my point of view as TBT's author."

"I don't recall what you concluded back then. What was it?"

"Nothing too profound, but helpful," I answered. "It was, *'Challenging the status quo for the sake of truth, justice, and compassion.'* I don't believe it's controversial, and it should help my followers know what to expect from me. More and more companies are being candid about their purpose beyond the product they are selling. I made a list." I slid the examples towards Brad.

- **Life Is Good**: "To Spread the Power of Optimism."

- **IKEA**: "To create a better everyday life for people."

- **Tesla**: "To accelerate the world's transition to sustainable energy."

- **TED Talks**: "To Spread Ideas."

- **Google**: "To organize the world's information and make it universally accessible and useful."

- **Twitter**: "To give everyone the power to create and share ideas and information instantly, without barriers."

- **Oprah Winfrey**: "To be a teacher. And to be known for inspiring my students to be more than they thought they could be."

"Except for Oprah, those are all corporate mission statements," Brad observed. I don't think I have ever seen an Op-Ed. that included a mission statement under the byline."

"Precisely!" I seized the moment. "That's what I love about TRUTH BE TOLD. We are different. We should be setting the trend, not following it. That's who we are. And there is one more thing I want to propose." I continued. "More and more columns include a single word sign off, like B.R.B. for Be Right Back, or C.U.L. for Catch You Later, or even the standard T.Y. for Thank You. I intend to end each column with an obscure Biblical reference, 'Micah 6:8'"

"Arghhhhhhhhhhhhhhh," Brad shook his head in disbelief. I could tell I was pushing him to his limit and beyond, but at this point I had nothing to lose. I was convinced it was God's will for TBT. I was placing my trust in the promise of the man in white that God's spirit would make a way when their seemed to be no way.

"I thought we agreed not to go Biblical," Brad objected.

"I don't intend to quote it," I countered. "Just lay the reference out there as a sign off. I think it will peak the curiosity of the reader and tantalize them to look it up for themselves. It's a bit mysterious which fits the nature of TBT perfectly in my opinion."

"What does it say? Why did you choose that passage?" I could sense Brad was at least giving the concept fair consideration.

"Well, it's not 'Jesus Saves!' if that's your concern." I laughed out loud. "I chose it because it's accepted by Christians, Muslims and Jews alike. I don't think even nonbelievers and agnostics will find much objectionable about it. It is true on its face. '*The LORD has told you what is good, and what*

He requires of you: to do what is right, to love mercy, and to walk humbly with your God.' [101]

"Just so I understand, you want the mission statement to be added under your byline and the Micah 6:8 reference to be added as a sign off at the bottom of every column? Is that correct?" Brad asked.

"Exactly. Nothing more, but nothing less. I feel compelled to be more transparent about my perspective in writing TBT, especially as I tackle issues that challenge national morality. I don't intend for TBT to become the Ann Landers of a new generation, giving advice on trivial matters. TBT has a greater purpose. And as you have always said, 'You don't mind controversy. It's apathy you can't stand.'"

"I want to think more about it, and I reserve the right to change my mind, but I'm willing to float a trial balloon."

Wow. I anticipated more push back than I was receiving. It was either Brad's response to the conviction in my voice, or the spirit of God had shown up in a big way, maybe both.

Brad continued, "It will be controversial and will attract the criticism of our atheist friends, but TBT kicked that door down a long time ago." Brad seemed agreeable with the changes, at least for now. It was more than I expected, and it saved me from making an ultimatum, which I was fully prepared to do.

We agreed to introduce the changes in the next four columns and make a final decision after that. I was fine with that. It allowed Brad and *The Herald* time to weigh the public and advertiser's response and provided me with an adequate opportunity to convince them of TBT's greater purpose.

The more I thought about it, the more I liked it. If the Lord intended TRUTH BE TOLD to stand out, these changes would accomplish the purpose.

St. Louis Herald

TRUTH BE TOLD

Edition 1, Column 17

"Challenging the status quo for the sake of truth, justice and compassion."

Life: An Unalienable Right

(The first of a three-part series: Life, Liberty and the Pursuit of Happiness.)

By: **James King**

"We hold these truths to be self-evident, that all men are created equal, that they are endowed by their Creator with certain unalienable rights, that among these are life, liberty, and the pursuit of happiness." (The Declaration of Independence)

L ife is precious.
The whole world was captivated by the nearly impossible rescue of twelve young boys and their soccer coach from a flooded cave in Thailand. They had been trapped for two weeks when a rainstorm flooded the cave behind them. Experts from across the globe gathered to engineer their rescue, ultimately achieved through the combined effort of eighteen Tai Navy Seal divers and 100 volunteers. From the time they were discovered on July 2nd, until the last boy was rescued on July 9th, the world held its collective breath.

On October 13, 2010, the last of 33 miners were rescued after a cave-in trapped them a half mile underground for 69 days. The operation required the help of experts and equipment flown to Chili from around the world. The rescuers had to determine the miners' location, bore a hole to deliver oxygen and needed supplies, and then drill a separate shaft large enough to accommodate a capsule capable of carrying one man at a time to the surface. The rescue cost over $20 million. President Sebastian Pinera declared the cost, "worth every peso."

Closer to home, who can forget the 1987, ordeal 18-month-old "baby Jessica" endured when she fell more than 20 feet into an eight-inch-wide water well while playing with other children in her aunt's backyard in Midland, Texas. The 58-hour nightmare required drilling a second shaft next to the well, then tunneling perpendicular through dense rock to rescue the child. For two days, the toddler was heard crying, humming, and singing while people frantically attempted her rescue. Jessica was hospitalized for more than a month and required a partial amputation of one foot due to gangrene. She is now living a normal and happy life as a married mother supported in part by a nearly $800,000 trust fund established by well-wishers from around the world.

All life is precious. Not just human life.

Parineeta was found near death on a road in India with a broken leg. Her owner had abandoned her because of the injury. The donkey was rescued, her leg mended, and adopted by a loving family who happily provide her a worry-free life roaming their pasture.

A black bear named Ben was rescued from a roadside zoo in North Carolina. He had spent the first six years of his life locked in a cage not much bigger than his body. Today he enjoys new-found freedom in a wildlife sanctuary in Northern California.

The list of animal rescues is endless. An emaciated dog named Blue was found near death in Virginia. His owner was charged for the starvation deaths of other animals found on his property. The man was given a one-year prison sentence and prohibited from owning any animals for three years. A Chimpanzee was saved from an 8ft. x 16ft, windowless cage as a roadside attraction in Georgia. And every spring ducklings that fall through the grates of rain sewers are rescued by bystanders as their anxious mother watches from a safe distance.

Americans are inclined to do everything they can to protect life.

The Animal Welfare Act of 1966 provides protection for animals in zoos, laboratories, the general population and even those raised for slaughter. It mandates certain procedures to protect livestock in transit and limit their suffering and pain when harvested. Significant criminal and civil penalties are imposed for any violation.

Wild animals are likewise protected by fish and game regulations that establish legal seasons and limits on hunters, trappers, and anglers. Animals considered endangered are especially protected. Selling, purchasing, possessing, and transporting a Bald or Golden Eagle bird, its eggs, or nest without permission, and any attempt to shoot, poison, capture or disturb an eagle can result in a fine of $10,000 and two years in prison. Felony convictions carry a maximum penalty of $250,000. Rewards are offered to encourage individuals to provide information leading to arrests.

In 2005, a Florida land development company was fined $356,000 for the destruction of a tree containing an eagle nest on property where it was constructing a housing development. That same year, in a separate incident, two Florida defendants were ordered to pay fines of $10,000 each and contribute $80,000 in restitution to the Audubon Center and the Florida Bald Eagle Conservation Fund for a similar offense.

Americans consider nearly every kind of life priceless.

Scientists and schoolchildren across the nation love to speculate about the possibility of life on Mars, the closest planet to earth. The belief that the planet was once partially covered by water has stirred their imagination, since water is deemed essential to the existence of microorganisms, which some believe is the first link in the chain of life. Mars' rovers have collected soil samples which are being examined for what scientists call "biosignatures," evidence of past life forms.

In July of 2018, Bill Whitaker of CBS traveled 2 miles beneath the earth's surface in a 60 Minutes broadcast to investigate a South African gold mine. Salt deposits and water supplies uncovered during the mining process fascinated the scientists who accompanied him. They discovered microscopic worms in one pocket of water that they speculated was 5,000 years old. It was a species of life never-before-seen, surviving at great depth without any exposure to sunlight. They identified a crustacean one-sixty-fourth-of-an-inch long, living off single-celled bacteria found in the same water. They were ecstatic.

TRUTH BE TOLD believes all life is sacred and must be shown the dignity and respect it deserves.

The word sacred is derived from the Latin word, 'sacrare,' meaning, "set apart, or holy." It implies an object deemed sacred is connected to God, holy, and entitled to special reverence and respect. Scientists, using the most advanced technology available, are incapable of affecting change in inorganic material in such a way as to create organic life, not even the formation of single-cell bacteria. Life alone must give birth to life. Those who deny God's existence struggle to accept the logical conclusion that God is the creator of all forms of life.

People of faith, by contrast, accept the simple statement, *"In the beginning, God created the heaven and the earth."* [102] To believe creation can occur apart from God is illogical and unproven. The belief that there was once absolutely nothing and nothing happened to the nothing, causing nothing to explode to create everything everywhere requires faith greater than belief in a God who created the world and everything in it.

For all the stated reasons that life is precious, life is valuable, and all life no matter how basic should be treated with respect and dignity, obligates TRUTH BE TOLD to declare life in the womb sacred and thus worthy of respect and protection. Bald and Golden Eagles are no longer endangered species, but stringent laws, fines and imprisonment still protect their eggs. It seems misguided at best, and hypocritical at least, to allow life-ending abortions to be performed after human conception and up to and including the day of a baby's birth.

Our nation is divided on the issue. The Supreme Court seems unwilling to reexamine their 1973, Roe Vs. Wade decision which granted women permission to make a choice to end their baby's life. The court is hesitant to rule on a matter of personal moral and religious belief.

Although TRUTH BE TOLD does not advocate for any form of abortion, it would be more honest in the opinion of TBT if the Supreme Court would grant permission to the states and to a woman carrying a fetus to euthanize her child as it does livestock and domestic animals. It is harsh and shocking to declare the truth about what is really happening in an abortion. Again, TBT does not support any threat to life in the womb. Based on what we know about the beginning of life, TBT must declare fetal life sacred. To call life not life, no matter how fragile, no matter how small, no matter how immature, is contrary to every value, protection, and legal status America provides to all other forms of life.

TRUTH BE TOLD has no power to declare anything legal or illegal; elected officials and the courts retain that authority for the nation. But it is TBT's stated purpose to espouse a viewpoint solely on the basis of self-evident truth. TRUTH BE TOLD believes people are better off when they freely exercise informed decisions on matters that are good, better, and best for us all.

TRUTH BE TOLD will not avoid an issue because it is controversial or divisive, nor refuse to take a stand on a matter that could jeopardize the popularity of this column. America was founded by imperfect people on the basis of principles they believed were universally self-evident. TRUTH BE TOLD believes self-evident truth still exists, even when that truth creates offense and provokes strong opposition. So be it.

The right to *Life, Liberty and The Pursuit of Happiness* is considered a self-evident principle our founders believed should be protected.

TRUTH BE TOLD agrees.
(Micah 6:8) ▪

St. Louis Herald

TRUTH BE TOLD

Edition 1, Column 18

"Challenging the status quo for the sake of truth, justice and compassion."

Liberty: An Unalienable Right

(The second of a three-part series: Life, Liberty and the Pursuit of Happiness.)

By: **James King**

> *"We hold these truths to be self-evident, that all men are created equal, that they are endowed by their Creator with certain unalienable rights, that among these are life, liberty, and the pursuit of happiness."* (The Declaration of Independence)

Two of my most prized possessions are an original 1903 lithograph poster of Abraham Lincoln, Frederick Douglas, and Booker T. Washington, drawn by the famous illustrator Ernest Haskell, and a first addition copy of Booker T. Washington's classic autobiography, *Up from Slavery.* Knowing my admiration for Booker T. Washington, Sarah acquired both of these treasures from the dusty confines of an antique store in our area. Unbeknownst to the dealer at the time, they are worth hundreds more than she paid for them. But their value to me is more than monetary. Those men are true heroes of liberty. They risked their lives to free those unable to free themselves.

The founders of our nation declared life, liberty, and the pursuit of happiness to be "self-evident" God-given rights. But if the Founding Fathers believed all men were created equal, and liberty was a God-given right, why did they permit slavery in the United States from its inception? Why did so many of them, including Thomas Jefferson and George Washington own slaves themselves? In a debate with Stephen Douglas, Abraham Lincoln was asked that very question.

"In the first place, I insist that our

fathers did not make this nation half slave and half free, or part slave and part free." Lincoln responded. "I insist that they found the institution of slavery existing here. They did not make it so, but they left it so because they knew no way to get rid of it at the time." [103]

There is no doubt what Lincoln thought on the subject. In a speech to a regiment of the Union Army he said, *"Whenever I hear any one arguing for slavery, I feel a strong impulse to see it tried on him personally."* [104] He repeatedly said in many of his speeches, *"As I would not be a slave, so I would not be a master... I am naturally anti-slavery. If slavery is not wrong, nothing is wrong. I cannot remember when I did not so think and feel."* [105]

Despite what many believe, the issue of slavery is not just a historic crime of past generations. There are more people enslaved today than at any other time in history. Experts calculate that roughly 13 million people were captured and sold into slavery between the 15th and 19th centuries; today, it is estimated more than 40 million people, three times as many, exist in some form of modern slavery. [106]

You rarely hear the word "slavery" used today but that doesn't mean it has been wiped from the face of the earth. The condition of being owned, exploited, dehumanized and treated as a piece of property is now more commonly called "human trafficking." Women and girls comprise 71% of all victims. Children make up 25% of the rest, an estimate of 10 million worldwide. They are compelled to work as prostitutes, clean houses, harvest crops, work on fishing vessels, mine for minerals essential to smart technology, as laborers in construction, and forced military service.

Although victims of war are often sold into slavery, most shackles of slavery are fastened more subtlety today than in the 19th century. Human traffickers are prone to use deception more often than violence, offering the promise of a better job, or the assurance of a better life *for a fee* that turns into a never-ending cycle of indebtedness. Impoverished mothers in third-world countries must often choose between selling their children, watching them starve to death, or turn to prostitution. Illegal immigrants in the United States are frequently forced to work under the threat of arrest and deportation if they complain about unfair treatment.

"According. to slavery expert Siddharth Kara, modern slave traders now earn up to 30 times more that their 18th and 19th century counterparts would have done. The one-off cost of a slave today is $450, Kara estimates. A forced laborer generates roughly $8,000 in annual profit for their exploiter, while sex traffickers earn an average of $36,000

per victim." [107]

Many patriots of every race, creed, and nationality paid dearly for the liberty we enjoy. Sixty-eight-hundred soldiers fought and died in the War for Independence from England. An equal number were wounded and seventeen thousand succumb to disease and deprivation. But freedom from England did not mean freedom from slavery. More would be required.

The civil war was fought from 1861–1865, to preserve the Union and free the nearly four million African Americans living as slaves in the South, one-tenth of the entire United States population. The war touched every aspect of the American culture. It cost the lives of 650,000 soldiers, in addition to 50,000 civilians and 80,000 African American slaves who were killed by violence or disease.

Who could have predicted the self-evident truth of Liberty would demand so high a price in human suffering and sacrifice?

TRUTH BE TOLD believes true liberty is defined by more than the absence of chains. Many who are free to come and go wherever and whenever they wish, who have never been owned by anyone, are not free. They suffer in prisons of a different kind. Theirs' are not bars of steel but chains of fear, prejudice, hatred, envy, lust, jealousy, bitterness, anger, poverty, ignorance, worry and pessimism. Harriet Tubman,

the most famous conductor on the underground railroad, responsible for leading hundreds of slaves to freedom, observed, *"If I could have convinced more slaves that they were slaves, I could have freed thousands more."* They had made peace with their chains. Many still do.

But by contrast, there are examples of imprisoned men and women who have refused to accept their condition and live in freedom despite the guards and conditions that enslave them.

Booker T. Washington, was six-years-old when President Lincoln issued the Emancipation Proclamation, freeing him from his chains. Freedom from legal slavery didn't automatically mean freedom from the conditions of slavery. The chains of inferiority and prejudice that continue to haunt African Americans to this day did their best to enslave Washington, but he refused to become a victim. He said, *"I confess that I do not envy the white boy as I once did. I have learned that success is to be measured not so much by the position one has reached in life as by the obstacles which he has overcome while trying to succeed. Looked at from this standpoint, I almost reach the conclusion that often the Negro boy's birth and connection with an unpopular race is an advantage, so far as real life is concerned."* [108]

Corrie ten Boom and her family were imprisoned for hiding Jews and assisting their escape from Nazi persecution in Holland, during WWII. Her eighty-four-year-old father was offered freedom if he would give his word to cause no more trouble. He replied, *"If I go home today, tomorrow I will open my door again to any man in need who knocks."* [109] He was returned to his cell to die ten days later. His daughters Betsy and Corrie, were sent to Ravensbruck concentration camp where Betsy succumbed to the abusive conditions ten months later. Despite the suffering they endured, the sisters preferred their enslaved status over the misery and darkness of the guards who imprisoned them.

Nelson Mandela was arrested and given a life sentence for conspiracy to overthrow the racist and corrupt South African government. Twenty-seven years later, fearing civil war, the president pardoned him. Four years after his release, Mandela was elected to become South Africa's president from 1994–1999. He humbly acknowledged the sins of his youth that led to his arrest, but wisely used the lessons learned during his imprisonment to free many others from prisons of the heart and mind.

"As I walked out the door toward the gate that would lead to my freedom," he said. *"I knew if I didn't leave my bitterness and hatred behind, I'd still be in prison. To be free is not merely to cast off one's chains, but to live in a way that respects and enhances the freedom of others."* [110]

Like ten Boom sisters before him, Mandela did not envy his jailers. *"A man who takes away another man's freedom is a prisoner of hatred. He is locked behind the bars of prejudice and narrow-mindedness."* [111]

TRUTH BE TOLD believes that true liberty is a state of mind.

The R&B pop group En Vogue's 1992, smash hit, *Free Your Mind*, had it right. The lyrics attack any form of prejudice that passes judgement on the basis of outward appearance.

Prejudice makes no sense to them. According to En Vogue, the problem is one of perception. The lyrics of their song remind people that before you can truly know another person, you have to see them as they are, not as you suppose them to be. In other words, you have to free your mind before you can accept a person without regard for the color of their skin. They conclude that if you can do that, the rest will follow. Prejudice by definition, is a "pre-judgement" made by closed-minded people who haven't taken the time or made the effort to get to know the person or race they subjectively deem unworthy.

Booker T. Washington refused to accept the opinion that his birth status rendered him inferior by reason of race. The Ten Booms refused to give Nazi authorities the power to alter their character. Nelson Mandela rose above his own prejudice and hatred of his enemies to unify his nation rather than use his newly acquired power to retaliate. Those who are truly free refuse to be defined by their status, the opinions of others, and the laws of the land. They are free because they refuse to accept the chains of injustice others attempt to impose on them.

The Declaration of Independence called Liberty a basic human right ordained by God. It was England's violation of that Divine right that justified America's succession.

"Whenever any Form of Government becomes destructive of these ends, it is the Right of the People to alter or to abolish it, and to institute new Government, laying its foundation on such principles and organizing its powers in such form, as to them shall seem most likely to effect their Safety and Happiness."[112]

Thomas Jefferson, the author of those words, called liberty a gift from God that could not have been achieved without His blessing. He warned that anyone who thought differently risked God's judgment.

"God who gave us life gave us liberty. Can the liberties of a nation be thought secure when we have removed their only firm basis, a conviction in the minds of the people that these liberties are the Gift of God? That they are not to be violated but with His wrath? Indeed, I tremble for my country when I reflect that God is just, and that His justice cannot sleep forever..."[113]

Our nation's past is littered with Liberty's mantras.

- "Live free or die." The motto of the state of New Hampshire.
- "Give me freedom or give me death." Patrick Henry
- "They who can give up essential liberty to obtain temporary safety deserve neither liberty nor safety." Benjamin Franklin
- "Those who deny freedom for others, deserve it not for themselves." Abraham Lincoln
- "Conformity is the jailer of freedom and the enemy of growth." John F. Kennedy
- "When this happens and when we allow freedom (to) ring... we will be able to join hands and sing in the words of the old Negro spiritual, 'Free at last, Free at last, Thank God Almighty we are free at last.'" Martin Luther King Jr.
- "Freedom is never more than one generation away from extinction." Ronald Reagan

The Statue called Liberty stands proudly on her own island in New York harbor, welcoming the world to America's shores. The sculptor Frederic Auguste Bartholdi modeled the colossus after Libertas, the Roman goddess of freedom. The broken shackles and chains lying at her feet symbolized America's abolition of slavery.

The words of Emma Lazarus' poem inscribed on her base give voice to her meaning,

"Give me your tired, your poor, your huddled masses yearning to breathe free. The wretched refuse of your teeming shore. Send these, the homeless, tempest-tossed to me. I lift my lamp beside the golden door!"

The sacrifice of thousands was considered a price worth paying to secure America's freedom.

Thousands more died in the Civil War to banish slavery from our land. Liberty is a God-given right that must be defended, an inheritance that must be prized by every generation.

Liberty is the value above all other values that makes America great.

(Micah 6:8) ▪

St. Louis Herald

"Challenging the status quo for the sake of truth, justice and compassion."

The Pursuit of Happiness: An Unalienable Right

(The third of a three-part series: Life, Liberty and the Pursuit of Happiness.)

By: **James King**

"We hold these truths to be self-evident, that all men are created equal, that they are endowed by their Creator with certain unalienable rights, that among these are life, liberty, and the pursuit of happiness." (The Declaration of Independence)

I've often wondered why "Life, Liberty and the Pursuit of Happiness," were Thomas Jefferson's *Big Three*. The first two are logical enough, but *The Pursuit of Happiness*? Not so much. I can think of several God-given rights that seem more worthy of a fight with the British army.

- Life, Liberty, and Prosperity.
- Life, Liberty, and Family.
- Life, Liberty, and Tax Relief.
- Life, Liberty, and Property.
- Life, Liberty, and Free Trade.
- Life, Liberty, and Self-Governance

Mark Setton is co-founder and CEO of an organization he calls, The Pursuit of Happiness (POH for short.). The POH is dedicated to overcoming depression and a quest for lasting happiness. Dr. Setton holds a PhD. from Oxford University and has taught at the University of New York, the University of California at Berkeley, and Oxford. He is currently the Professor of East Asian Studies and International Affairs at the University of Bridgeport. Although a recognized expert on Confucian Thought and Asian Philosophy,

Setton is better known for his obsession with the scientific, biological, and philosophical basis for the God-given, unalienable right that Thomas Jefferson called *The Pursuit of Happiness*.

According to Setton most historians believe Jefferson's emphasis on happiness came from the English philosopher, John Locke 1632–1704. Locke championed "Life, Liberty and Estate," in his famous work, *Two Treatise of Government*. Many historians believe, Jefferson simply chose a less aristocratic, more American word to describe the same concept, i.e. the pursuit of wealth. But Setton does not agree. He uncovered a lengthy letter from Jefferson to his private secretary in Paris, declaring himself an Epicurean. Setton believes Jefferson's choice of the phrase,

"The Pursuit of Happiness," was a rejection of Locke's pursuit of estate (i.e. wealth) in favor of the Epicurean values of "close friendships, limited desires, simplicity, and contentment" that produce happiness in life. Setton rests his case on the clarity of Jefferson's letter that concludes by declaring, "happiness, not wealth, is the aim of life." [114]

A team of highly qualified PhDs maintain The Pursuit of Happiness Institute. Their official website is worth the time it takes to examine it. The website offers dozens of articles, courses of study, profiles of historic proponents of happiness

and their theories, a quiz to measure your degree of happiness, and an in-depth discussion of the seven habits they believe are characteristic of happy people.

1. Close Relationships – People considered safe to share your feelings.
2. Acts of Kindness – Caring for others leads to greater happiness.
3. Exercise & Physical Well-being – Keep moving and eat healthy.
4. Flow – Engage in activities that bring joy and personal satisfaction.
5. Spiritual Engagement – The pursuit of life's deeper meaning.
6. Self-Awareness – Accepting one's uniqueness and personal value.
7. Optimism – Defined as gratitude leading to courage.

Introspection, an aspect of the sixth habit, is a quality they have found common among happy, well-adjusted people. They contend it is helpful to examine your past and analyze those moments when you felt most content. Some of us have a longer past than others to examine.

As a reporter, I've interviewed hundreds of people of both the happy and unhappy kind. Most of my weekend columns were based on interviews of people celebrating an extraordinary accomplishment, or who demonstrated a quality of life worthy of admiration. When asked to describe the happiest moment of their life, they predictably mentioned a time when they overcame a great difficulty or period of struggle.

They may not have realized it at the time, but overcoming their struggle usually led to a greater sense of satisfaction and happiness than if they had experienced no struggle at all. People tend to feel most alive and invigorated when confronting a nearly insurmountable challenge. Difficulties in life often necessitate reliance on others: a spouse, a friend or colleagues. Overcoming hardship also requires sacrifice, hard work, determination and focus. Few realize the essential role struggle plays in sharpening their skills and deepening their character. Like fire is used to remove dross from gold and tempers steel, hardship refines people and strengthens resolve.

Our family has weathered its share of setbacks like everyone else, but we've not succumbed. We've been blessed to raise two healthy, type-A sons. The lessons learned during their formative years were not easy. We didn't sign up for easy. My theory is that compliant children rarely make a difference in things that matter. We preferred outgoing over docile. Some parents struggle with the terrible twos or the challenge of teenage upheaval. We were not strangers to frustration, but attitude

is everything. Anyone can parent an obedient child, real parenting requires the skill to navigate your child's first detention, wrecking the family car, overcoming heartbreak, underage drinking, hospitalization, or engaging in one of a hundred other activities guaranteed to disrupt the flow. Happiness is not defined by the absence of turmoil. The ability to overcome turmoil, taking the good, the bad and the ugly in stride is the key to happiness.

Looking back over sixty-plus years provides perspective. We were married the weekend after graduating from college and immediately moved to a new city so I could enroll in graduate school. We didn't have two nickels to rub together, but that was part of the charm. Our three-room tenement cost $100/mo., which included utilities. Our next-door neighbor entertained men at all hours of the day and night in the practice of her profession. Ferrell cats kept the rodent population at bay. The blare of police sirens and gunfire were usual on our street. We purchased a $1,500 used car for my college-educated wife to drive to her job as a receptionist. I rode a bike to the university which I placed inside the apartment every night to keep it from being stolen. Our Christmas decorations were made from egg cartons and cookie cut outs of hardened dough that we painted. My wife still cherishes a candy dish with a silver edge that I purchased as a gift from a Goodwill store. I'm quite certain I spent at least $3 for it. We still consider those, "the good old days" that we experienced with other grad students who lived much the same way.

TRUTH BE TOLD agrees with Jefferson that a person's attitude about their situation is more important than the reality of their circumstance. During those years of struggle, we were in hot pursuit of a better career, a better address, a better salary, a better car, and a better life all around. But in the midst of the pursuit, we were never unhappy. As the old proverb says, the journey is as important as the destination. The pursuit of our goals provided as much satisfaction as their achievement.

A good friend likes to quote the Bible to me now and then when it applies to an article I'm writing. While discussing this series on God-given rights, he referenced a letter the apostle Paul wrote to his understudy Timothy.

"Godliness with contentment is great gain. For we brought nothing into the world, and we can take nothing out of it. If we have food and clothing, we will be content with that. Those who want to get rich fall into temptation and a trap and into many foolish and harmful desires that plunge people into ruin and destruction." [115]

The Lord is not opposed to riches,

just the misguided love of riches. Some of the most prominent people in the Bible grew rich through the Lord's blessing: the patriarchs Abraham, Isaac, Jacob, and Job as well as kings David and Solomon. When Solomon, the richest and most accomplished man in the world reflected on all he had achieved, he called his many earthly accomplishments, "a meaningless, chasing after the wind." [116]

But not everything is meaningless. According to Solomon, God provides true happiness through the simple things of life, things available to everyone regardless of social status or financial standing.

"A person can do nothing better than to eat and drink and find satisfaction in their own toil. This too, I see, is from the hand of God, for without Him, who can eat or find enjoyment? To the person who pleases him, God gives wisdom, knowledge, and happiness, but to the sinner he gives the task of gathering and storing up wealth to hand it over to the one who pleases God." [117]

The prophet and the apostle agree, "Godliness when accompanied by contentment is the key to true happiness." [118]

In the Declaration of Independence, the big three unalienable rights were defined by Jefferson as *Life, Liberty and The Pursuit of Happiness.* God's big three, memorized by many children in Sunday school, are

Faith, Hope and Love. Although the lists are not exactly the same, they both emphasize the internal qualities of a person, not an outward circumstance, as the keys to unlock happiness.

TRUTH BE TOLD believes The Pursuit of Happiness is an elusive God-given right, but of a different sort than Life and Liberty.

The Pursuit of Happiness is not something a person can possess and locked down after it has been won. It is an action not an accomplishment. The thrill of the chase yields the result. The pursuit, not the capture.

When you stop the pursuit, happiness will vanish.

Long live the chase.

(Micah 6:8) ▪

St. Louis Herald

TRUTH BE TOLD

Edition 1, Column 20

"Challenging the status quo for the sake of truth, justice and compassion."

The Question of Faith

By: **James King**

Kindness, compassion, and forgiveness are qualities especially needed in times of controversy, and controversy is rampant these days. Whatever happened to the axiom, "I disapprove of what you say, but I will defend to death your right to say it." The values of tolerance and inclusion are often touted, but rarely practiced. Battles rage over race, immigration, socialism, capitalism, faith, abortion, politics, nationalism, globalism, community standards, environmentalism, free trade, tariffs, freedom of speech, gun laws, vaccination, and on and on and on.

Some say our nation has never been more divided, but I'm not so sure. Americans have always been known to hold strong opinions. The unity evidenced among the founding fathers during the nation's formative years is often praised. Benjamin Franklin described the moment when he said, "We must indeed all hang together or most assuredly, we will all hang separately." It was especially true of John Adams and Thomas Jefferson who exchanged more than three hundred letters between them before dying on the same day, July 4, 1826, exactly fifty years after signing The Declaration of Independence. But their relationship was also marred by a season of deep alienation.

During the election of 1800, Jefferson, who served as vice-president under Adams, attempted to unseat the President by any means necessary. Although campaigning by the candidates was considered inappropriate at the time, it didn't stop their surrogates from vicious character attacks.

It got nasty. Jefferson's camp said Adams, "...has neither the force and firmness of a man, nor the gentleness and sensibility of a woman." Adam's people called Jefferson, "a mean-spirited, low-life fellow, the son of a half-breed squaw sired by a Virginia mulatto father." [119] Jefferson won the election but the damage seemed irreparable. Neither man spoke to the other for years.

When a fellow signer of The Declaration died a decade later, Jefferson sent word of their mutual friend's death to Adams. He included, "We too must go and that ere long, I believe we are under half a dozen at present; I mean the signers..." [120]

Twelve years of silence was broken. Adams responded, "You and I ought not to die before we have explained ourselves to each other." [121] Although they continued to disagree about politics, religion and other matters, they reestablished a sincere and true friendship. One observer wrote,

"Historians regard the letters that they exchanged as an intellectual dialogue of the highest plane. In all, it spanned half a century and embraced government, politics, philosophy and religion as well as the vicissitudes of aging and various family sorrows and joys." [122]

For as long as I can recall, religion and politics have been identified as the two subjects people should avoid discussing in polite conversation. TRUTH BE TOLD believes we could learn a thing or two from the example of Adams and Jefferson. Too much time is wasted and relationships ruined over disagreements in belief and perspectives that friends should accept and respect in each other.

During the contentious days of the 16th century Reformation, a phrase was born that bears remembering, "In necessariis unitas, in dubiis libertas, in omnibus caritas." These words are translated, "In essentials unity, in non-essentials liberty, and in all things charity," or, "Unity in necessary things; liberty in doubtful things; charity in all things."

TRUTH BE TOLD believes no one should be forced to accept or deny anything, so long as their opinions do not result in actions that bring harm to others. There is value in rigorous debate. Originalists believe the Constitution of the United States should be considered a fixed document and interpreted according to its meaning at the time it was enacted. Relativists believe the Constitution should be considered a fluid document written to provide guiding principles that ought to evolve with the culture. TRUTH BE TOLD, believes the tension between these viewpoints serves both sides well. It ensures America will not stray far from her roots while encouraging a thoughtful approach toward issues the founding fathers could not have foreseen.

TRUTH BE TOLD believes an attitude of mutual respect is also essential when discussing matters of faith between friends and strangers. No one should be forced by war, penalty of law, or cultural prejudice to accept or deny their religious belief. The first amendment to the Constitution is first for a reason.

Congress shall make no law respecting an establishment of religion, or prohibiting the free exercise thereof; or abridging the freedom of speech, or of the press; or the right of the people peaceably to assemble, and to petition the government for a redress of grievances.

A small but spirited controversy erupted in 1979, between two prominent social activists. Bob Dylan's public comments and the lyrics of his songs epitomized his generation's rejection of America's abysmal civil rights record and the Vietnam War. Songs like, *Blowing in the Wind, A Hard Rain's Gonna Fall, The Times They Are a Changing* and *Like a Rolling Stone,* made Dylan a cultural icon and an inspiration to many, including The Beatles.

Dylan was born Robert Allen Zimmerman to Jewish parents in Duluth, Minnesota on May 24, 1941. His grandparents had emigrated from present day Ukraine and were part of a tight-knit Jewish society in the ethnically divided shoreline community.

But it wasn't only mainstream America that Dylan's music challenged and confused. The album *Slow Train Coming* was somewhat of a surprise to even his devotees when released in 1979. The songs in the album showcased Dylan's conversion to Christianity especially the featured track, *Gotta Serve Somebody.*

The song makes the point that no matter what your political, social, financial, or cultural standing, everyone eventually chooses sides, everyone eventually serves somebody.

Gotta Serve Somebody isn't an overt proclamation of Dylan's new found Christian faith. It's not a Christian song by any stretch of the imagination. But it was viewed by those who knew his music as an explanation of his decision to become a Christian. The refrain contains a thinly veiled reference to the contrast between good and evil, serving God or the devil.

Surprisingly, *Gotta Serve Somebody* won the Grammy for the best male rock vocal performance in 1979. Not everyone was supportive of Dylan's conversion or the Grammy-winning song. No one reacted more negatively than John Lennon of Beatle's fame. A few years earlier, John had been quoted in the London Evening Standard declaring the Beatles more popular than Jesus and that Rock and Roll may outlast Christianity. Lennon, like most singer/songwriters of the

60's idolized Dylan. The album *Slow Train Coming* stunned John. In a 1980 interview, published in Playboy magazine, Lennon commented,

"I must say I was surprised when old Bobby boy did go that way... I don't want to say anything about a man who is searching or has found it. But it is unfortunate when people say, 'This is the only way.' That is the only thing I've got against anybody, if they are saying, 'This is the only answer.' I don't want to hear about that. There isn't one answer to anything." [123]

A few months after *Gotta Serve Somebody* was released by Dylan, Lennon wrote a rebuttal song called *Serve Yourself* to air his grievance.

To his credit, John didn't attack Dylan's faith, but objected to the notion that any one faith held all the answers. He chides those who proclaim that Jesus, Buddha, Mohammed, or Krishna is the one faithful source of all truth. John's song suggests there are many paths that lead to truth. No one faith, creed, or religion has a corner on the market.

Lennon's song, *Serve Yourself,* took many forms. He routinely changed the lyrics adding and deleting various thoughts and phrases each time he sang it. He had fun with it.

The search for truth and the meaning of life was not a new concept for Lennon or The Beatles. At the height of their fortune and fame the foursome traveled to India with other celebrity friends to visit the Maharishi Mahesh Yogi who taught them Transcendental Meditation.

They left mostly disillusioned, which may explain John's reaction to Dylan's song. John said, "We made a mistake there. We believe in meditation but not in the Maharishi and his scene... we thought he was something other than he was." [124]

His experience led John to conclude each person must decide what is true and best for themselves. As the song explains, he suggest serving yourself because no one else will.

Lennon called the religious search for spiritual truth a kind of "stew" and reminded those searching to think long and hard about their mother. When it's all said and done, Lennon conjectured the things you are taught as a child may be the best explanation of your adult beliefs.

Two days after his critical Playboy interview was published in 1980, John Lennon was shot dead by a disgruntled fan on the sidewalk in front of his apartment in New York City.

The bumper sticker COEXIST used to bother me. It is typically spelled with the disparate symbols of an Islamic crescent moon for the "C", a peace sign for the "O", the Hindu Om symbol for the "E", a Star of David for the "X", a pentagram for the dot of the "I", a yin-yang symbol for the "S", and a Christian cross for the "T". Senseless wars and well-intentioned arguments have been fought over the contradictions of these beliefs without the desired effect of converting anyone to the protagonist's point of view. How much better to maintain a respectful dialogue between friends and so-called "enemies." TRUTH BE TOLD does not advocate keeping beliefs private to avoid offense. Truth is discovered in dialogue. There is a Scripture that says, "Test the spirits to see if they are from God." [125]

During his trial for heresy, the reformer Martin Luther made an appeal for evidence and clarity.

"Unless I am convinced by Scripture and plain reason - I do not accept the authority of the popes and councils, for they have contradicted each other - my conscience is captive to the Word of God. I cannot and I will not recant anything for to go against conscience is neither right nor safe. God help me. Amen."

TRUTH BE TOLD believes in the open sharing of divergent beliefs. An honest and respectful discussion of opinions without the threat of violence is how truth is best transmitted from one person to another. "Eat the fish, spit out the bones."

In an attempt at full disclosure, the author of TRUTH BE TOLD wants it known he is a believer in Jesus Christ and accepts the Bible as God's inspired, inerrant and efficacious truth. It has been a long time coming.

Although raised in the faith, I wandered away from the beliefs of my childhood. The publication of TRUTH BE TOLD caused a reexamination of my values. TBT forced me to consider the basis for the truth that The Declaration of Independence calls "self-evident." If truth is self-evident as The Declaration asserts, it is by definition established on a logical expression of *common* sense which is not as common as it used to be.

I base my acceptance of the Christian faith on objective facts that can be examined and found to be true and on a subjective observation of faith outcomes in life, mine and others.

Christianity unlike other philosophical and religious belief systems, is a faith established and verified in history. The facts of Christianity can be examined against the facts of secular history. Because the facts of the Bible stand up against the scrutiny of history, its truth and claims also merit consideration.

Ancient written histories are rare but not lacking. The Merneptah Stele discovered in Northern Egypt in 1896 describes the Egyptian victory over Israel during the reign of Josiah, the thirteenth king of Judah after the death of Solomon. The Lachish letters discovered in 1935 just north of Beersheba describe the Babylonian capture of Jerusalem. The Cyrus Cylinder discovered in Iran in 1879, records the Persian king's overthrow of Babylon and release of the Jewish slaves. Historic references that verify the events of the New Testament are numerous enough to fill a sizeable book, including the writings of Josephus a non-Christian historian who documented Jewish history for the Roman Empire.

In addition to secular history, archaeological discoveries over the centuries corroborate the people, places, and stories of the Bible. Complex prophecies contained in ancient manuscripts centuries before they were fulfilled offer additional authentication of the Bible's trustworthiness. Specific prophecies concerning Jesus' birth, life and death validate His claim to the office of Jewish Messiah.

Other support for God's existence is found in the miraculous factors of creation. The earth is perfectly positioned in the solar system for life to exist. It is the exact size required to produce the gravitational pull necessary to hold the atmosphere fifty miles above the earth's surface. If the earth were further from the sun it would be too cold for life to exist, if it were any closer it would be too hot. A fraction of a difference would make life impossible, all while rotating on a precise axis allowing the planet's surface to heat and cool daily and for seasons to exist while moving at a speed of 67,000 miles per hour around the sun.

The witness of those who knew Jesus is also compelling. Jesus' disciples were not seasoned soldiers familiar with the atrocities of war. They were fishermen, tax collectors, shepherds and farmers who endured torture and martyrdom rather than deny their faith in Jesus. You have to ask yourself, "Who would die for something they knew to be a lie?" They suffered all, even death rather than deny the Christian faith which they knew to be true and verifiable.

TRUTH BE TOLD readily admits the Christian faith appears foolish and unreasonable to nonbelievers. Who has ever witnessed a virgin birth, or a dead man rise from the grave? But as history has demonstrated, faith in God and in the miracles of God are not without evidence. Belief in the Christian faith will always be a matter of personal conviction, but it is a faith based on facts that are verifiable and authenticated by sources outside the Bible.

John Lennon spent much of his life engaged in a personal search for truth and life's meaning. He aligned himself with, and then rejected, the teaching of Maharishi Mahesh Yogi. Whether Bob Dylan remained a Christian or reverted to his Jewish heritage is strongly debated. When Dylan's former wife asked if he was still a believer, he answered, "I believe the whole Bible." It's fair to say he still believes, *"You're gonna have to serve somebody,"* Some viewpoint of life is going to dictate your path. It will determine what you live to achieve, to promote, to enjoy, and the daily decisions every person must make.

There is an interesting story told by the apostle Paul in a book of the Bible called, The Acts of the Apostles. It describes Paul's escape from an angry mob in a city of Thessalonica to the safety of a city called Berea.

Paul referred to the Bereans as, "More noble-minded than the Christians in Thessalonica, for while they received his words with great eagerness, yet every day they examined everything he said in the light of the Old Testament to see if it was true." [126] Doubting is a God-honored quality, as long as it drives a person in search of what is true and verifiable.

The motto established during the Reformation of the 16th century is still sound advice to anyone discussing religion today, "In necessariis unitas, in dubiis libertas, in omnibus caritas." *Unity* in necessary things; *liberty* in doubtful things; *charity in all things.*

(Micah 6:8) ▪

"There's no use trying," she said. "One can't believe impossible things."
"I daresay you haven't had much practice," said the Queen. "When I
was your age, I always did it for half-an-hour a day. Why, sometimes
I've believed as many as six impossible things before breakfast."
—Through the Looking Glass, *by Lewis Carroll*

CHAPTER 18

Perspective

"Do you think we've changed? Sometimes I try to remember the things we took for granted before TRUTH BE TOLD transformed our life."

My question was directed to Sarah as we watched the sun set over the horizon from our backyard patio.

"How could we not? Who do you know who's been visited by a man in white in the middle of the night, or crossed paths with the likes of Mordecai and Sam?"

"No one willing to admit it," I replied. "It reminds me of the many times I took the boys deer hunting, and the treks we made into the mountains chasing elk."

"I don't see the connection," Sarah quipped as she sipped her wine while staring into the fire. Her comment made me smile. I loved moments like this. Our give-and-take conversations were always honest and always safe. In my past life as a reporter, I could speculate about a story, wondering if my coverage had helped or hurt a situation. Sarah was always a faithful sounding board.

I responded, "This business with the man in white, Mordecai, Sam and all that's happened has really opened our eyes to God's involvement in our world. When we ventured into the backwoods during deer season, or climbed 10,000 feet up King Mountain, we were forced to adjust our thinking."

I can still recall our first hike up King Mountain, near Steamboat Springs, Colorado. The weather was cool but sunny. A perfect day for hiking under the weight of our gear. But later that night after setting up camp, a blizzard unleashed its fury on us. Sixty mph winds rattled our tent with pelting rain, threatening to pull the anchors out of the ground. The temperature dropped turning the rain into snow, dumping two feet of misery on us. We had to leave our shelter several times in the middle of the night because the weight of the snow threatened to buckle the aluminum rods that held up our tent. I wondered if we'd ever get back to our truck parked ten miles down the mountain at the trailhead.

Those conditions weren't unusual for King Mountain. They were just unusual to us. Weather conditions in the mountains can change without warning in November. We were flatlanders. It took us a couple of days to make the mental adjustment before we realized we were in no danger if we remained calm and made good decisions. After that we took the cold and snow in stride. Our attitudes changed 180 degrees. We began to see the snow as an asset that helped track the movement of game.

Sarah brought me back to our discussion. "So our perspective before and after TBT has more to do with how we've changed than how things have changed around us? We know now what we didn't know then? Is that what you're saying?"

"Absolutely. Our situation hasn't changed dramatically. Our kids are grown with kids of their own and of course we are getting older. We live in the same house, have the same friends, dine at the same restaurants and enjoy the same routines we've come to love. But our understanding of what constitutes 'normal' has changed."

"How so?"

"God's interventions no longer surprise us or seem unusual; in fact, we've come to expect them, even seek them out. Before our first visitation with the man in white, the idea of divine encounters was something I thought about only at Christmas and Easter, or on those rare occasions when we read the Bible or went to church. Now we expect His advocates to show up on a regular basis."

My mind wandered. "When we ventured miles from civilization on our hunts, the contrast between normal life and 'off-grid-life' was considerable. There were no cars whizzing past, no lawn mowers rumbling two doors down, no children playing, no shopping lists to remember, no online menus to check, no deadlines to meet, no text messages or phone calls to return, no television, electricity, micro-waves beeping, stoves to watch, doors to lock, no running water, shower and no toilet. Nothing says 'you're not in Kansas anymore,' like hanging your butt over an icy log to do your business miles from nowhere!"

Sarah laughed at the mental picture I was painting of life in the mountains. "When I saw The *Wizard of Oz* was about to be broadcast again this weekend, I thought about how our lives had changed like Dorothy's. One moment she was living the ho-hum life of a country girl, and the next she was fighting flying monkeys while skipping down the yellow brick road with strange companions towards Oz. The phrase, "Toto, I have a feeling we are not in Kansas anymore..." crossed my mind more than once."

"It does feel a lot like that," I laughed. "Think of all the classic stories based on altered reality. *Alice in Wonderland*, and *Alice Through the Looking Glass*. The Cheshire Cat's comment comes to mind. 'I'm not crazy. My reality is just different than yours.' That about sums it up."

"Don't forget *Rip Van Winkle*," Sarah smiled as she recalled the fairy tale. "He fell asleep for twenty years and missed the Revolutionary War. His world was turned upside down. Talk about a new reality."

We were on a roll. "The *Chronicles of Narnia* come to mind, especially *The Lion, The Witch and the Wardrobe*," I injected. "Lucy's trip through the wardrobe opened a whole new world to Lucy and her siblings."

C.S. Lewis' books sit prominently on my shelf of classics, including *The Screwtape Letters*. I pulled that volume down last night to read some of the insights I had highlighted. I love the way he depicts the devil targeting people for temptation.

"That must have been an interesting experience for you," Sarah chuckled. "I've seen how you underline your books. I'd be surprised if there was even one page without a comment in the margin." She was not far from wrong.

"These are some of my favorites..."

- "It's funny how mortals always picture us putting things into their minds: in reality our best work is done by keeping things out."

- "Talk to him about moderation in all things. If you can once get him to the point of thinking that religion is all very well up to a point, you can feel quite happy about his soul. A moderate religion is as good for us as no religion at all—and more amusing."

- "All said and done, my friends, it will be an ill day for us if what most humans mean by 'religion' ever vanishes from the Earth. It can still send us the truly delicious sins. The fine flower of unholiness can grow only in the close neighborhood of the Holy. Nowhere do we tempt so successfully as on the very steps of the altar."

- "Do not be deceived, Wormwood. Our cause is never more in danger than when a human, no longer desiring, but still intending, to do the Enemy's will, looks round upon a universe from which every trace of Him seems to have vanished, and asks why he has been forsaken, and still obeys." [127]

Lewis' insights revealed a deep understanding of human nature. In my estimation, he had zeroed in on the thoughts and attitudes of most church-going Christians.

Sarah reacted, "I thought the first quote was the most intriguing. That the devil attempts more often to remove thoughts from people's heads rather than suggest new ones. That's profound."

"For sure. I wonder how many Christians think about God in the midst of their hectic schedules. I doubt many believe He intervenes in important matters on earth, let alone in their personal lives."

"'A moderate religion is as good as no religion at all.' That advice from Screwtape to Wormwood rings true. By contrast, Lewis recognized there are believers confused by God's action or inaction, but who still trust Him. He said, 'Christians who still honor and obey God despite their confusion are the greatest threat to evil's plans.' C.S. Lewis was a genius."

It caused me to recall Jesus' interaction with a man who was born blind. Before being healed, that man, much like myself, had a feeble understanding of who Jesus was and what He was capable of doing. The religious elite demanded the man whose sight had been restored, denounce Jesus as a sinner, no different than anyone else. Despite his uncertainty, the man whose sight had been restored refused to deny the miracle.

"Give glory to God by telling the truth," they said. "We know this man is a sinner."

He replied, "Whether he is a sinner or not, I don't know. One thing I do know. I was blind but now I see!" [128]

Rather than embrace a God who can perform miracles, the religious leaders preferred what Lewis called, "a moderate religion." They promoted obedience over belief as their standard of faithfulness. When the blind man refused to denounce Jesus as a sinner, he was banned from worship in the synagogue. When Jesus heard it, He circled back to reconnect.

"When Jesus found him, He asked, "Do you believe in the Son of Man?"

"Who is he, sir?" the man asked. "Tell me so that I may believe in him."

Jesus said, "You have now seen Him; in fact, He is the one speaking with you."

Then the man said, "Lord, I believe," and he worshiped Him.

Jesus said, "For judgment I have come into this world, so that the blind will see and those who see will become blind." [129]

In other words, those who think they know all the answers are often blind to the truth, but those who humbly admit their confusion are able to see God at work in the world.

Einstein once said, *"Two things are infinite: the universe and human stupidity; and I'm not sure about the universe."* The Screwtape Letters of C.S. Lewis are a creative way of describing the devil's attempts to exploit the stupidity of human nature.

I suggested to Sarah, "Like the blind man, our eyes have been opened,"

"I wonder what the Lord must think of Christians who remain oblivious to His activity on earth." Sarah was in a thoughtful mood.

"When I consider a believer's relationship to God, I think of how we relate to our own children. We make allowances for age-appropriate, education-appropriate, and experience-appropriate behavior. If parents hesitate to judge children who act in ignorance, I suspect God does the same. But those who know better should anticipate His judgment. That's just my humble opinion," I offered with a shrug.

"Do you think God has a plan for every life? Is it our job to figure out what He wants us to do?" Sarah asked.

"I doubt God is overly concerned about what we do, but I do believe He cares about *HOW we go about it.* He obviously taps some people for special assignments. That was true in the Bible, and it's been our experience as well, but I don't believe God prefers one profession over another. Jesus' earthly father was a carpenter, not a priest or a rabbi. Mark Twain said, 'God must love the common man. He made so many of them.'"

"Do you believe He directs our lives by opening doors and closing others?" Sarah was on a roll.

"I suppose God provides guidance when it's needed, but I'm not a fatalist. I'm not of the opinion He has a predetermined path He expects us to discover and follow. He knows in advance what path we will choose, but that's not the same as causing it. He gave humans free will."

"Ah, free will." Sarah sighed. "Was that a mistake on His part? Just kidding of course, but why in the world did God give people free will if He knew we would make such a mess of things?"

"What was His alternative?" I had already given this subject some thought. "Should He program people like robots to obey a predetermined course of action? Like any good parent, the Lord prefers behavior that is motivated by love not forced compliance."

The sunset was turning the sky a stunning tapestry of orange, yellow and red as we reflected on the shift in our life's perspective.

Sarah spoke for both of us, "I can't believe we lived so many years oblivious to God's involvement in our day-to-day life. I will never again consider anything 'lucky or unlucky.' Now when something unexpected happens, I simply wonder, 'What's God up to?'"

I joined in her wonder. "Knowing God is involved in our life is not the same as knowing what God is doing. There is a Scripture that says, 'How great are God's riches, wisdom and knowledge! How impossible it is for us to understand His decisions and His ways! For who can know the LORD's thoughts? Who knows enough to give him advice?'" [130]

"I agree dear Sarah, it's important to remember the Lord is God and we are not. That was enough for the blind man. His faith was simple, but it was sufficient."

When asked if he knew the Lord, he replied, "Tell me so I may believe... for I was blind but now I see." [131]

It was true for the man born blind. It was true for us.

We were blind, but now we see.

EPILOGUE

"Do not say, 'Why were the old days better than these?'
For it is not wise to ask such questions."

—*Ecclesiastes 7:10*

Before you jump to conclusions about my sanity or Biblical acumen, let me assure you I am an ordained member of a Christian tribe that is theologically right of center. We subscribe unashamedly to the Reformation mantra, "By GRACE alone, by FAITH alone, by SCRIPTURE alone."

I am old school enough to believe not only in the efficacy (the spiritual power) of Holy Scripture, but also in its inerrancy. But having said that, other than the Bible, I am not captive to the books I have read nor the theology I have studied for I know the men who wrote those books and taught those classes were limited by their humanity, just as I am. When we limit God to our understanding, we make Him inferior. I cannot limit God's capabilities to the constraints of my comprehension. I refuse to confine a limitless God to the limits of anyone's humanity.

I choose to follow a God greater than my understanding... and therein lies the rub. I'm asking an almighty God to pour His unlimited wisdom into my limited mind so I can communicate His truth by means of my limited ability. That is unreasonable, even impossible by definition. But God can do it. Helping people understand things beyond human reason may be God's greatest miracle. If it were reasonable and usual, it would not be miraculous.

You are within your rights to ask why God would select me as His spokesperson. I'm pretty sure I know the answer. He embraces the opportunity to accomplish extraordinary things by means of very ordinary people. No one is more ordinary than I am. The apostle spoke bluntly to the Christians at Corinth when he wrote,

"Think of who you were when you were called. Not many of

you were wise by human standards; not many were influential; not many were of noble birth. But God chose the foolish things of the world to shame the wise; God chose the weak things of the world to shame the strong. God chose the lowly things of this world and the despised things—and the things that are not—to nullify the things that are, so that no one may boast before Him." [132]

To be unqualified is my greatest qualification. I was born into a family of modest means. My dad was a WWII veteran who spent most of his working life on an assembly line for International Harvester. My mom corralled seven children, tended a huge garden, and helped on her parents' farm. Most of my childhood friends, like my parents and most of my siblings finished their education with a high school diploma. I'm proud of my working-class roots and consider them an asset, but there is nothing about the place of my birth or the circumstance of my childhood that anyone would consider "sophisticated."

I was fortunate to have mentors who encouraged me along life's path. My childhood pastor encouraged a parishioner to subsidize my tuition so I could attend a private Christian high school in a city some distance from my hometown. He then convinced my parents (and me) that attending there would be to my benefit. I never promised to serve in any Christian profession and he never made it a condition of our agreement. Shortly before his death, I tracked him down to thank him for his kindness. He revealed I was the only child in the history of his ministry that he felt compelled to help in that way. How strange I thought. I'm not sure what motivated his considerable effort. Perhaps he too was merely being faithful to a strange and personal prompting from God.

After high school, and because of it, I attended a Christian college and then a biblically conservative Christian seminary. After four years of graduate study, I was ordained as the pastor of a small-town church in central Michigan. In other words, while formally trained in conservative Christian doctrine, there is nothing in my resume that would catch the notice of anyone, let alone God.

Based on a casual reading of the Bible and a study of the leaders God chose as His spokesmen, the Lord seems to prefer nobodies. *Abraham* was an old man when God asked him to leave the security of the familiar to explore a land He would show him. *Moses* was the son of a slave, then an outlaw hiding in obscurity when God appeared to him in the guise of a burning bush. *Saul* was so insecure he hid in the baggage, but God caused the lots to fall in such a way he was chosen as the first king of Israel. *Gideon* was literally the least son, of the least family, from the least clan in the least tribe of all Israel. The idea that God would choose *David* from all the sons of Jesse, surprised even his own father. *Matthew* was a despised tax collector. *Peter* and *John* were fisherman. *Paul* was complicit in the arrest and martyrdom of Stephen and other Christians, but God called him to be His chief representative to the world's gentiles. The very same "chief of sinners" (his words not mine) would eventually become the author of most of the New Testament.

I am an ordained pastor in a church body that routinely touts God's Word and Sacraments as the Lord's *only* means of grace. And while I agree that God requires Christians to weigh all matters in the light of His Word, He has not limited Himself to those two means of revelation.

As the Lord's poet acknowledged: "The heavens declare the glory of God; the skies proclaim the work of his hands. Day after day, they pour forth speech; night after night, they reveal knowledge. They have no speech, they use no words; no sound is heard from them. Yet their voice goes out into all the earth, their words to the ends of the world." [133]

Although all promptings, visions, and beliefs of Christians must be examined in the light of God's Word, we must not impose human limitations on God's freedom to reveal Himself as He chooses. He has always been and always will be a God of creativity.

His Word and His ways have been proclaimed through many mediums including: rainbows, a prophet's staff, a talking donkey, a burning bush, droughts and deluges, plagues, hailstones, miraculous catches of fish, miraculous water crossings, fiery chariots, floating axe-heads, thunder, a star, and even once through a séance conducted by a witch from the village of Endor. Has God suddenly changed? Are those accounts only quaint stories of God's past, and not a true representation of His divine nature? Do we worship the same God as the patriarchs, the prophets and apostles? The Bible affirms the truth of it. "Remember your leaders, who spoke the word of God to you. Consider the outcome of their way of life and imitate their faith. Jesus Christ is the same yesterday and today and forever." [134]

God can do whatever God desires to do. It's the prerogative of being God. His ways remain as mysterious as the wind, and like the wind His presence and impact cannot be denied. I for one, am determined to follow wherever the wind of God's Spirit is blowing, always examining my feelings and experiences by the truth of His Word.

There is a Scripture that says, "Without faith it is impossible to please God, because anyone who comes to Him must believe that He exists and that He rewards those who earnestly seek Him." [135] I am resolved to be that guy, committed to believe and earnestly seek His guidance.

I know for a fact Jesus appeared to Paul no less than four times. First at his conversion, then in Corinth, later during his first visit to Jerusalem and finally in Caesarea before going to Rome to stand trial. And those are just the occasions the Bible describes. Were there more? Perhaps. God and Paul are the only ones who know for certain. Those four appearances don't take into account the three years Paul spent in the wilderness of Arabia[136] with the Lord, or the time he was swept up into what he calls, "the third heaven." [137]

I tell myself, God did not love Paul more than me, nor me less than Paul. If God was willing to visit Paul in his confusion, He might be willing to do the same for me. I don't consider my life as important as Paul's, but neither do I consider it unimportant. I am willing to be used by God if God is willing to use me. I am willing to do whatever God asks of me.

Personal appearances were not the only means God used to recruit and direct the activities of His representatives. Paul had visions. One night he saw a man of Macedonia standing and begging, "Come over to Macedonia and help us." [138] John the Baptizer saw a dove-like image descend upon the head of Jesus as he baptized Him and heard a voice out of heaven declare,

"This is my beloved son..." [139] Whether others saw it or only John, is not made clear. As Jesus entered Jerusalem for the last time, God verbally endorsed His mission, but most mistook it for the sound of thunder. [140]

God's endorsement of Jesus by means of miracles and a voice from heaven was customary, but those were Messianic moments worthy of extraordinary signs. There are other times when God used miraculous and unusual approaches to recruit, affirm and provide guidance to representatives other than Jesus.

Abraham entertained three "heavenly" strangers who announced Sarah's pregnancy while on their way to pass judgment upon Sodom and Gomorrah. [141] *Moses* encountered his burning bush. [142] *Gideon* tested God with a lambskin fleece. [143] (By the way, am I the only one amazed at God's patience over Gideon's request for continual affirmation?) *Balaam* was challenged to obedience by a talking donkey. [144] (The angels must have laughed over that one.) *Jacob's* sleep was interrupted by the vision of a stairway leading into heaven. [145] The young boy *Samuel* heard God's voice call his name in the night. [146] *Elijah* was visited in the wilderness by tornadic winds, an earthquake and consuming fire before hearing the voice of God in a whisper. [147] *Elisha* parted the waters of the Jordan by striking them with the robe that fell from Elijah when he was snatched into heaven on a fiery chariot. [148] As Elisha struck the waters he demanded, "Where is the Lord, the God of Elijah?" [149] King *Hezekiah* saw a shadow move backward up his staircase. [150] And *Jeremiah* was taught an important lesson by watching a potter shape and then reshape a vessel on a potter's wheel. [151]

Theologians call them, "theophanies," a word composed of two Greek words, "Theo" meaning: God, and "phanien" meaning: to show. I have always chafed a bit at theologians who render God impotent by saying, "Such theophanies are exclusive to Biblical times." How do such teachers quote the Scripture that declares, "Jesus Christ is the same yesterday, today and forever." [152] Either He is or He isn't.

I remember sitting in a seminary class designed to teach aspiring pastors doctrines concerning the nature of God. We began by studying the ancient Athanasian Creed that declares, "The Father is incomprehensible, the

Son is incomprehensible, the Holy Spirit is incomprehensible...." Shortly thereafter, the professor invited us to open our textbook and follow along while he explained the true nature of God. How ironic.

God never declared a moratorium on personal appearances by Himself or His angels. Just the opposite. The Scripture cautions, "Do not forget to show hospitality to strangers, for by so doing some people have shown hospitality to angels without knowing it." [153]

I understand. I get it. After years and years of "business as usual," the mystery goes out of life. God anticipated that attitude. Peter wrote, "In the last days scoffers will come, scoffing and following their own evil desires. They say, "Where is this 'coming' He promised? Ever since our ancestors died, everything goes on as it has since the beginning of creation." But they deliberately forget that long ago by God's word, the heavens came into being and the earth was formed out of water and by water...and by these waters also the world of that time was deluged and destroyed." [154] God's promises are trustworthy. He came, He comes, He will come again.

"Ho hum. Life continues as it always has." So say the scoffers. I refuse to be numbered among the doubters. I refuse to live in a world ruled by what is reasonable. The miraculous is not reasonable. God is not usual. His Words like snow and rain fall on the earth with power to accomplish the miraculous.[155]

So why me? Why now? Why should I expect God to make Himself known in miraculous ways?

Why not?

Endnotes

Chapter 1
1. Romans 11:33,34
2. Matthew 5:11

Chapter 2
3. Luke 2:8,9
4. Luke 1:26–38
5. Luke 10:27

Chapter 3
6. Hebrews 13:2
7. Amos 8:11
8. 2 Corinthians 14:33
9. Jeremiah 29:11–13
10. Mark 9:24

Chapter 4
11. Matthew 22:37,38
12. Luke 10:36
13. Luke 10:25

Chapter 5
14. 1 Corinthians 2:6,7
15. Genesis 11:4
16. Genesis 11:6,9
17. Genesis 11:6
18. Acts 2:9–12
19. Revelation 7:9

Chapter 6
20. Joshua 24:15
21. Exodus 4:11
22. Esther 4:14
23. Esther 4:14
24. James 4:17

CHAPTER 8

25. Frederick Douglass, *Narrative of the Life and Other Writings*, 2006, Borders Classics, Borders Group Inc., 2500 South State Street, Ann Arbor, Michigan, 48104.

26. Bruce Springsteen, *Bruce Springsteen*, Born to Run, 2016, Simon and Schuster, 1230 Avenue of the Americas, New York, NY, 10020.

27. Laura Schroff and Alex Tresniowski, *An Invisible Thread*, 2011, Howard Books, A Division of Simon & Shuster Inc., 1230 Avenue of the Americas, New York, NY, 10020.

28. Booker T. Washington, *Up from Slavery*, page 39, Penguin Group, Viking Penguin Inc., 40th West 23rd Street, New York, NY., 10010. First published by Doubleday, Pages and Company 1901.

29. Ibid. Page 99.

30. James 1:22–25.

31. Laura Schroff and Alex Tresniowski, *An Invisible Thread*, 2011, Howard Books, A Division of Simon & Shuster Inc., 1230 Avenue of the Americas, New York, NY, 10020.

32. Ibid.

33. Frederick Douglass, *Narrative of the Life and Other Writings*, 2006, Borders Classics, Borders Group Inc., 2500 South State Street, Ann Arbor, Michigan, 48104.

CHAPTER 9

34. Matthew 12:31

35. 1 Corinthians 12:3

36. Galatians 5:19–21, 1 Corinthians 6:9,10, Romans 13:13,14

37. John 13:35

38. Proverbs 27:6

CHAPTER 10

39. The LGBTQ Data was published in 2016 by The Williams Institute with support from the Ford Foundation. In 2018, Shoshana Goldberg and Kerith Conron added to this foundation and provided updated and expanded Gallup estimate about LGBTQ people to the study. The Williams Institute is associated with the UCLA School of Law.

40. Ecclesiastes 4:9–12

41. 2 Samuel 1:26

42. Hebrews 13:2 "Do not forget to show hospitality to strangers, for by do doing some people have shown hospitality to angels without knowing it."

43. Job 11:7

44. 1 Corinthians 4:5

45. Romans 13:8–10

46. Romans 10:21

47. 1 Timothy 2:4

48. Romans 3:12

49. Ephesians 2:8

50. Ephesians 4:15

51. 1 Timothy 2:4

52. 1 Corinthians 4:2

53. 1 Corinthians 13:4–7

54. 1 Corinthians 13:13

55. Genesis 2:18

56. Statistics from Fact Tank, *News in the Numbers,* February 13, 2019, published by the Pew Research Center based in part on the 2018 US Census Bureau findings.

57. Galatians 5:19–21, 1 Corinthians 6:9–11, Romans 1:26–32

58. Matthew 22:21

59. Genesis 1:27

60. John 4:24

61. Psalm 17:15

62. Revelation 21:4

63. John Gray, *Men Are from Mars, Women Are from Venus,* 1992, Harper Collins Publishers, 10 East 53 Street, New York, NY, 10022, page 16.

64. Ibid, pages 19,20

65. 1 John 4:8

66. 1 Corinthians 13:2,2

CHAPTER 11

67. Hebrews 4:12

68. 1 Corinthians 14:8

69. Hebrews 13:2

CHAPTER 13

70. Ecclesiastes 9:11

71. Proverbs 30:7–9

CHAPTER 14

72. Psalm 17

73. 1 Timothy 6:17–19

74. 1 Timothy 6:19

75. Matthew 6:21–24

76. 1 Timothy 6:10

77. I Timothy 6:17–19

78. Ecclesiastes 4:8–10

79. 2 Thessalonians 3:19

80. Booker T. Washington, *Up from Slavery*, Penguin Group, Viking Penguin Inc., 40th West 23rd Street, New York, NY., 10010. First published by Doubleday, Pages and Company 1901.

81. Iacocca, Lee with William Novak, *Iacocca: An Autobiography*, Batam Dell Publishing Group, November, 1984.

CHAPTER 15

82. Matthew 16:26

83. 1 Corinthians 15:19

84. 1 Corinthians 1:23,24

85. Proverbs 27:6

86. Norman Vincent Peale, *The True Joy of Positive Living, an Autobiography*, William Morrow and Company, December 31st, 1984, page 231.

87. Hebrews 11:1

CHAPTER 16

88. Romans 10:13–15

89. 2 Timothy 1:7

90. Isaiah 55:1,2

91. Isaiah 65:2

92. 1 Kings 19:10

93. 1 Kings 19:18

94. Hebrews 12:1,2

95. Revelation 2:1–7

96. Ephesians 1:15

97. 1 Corinthians 10:23,24

98. Matthew 16:26

99. Micah 6:8

CHAPTER 17

100. Micah 6:8

101. Micah 6:8
102. Genesis 1:1
103. *The Collected Works of Abraham Lincoln*, edited by Roy P. Basler, Volume VII, The Lincoln, Douglas Debate at Quincy, October 13. 1858, page 276.
104. Ibid, Volume VIII, "Speech to the one hundred fortieth Indiana regiment," March 17, 1865, page 361.
105. Ibid, Volume VII, "Letter to Albert G. Hodges," April 4, 1864, page 281.
106. *The Guardian*, Kate Hodal, "One in 200 People Is a Slave," February 25, 2019, page 1.
107. Ibid, page 3.
108. Booker T. Washington, *Up from Slavery*, Penguin Books, 1901, page 39.
109. Corrie Ten Boom, *The Hiding Place*, Bantam Books, November, 1971.
110. Nelson Mandela, *Long Walk to Freedom*, Macdonald Purnell Publishers, 1994.
111. Ibid.
112. The Declaration of Independence.
113. Thomas Jefferson, *Notes on the State of Virginia*, Query XVIII, page 237.
114. Setton, Mark, *Jefferson's Happiness, Bringing the Science of Happiness to Life*, www.pursuitofhappiness.org, 2018.
115. 1 Timothy 6:6–9
116. Ecclesiastes 1:11
117. Ecclesiastes 2:24–26
118. 1 Timothy 6:6
119. Cappon, Lester, "The Adams – Jefferson Letters," The UNC Press, September 1988.
120. Glass, Andrew, "Adams-Jefferson Correspondence Resumes, May 27, 1813," *Politico*, May 26, 2017.
121. Andrew Glass, "Jefferson And Adams Die Hours Apart, July 4, 1826. *Politico*, July 4, 2016.
122. Glass, Andrew, "Adams-Jefferson Correspondence Resumes, May 27, 1813," *Politico*, May 26, 2017.
123. Sheff, David, "All We Are Saying," An interview with John Lennon, *Playboy Magazine*, December, 1980.
124. *The Beatles Anthology,* by The Beatles. (A profusely illustrated volume in which John Lennon, Paul McCartney, George Harrison and Ringo Starr tell their own story.) *Chronicle*, October 2000.
125. 1 John 4:1
126. Acts 17:11

CHAPTER 18

127. C.S. Lewis, *The Screwtape Letters*, Geoffrey Bles, publisher, 1942.

128. John 9:24,25
129. John 9:35–39
130. Romans 11:33,34
131. John 9:36

EPILOGUE

132. 1 Corinthians, 2:26–31
133. Psalm 19:1–3
134. Hebrews 13:7,8
135. Hebrews 11:6
136. Galatians 1:16,17
137. 2 Corinthians 12:1–3
138. Acts 16:9
139. Luke 3:22
140. John 12:28,29
141. Genesis 18:1–3
142. Exodus 3:2,3
143. Judges 6:37–40
144. Numbers 22:28
145. Genesis 28:12
146. 1 Samuel 3:1–10
147. 1 Kings 19:12
148. 2 Kings 2:11,12
149. 2 Kings 2:14
150. 1 Kings 20:9–11
151. Jeremiah 18:1–4
152. Hebrews 13:8
153. Hebrews 13:2
154. 2 Peter 3:3–6
155. Isaiah 55:10

Study Guide

Man in the Middle

The Problem of Political Correctness
Speaking the Truth in Love

SESSION ONE

TRUTH BE TOLD – Columns 1 thru 4

Column 1: An Auspicious Beginning

1. Who has been the greatest influence in your life?

2. How do you decide what is good, better, or best for your life? Describe your decision-making process.

3. What three phrases would you use to describe yourself to a new acquaintance?

4. Do you tend to a.) go with the flow, b.) challenge the P.C. crowd, c.) avoid controversy as much as possible?

5. Where do you stand on the existence of God, the trustworthiness of the Bible, and the many religions of the world?

Column 2: Self-Evident Truth

1. Do you believe in self-evident truth? What makes you so sure of your answer?

2. Do you agree that certain rights are unalienable and that all people are created equal and endowed by the laws of nature and nature's God with the right to life, liberty, and the pursuit of happiness? What did Jefferson mean by basing The Declaration on the "laws of nature and nature's God?"

3. What is right or wrong with the statement, "You have your truth and I have mine."

4. How would you describe your inner voice (conscience) that either excuses or accuses you of being right or wrong? Where does that voice come from?

5. What point was Jesus making when He said, "If you hold to my teaching, you are really my disciple. Then you will know the truth, and the truth will set you free." (John 8:31,32)

Column 3: Is God Dead?

1. What causes people to believe or disbelieve in God?

2. Do you pray to God? If so why? If not, why not?

3. What role if any, has the Bible played in defining your view of God?

4. On what basis do you decide what is morally right or wrong? Do you accept the Ten Commandments as the sum of all moral law?

5. Do you believe in life after death? What determines a person's eternal destination?

Column 4: R-E-S-P-E-C-T

1. How do you define respect? Do you believe mutual respect is more (or less) common in America than most people think?

2. Do you agree or disagree with Dr. MLK's nonviolent approach to achieving respect for minorities in America? Is his approach still appropriate and effective?

3. Why is it so hard for people to agree to disagree and still live in harmony and mutual respect?

4. What does the Bible mean when it says, "God has made us competent as ministers of a new covenant—not of the letter

but of the Spirit; for the letter kills, but the Spirit gives life." (2 Corinthians 3:6)

5. Describe your reaction to the phrase, "Truth needs no defense, just opportunity." Do you think people recognize truth when they hear it? Why? or Why not?

SESSION TWO

TRUTH BE TOLD – Columns 5 thru 8

Column 5: Created Equal

1. If your explanation of race origin is derived from the evolutionary theory, how does natural selection and survival of the fittest, square with the concept of racial equality?

2. On what basis did the Founding Fathers declare that all people are equal and deserve equal rights?

3. Explain the term "inalienable."

4. Is it possible to declare a thing to be true, (i.e. all men are created equal and are endowed by their creator with certain inalienable rights), even though the Founding Fathers owned slaves themselves? How do you explain that?

5. If God created everything good, how did things go so wrong?

Column 6: Racial Distinction

1. How old were you when you first realized the existence of racial differences.

2. Did you grow up in an environment concerned about social rights and racial equality? Was that something discussed by your family of origin, or did you learn of it later in life?

3. Are you more or less sensitive to racial equality issues than your family of origin or about the same?

4. According to TBT what's wrong with the theory of geographic isolation as an explanation for race distinction? How do you explain the existence of different races in the world?

5. According to the Biblical explanation in Genesis chapter 11, why did God create separation between people?

Column 7: Minority Status

1. How do you react to Kermit the Frog's lament that it's so hard to be who he is? What's the point of the lyrics?

2. What did Booker T. Washington mean when he said, "Success is to be measured not so much by the position that one has reached in life as by the obstacles which he has overcome while trying to succeed."

3. What opportunity does racial diversity provide to make the world and lives of people better?

4. Do you believe every person, no matter their race, gender, or social status, has the same opportunity to make a difference in things that matter? Are some races more "privileged" than others?

5. How would a world where everyone looked the same, thought the same, believed the same and acted the same be different? Would that be better? What insight does 2 Corinthians 8:13–15 provide?

Column 8: Man in the Mirror

1. What kind of music do you prefer and why?

2. Consider the lyrics to Michael Jackson's famous song, *Man in the Mirror.* Do you agree or disagree with the message of the song?

3. What keeps most people from crossing racial, social, cultural and faith lines? Explain the term, "segregation by personal choice."

4. How did helping the less fortunate change Mother Theresa, and Laura Schroff? Who benefits most, the ones helped or the ones who help others?

5. How do you feel about the concept of, "Doing for one what you wish you could do for all?" Is that something you practice routinely?

SESSION THREE

TRUTH BE TOLD – Columns 9 thru 12

Column 9: What's Love Got to Do with It?

1. TRUTH BE TOLD suggests love cuts both ways. What does that mean?

2. Why does the Bible say, "These three abide: Faith, Hope and Love, and the greatest of these is love?" What makes love supreme?

3. Other than Jesus, who do you know that best exemplifies love? Explain.

4. What act of kindness have you recently experienced that demonstrated love towards you?

5. Name your favorite love song and explain why you chose it.

Column 10: Marriage: Till Death, Debt, or Divorce Do Us Part

1. Explain the statement, "No one gets to steer the stream, only their boat that floats on its surface."

2. What statistic about marriage surprised you the most?

3. Is it possible for the church and Christians to oppose same sex

relationships while simultaneously accepting and loving those who are a part of the LBGTQ community?

4. What other sins are also listed in the Biblical passages that oppose homosexuality as a sin that can lead to separation from God?

5. What is the only sin that damns? Why do certain sins more than others put people in danger of succumbing to that unforgiveable sin?

Column 11: Gender: He, She, Us, and Them

1. What does the phrase, "We don't know what we don't know." mean? Why is it an important concept in a discussion about gender?

2. What do you think the statement means, "God created mankind in His own image, in the image of God He created them; male and female, He created them." In your opinion, what constitutes the image of God?

3. Do you believe a person's gender identification is formed mostly by nature or nurture?

4. Other than physical attributes, what other distinctives (typically but not always) reflect a male or female orientation?

5. How is it possible to uphold absolute moral standards while demonstrating acceptance of those whose moral behavior opposes your belief?

Column 12: Sex Is Not a Four-Letter Word

1. Explain the statement that sexual relationships can be beneficial or detrimental but rarely neutral.

2. Describe intimacy. Do you agree that sex for the sake of sex is a poor substitute for intimacy?

3. How do feel about the statement, "Women need to feel loved to have sex and men need to have sex to feel loved?"

4. What was God's purpose in creating sexual interaction between people? Other than a means of procreation, what purpose does it serve?

5. Why is it so difficult for people to have honest and transparent conversations about sexual matters?

SESSION FOUR

TRUTH BE TOLD – Columns 13 thru 16

Column 13: The Gratitude Factor

1. Are you a person that is easily satisfied, sometimes satisfied, or rarely satisfied by outcomes personal or professional?

2. Do you believe it is more advantageous for a person to struggle early in life or be raised in a privileged environment? Why do you feel that way?

3. Are you more inclined to compare your circumstance to people with greater resources or those with lesser resources than you? What has been the consequence of that perspective?

4. How did you react to the syllogism TBT postulated to explain the impact of a grateful spirit?

5. What was your take-away from the essay Laura wrote about her high-school mission trip to Mexico?

Column 14: The Haves and The Have Nots

1. Do you tip when paying a bill for carry-out food? Why or why not?

2. Do you consider yourself generous by nature?

3. Do you consider yourself underprivileged, middle class, or wealthy by comparison to others?

4. How do you react to John Rockefeller's answer to the question, "How much is enough?" He replied, "Just a little bit more."

5. What did Jesus mean when He said, "Where your treasure is, there your heart will be also?" Is it harder to be a faithful Christian and wealthy? Explain.

Column 15: Work Ethic

1. Do you agree or disagree with Thomas Edison's comment, "Opportunity is missed by most people because it comes dressed in overalls and looks like work?"

2. How old were you when you landed your first job other than an allowance for doing chores at home? How would you describe the work-ethic of your family of origin?

3. Is it an advantage or disadvantage to be raised in a relatively affluent home? (Booker T. Washington concluded he no longer envied the white child as he once did since the difficulties of his life taught him essential skills to succeed.) Do you agree with Booker T.'s perspective?

4. When does a strong work ethic cross the line and become work-a-holism? Which do you feel is more common, work-a-holism or laziness?

5. What advice would you offer to maintain the balance between work and pleasure?

Column 16: Get Smart

1. Are you working in the field you trained for and expected to enter as a young person? Has that been a good decision for you?

2. What qualities are required beyond education for success in life?

3. Do you agree with Mike Rowe's assessment that "acquiring a bachelor's degree by at least half of America's young people is a big waste of time and money?" What's his point?

4. What does the old proverb, "Too soon old, too late smart," mean to you? Describe the difference between being highly educated and being wise?

5. What have you always wanted to achieve or learn that you haven't yet accomplished?

SESSION FIVE

TRUTH BE TOLD – Columns 17 thru 20

Column 17: Life: An Unalienable Right

1. What is there about a heartwarming rescue of endangered life that captivates the world?

2. How do people justify the severe penalties for endangering the life and eggs of animals but fight passionately for the right to end a human pregnancy?

3. What constitutes life? How can we call single-celled bacteria found on other planets or in the deepest mines in the world life and simultaneously dismiss an unborn fetus as less than life?

4. How do people explain the origins of life apart from God? How is it possible to believe in the evolutionary origin of life when no scientist is capable of creating life from inorganic material, let alone out of nothing?

5. Is the issue of abortion a question of faith or science or both in your opinion?

Column 18: Liberty: An Unalienable Right

1. What do you think of Lincoln's explanation for why the Founding Fathers declared all men are created equal but still owned slaves themselves? He said, "They did not make it so, but they left it so because they knew of no way to get rid of it at the time." In other words, they could not afford to be divided when fighting for their independence from England. It would have to come later.

2. Does it surprise you that more people are enslaved today than at any other time in the world's history? According to TBT, what forms does slavery take in our day and age?

3. Do you believe that Juneteenth… (June 19th, recognized as the day Lincoln emancipated slaves in America) should be declared a national holiday? How might it impact Independence Day and Martin Luther King Jr. Day as an additional celebration?

4. Do you agree with TBT's statement "Many have never been owned by anyone, but they are not free. They suffer in prisons of a different kind." How did Harriet Tubman describe the frustration she experienced from slaves who chose slavery rather than risk their lives for freedom? Does her opinion still apply today?

5. Do you agree or disagree with the lyrics from En Vogue's song, *Free Your Mind*?

Column 19: The Pursuit of Happiness: An Unalienable Right

1. What does the term, "Pursuit of Happiness," mean to you?

2. What is required for happiness? In your opinion, what aspects of life are the key to true happiness?

3. Looking back over your life, describe the time(s) you were most happy. Were they difficult times, easy times, times of certainty, or uncertainty?

4. What's the definition of contentment? How do you feel about the Bible verse that says, "Godliness with contentment is great gain. For we brought nothing into the world, and we can take nothing out of it. But if we have food and clothing, we will be content with that." (1 Timothy 6:6–8... If time allows you may want to read the entire chapter.)

5. Why do you think the Declaration of Independence guarantees the right to pursue happiness, but doesn't guarantee happiness?

Column 20: The Question of Faith

1. Why was the first amendment to the Constitution considered so important? "Congress shall make no law respecting an establishment of religion, or prohibiting the free exercise thereof..."

2. Do you agree with the sentiment Bob Dylan expressed in his song, *Gotta Serve Somebody*? What was John Lennon's objection to the song?

3. How do you feel about the bumper sticker, "COEXIST"?

4. What's the difference between compromising your faith and being tolerant of people who believe differently?

5. If you had to describe your view of faith in God, what would you say?

SESSION SIX

TRUTH BE TOLD – An Overview

Overview 1: Angels, Friends, and Circumstance

1. There is a passage in Scripture that says, "Do not neglect to show hospitality to strangers for by this some have entertained angels without knowing it." (Hebrews 12:2) Have you ever had a

suspicious encounter with someone that caused you to question if they were of this world?

2. Solomon once said, "Faithful are the wounds of a friend, but deceitful are the kisses of an enemy." (Proverbs 27:6) What was he implying?

3. What's the best decision you never made?

4. How do you go about deciding a potentially life-changing matter? Do you consult others, spend time alone, analyze every possible outcome, or just trust your intuition?

5. What's your purpose in life? If you had to write a simple mission statement for yourself, what would it be?

Overview 2: Deciding Good, Better, and Best

1. Do you believe self-evident truth is a reality or a myth? Is truth subjective or objective?

2. Were you raised in a permissive/lenient household, or a more disciplined environment? Which is better in your opinion?

3. Are you a "live and let live" kind of person, or do you have a compelling need to convince other people of right and wrong?

4. There is a passage that says, "Humans plan their course, but the Lord determines the outcome." (Proverbs 16:9) What's the danger of any person having absolute control of anything?

5. Do you believe the ten commandments should serve as the basis for most moral decisions? Why or why not?

Overview 3: Tolerance, Acceptance, and Political Correctness

1. Is it possible to hate the sin and love the sinner? What's the difference between loving acceptance and affirmation?

2. How do you feel about political correctness?

3. There is a passage that says, "Let everyone be quick to hear, slow to speak and slow to anger for the anger of man does not achieve the righteousness of God." (James 1:19) How does that apply to taking offense on issues of disagreement?

4. What's good about social media and 24-hour news broadcasts? What's troublesome about those things?

5. What phrase strikes you the most from the poem by Rudyard Kipling, "If you can keep your head when all about you are losing theirs and blaming it on you. If you can trust yourself when all men doubt you, but make allowance for their doubting too; If you can wait and not be tired by waiting, or being lied about, don't deal in lies, or being hated, don't give way to hating... then you will be a man my son."

Overview 4: Faith and Religion

1. How would you describe your belief in God?

2. How often do you have conversations with people of a different faith?

3. What do you believe is the best way to share your faith without giving offense or ruining a relationship?

4. Do you agree or disagree that the two subjects you should avoid in all discussions are religion and politics? Why?

5. How do you nurture your belief? Do you believe in the organized church? Why or why not?

ABOUT THE AUTHOR

Stephen Hower is a freelance writer who resides with his wife, Carol, in St. Louis, Missouri. Hower has published four previous books and countless articles and poems on a wide range of issues. His books and writings are available on Amazon or from the author directly at **howerbooks.com**, or **howerstl@gmail.com**. His published works include:

Sharpening the Sword: A closer look at the lives of fifty outstanding historic leaders including Booker T. Washington, Helen Keller, Dwight Moody, Sam Walton, Thomas Jefferson, Walt Disney, and many others. Not all fifty subjects were outstanding Christian leaders, but each one demonstrated godly principles of leadership and courage in action. Each study includes a Biblical parallel, additional insight for discussion, and a concluding prayer inviting God to guide the reader into an application of the principle in their life.

Serenity Principles: Using Scripture and the familiar Serenity Prayer as a foundation, the reader will learn the difference between things one can change and things they cannot. You will identify Biblical principles that can empower you to accomplish difficult personal change in the face of paralyzing crisis. You will discover how faith in God can help you adapt to change and triumph through struggle. Change is inevitable, but victimhood is not. The Lord—who is the same yesterday, today, and always—can guide you through trauma to a peace beyond explanation.

Contrary to Popular Belief: Zig Ziglar called it "a no-nonsense but loving approach of taking God at His word and living by it. Hower tells it like it is in a loving, Biblical manner. He touches all the bases and gives a clear guide to serving Christ well while we're here and enjoying our eternity with Him forever." John Maxwell said, "Hower tackles the rough questions and issues that come between Christians and their nonbelieving friends. An honest look at the seemingly foolish and paradoxical truths of the Christian faith. As Stephen effectively points out, truth needs no defense, just opportunity."

God Had a Better Plan: A co-authored biographical book with Robert Hillard. It relates a compelling story of struggle, redirection, hard work, redirection, success, redirection, failure, redirection, and eventual achievement. It is the miraculous account of how God enabled a disadvantaged farm boy to establish a multi-million-dollar endowment to provide financial assistance to elderly, impoverished Christian leaders. Readers will discover how God recruits people like Bob to get important things done, employing hard work to change their lives along the way. Bob's story is unique, but the lessons it teaches are universal.

Book Sales

For more purchasing options and information on the book,
visit the publisher at **www.tenthpowerpublishing.com**.
For quantity discounts, contact the author directly.

Contact the author for more information at his website.
www.howerbooks.com